HORSE FACILITIES HANDBOOK

HORSE
FACILITIES
HANDBOOK

Eileen Wheeler
Bill Koenig
Jay Harmon
Pat Murphy
David Freeman

MWPS
MidWest Plan Service
A Foundation of Knowledge

Designed by Kathy J. Walker

MidWest Plan Service

122 Davidson Hall

Iowa State University, Ames, Iowa 50011-3080

For additional copies of this publication and a free catalog

of other agricultural publications, call 1-800-562-3618

or visit our website at: www.mwpshq.org

Library of Congress

Cataloging-in-Publication Data

Horse facilities handbook / [Eileen Wheeler ... et al.].

   p. cm.

Includes bibliographical references and index.

ISBN 0-89373-098-X

1. Stables—Design and construction—Handbooks, manuals, etc.

2. Horses—Housing—Handbooks, manuals, etc.

I. Wheeler, Eileen.

TH4930.H67   2005

636.1'0831—dc22   2004061036

   CIP

Final Author Committee
Eileen Wheeler (Chair), Associate Professor and Extension
    Engineer, Penn State University
Bill Koenig, MWPS Engineer
Jay Harmon, Associate Professor and Extension Engineer,
    Iowa State University
Pat Murphy, Professor and Extension Engineer,
    Kansas State University
David Freeman, Professor and State Equine Specialist,
    Oklahoma State University

Special Acknowledgement
This book has gone through drafts over a more than 15 year
period. MWPS would like to acknowledge the following
individuals for their significant contributions to the many
drafts of this book:

Raymond Huhnke, Agricultural Engineer, Oklahoma State
    University
Mike Brugger, Agricultural Engineer, the Ohio State University
Larry Turner, Agricultural Engineer,
    University of Kentucky
John Leech, former Livingston County District Equine Agent,
    Michigan State University
Eldridge Collins, Agricultural Engineer,
    Virginia Tech (retired)
Howard Person, Agricultural Engineer,
    Michigan State University (retired)
Mark Russell, Professor, Animal Science,
    Purdue University
Craig Wood, Professor, Animal Science, University of Kentucky

MWPS would like to thank the following equine facilities for
allowing us to take or use photographs of their facilities:

Clear Creek Stables, Inc., Ames, Iowa
Fox Creek Equestrian Center, Manhattan, Kansas
Iowa State University Horse Farm, Ames, Iowa
Red Horse Ranch, Ames, Iowa
Shamrock Stables, Ames, Iowa
Timber Ridge Stables, Boone, Iowa

Reviewers
Michael Brugger, Associate Professor of Agricultural
    Engineering, The Ohio State University
Bob Coleman, Animal Scientist and Extension Horse Specialist,
    University of Kentucky
Ted Funk, Associate Professor and Extension Engineer,
    University of Illinois
Debra Hagstrom, Associate Professor of Animal Science,
    University of Illinois
Jay Solomon, Extension Educator of Engineering Technology,
    University of Illinois

CONTENTS

————◆◆◆◆◆————

PREFACE

This handbook has been developed to help engineers, designers, and horse owners, and enthusiasts who are developing new facilities, remodeling existing facilities, making plans for a future project, or doing research about facilities so that their horse will receive the best care as they make a decision on where to board their horse. This book is a revision of and replaces the book titled *Horse Handbook: Housing and Equipment*, MWPS-15, first edition, 1971.

Like the first edition, this book still has a wealth of great construction details, but now has vastly expanded discussions and information on:
- Site selection and site layout,
- Building and stable designs and layouts,
- Manure handling and treatment,
- Ventilation and environmental control, and
- Fire safety.

In addition to the expanded discussions, this handbook now includes detailed information on:
- Roadways that will allow for easy and safe entry to the farmstead,
- Parking and turn-around areas for cars, trucks, trucks and trailers, and semi-trailers,
- Pastures, paddocks, and outdoor facilities,
- Arenas and training facilities,
- Breeding facilities,
- Bulk feed and bedding storage,
- Fencing,
- Water, electrical, and domestic waste designs, and
- Emergency response planning.

People using this handbook will gain knowledge on many design and safety issues including:
- How horse behavior affects design,
- How to design pastures so that a dominant horse will not injure a less dominant horse,
- What are the keys to successfully ventilate a stable and to keep it cool or warm,
- How farmstead and stable layout can increase labor efficiency,
- What to do with the manure that accumulates,
- How to avoid drainage problems, and
- What can be done to minimize the negative effects of an emergency situation such as fire or severe weather.

CHAPTER 1

Quick Reference

The daily activities on horse farms vary according to a farm's primary function, be it breeding, training, or public use. Though each farm requires specialized facilities, the basic goals of facility design and construction are similar. Facilities should promote safety as well as the efficient care and handling of horses. Well-planned facilities allow for lower operational costs and an overall increased efficiency of facilities. Poorly planned or improperly constructed facilities interfere with daily operations, increase costs such as labor and maintenance, and compromise the safety and health of both horses and people.

Influence of Horse Behavior on Design

To develop well planned facilities, a designer must understand horse psychology and behavior. When designing and constructing a facility, keep in mind that the expected behavior of horses will vary under different situations. It is also important to realize that horses have traits that differ from other livestock species. People who have little previous experience with horses and/or the planned activities of the farm should research horse behavior and training. Safe and sound designs respect horses' uniqueness and provide convenience and safety for both horse and handler.

A horse's natural defense mechanism is the *fight* or *flight* instinct. Horses are generally non-aggressive, but when threatened, excited, impatient, scared, or in pain they will typically first try to escape by running away. If escape is not possible, they will fight by kicking, striking, or biting. Those defenses explain the high-strung, excitable nature of the horse. The degree of excitability and nervousness varies between individuals and blood lines. Properly designed handling facilities allow for horse and handler safety while diminishing the horses' instinct or desire to escape by running through or jumping over barriers. Some classes of horses, such as breeding stallions, can be naturally aggressive and require specialized facility design to guard against horse or handler injury.

General horse traits include:
- Major preoccupation with food and security. A stable area typically represents an area for food and security. An excited horse may re-enter a burning barn because of this connection between food and security.
- Herd instinct with its security and the acceptance of discipline and a degree of submission. This instinct is a prime factor in training.
- Low pain tolerance. This low pain tolerance is sometimes used by people to control and train horses.
- Desire to stand to rest or doze while standing but will lie down for prolonged sleep. Sleeping patterns mean that horses need a comfortable area in which to stand and lie down.
- Highly developed senses of sight, smell, and hearing. Horses have an excellent range of vision. Their vision range is 340°, which makes them very sensitive to motion.

Horses in stalls quickly become bored, which leads to stable vices such as:

- Wood chewing.
- Pawing or striking the ground with either front foot.
- Weaving nervously and rapidly shifting weight from one front leg to the other.
- Placing the upper incisors on a solid object and expanding the larynx, which results in the gulping of air into the digestive tract, a condition known as *cribbing*.

Horses are also social creatures. Most will try to group with other horses if they can because they need the security of a group. Isolated horses lack the security of a group and often develop peculiar or even neurotic behavior not found when a number of horses live together.

Other horses often copy these undesirable stable vices. Horses housed individually are calmer if they can maintain visual contact with other horses. If possible, horses should be allowed to see other horses and outside activities to decrease neurotic behaviors and to reduce anxiety from being isolated

Horses housed in group situations, such as pastures and paddocks, develop a dominance hierarchy. Each horse uses a combination of aggressive and submissive behaviors to place itself in the dominance hierarchy of the herd. Pastures and paddocks with corners and other small-enclosed areas that allow a dominant horse to trap a submissive one increase the frequency of injury.

Designing facilities to account for horse behavior does not have to be complicated or expensive. Horses have flourished for ages on open grassy plains. Excellent horse husbandry can be achieved with a paddock and simple shelter. This publication provides specifications for planning and constructing facilities for commercial equine production and use farms, including specific chapters on environmental control, manure management, utilities, and protective systems. Additional

chapters cover recommendations for fencing, feed storage, breeding farm equipment, and arena and show facilities. For individuals considering entering into a commercial or pleasure horse farm enterprise, this book will help in the design and construction of horse housing and equipment that best meets the operational and production goals.

Horse Size Estimation

Table 1-1 Horse Heights.

Height in hands (4 inches) to the top of the withers.

Type	Normal	Range
Riding horses	15 to 16.2 hands	14 to 17 hands
Carriage horses		Up to 17.2 hands
Draft horses	16 to 17.2 hands	15.2 to 18 hands
Ponies	By definition, less than 14.2 hands	

Table 1-2 Heart girth versus weight.*

For estimating weight. It is best to determine weight with a scale.

Heart girth (inches)	Approx. weight (lbs)
29½	100
39½	200
45¾	300
50¾	400
55½	500
59¼	600
62	700
65	800
68	900
70¾	1,000
73¼	1,100
75½	1,200
76¾	1,250
77¾	1,300
78¼	1,310
79¾	1,375
81¼	1,445
82¾	1,515
84¼	1,590
85¾	1,665
87¼	1,745
88¾	1,830
90¼	1,920
91¾	2,010
93¼	2,105
94¾	2,200
96¼	2,300

*Weights above 1,300 pounds were developed by Brad Kruse, DraftResource.com (http://www.draftresource.com/).

To measure heart girth, wrap a tape snugly around the horse directly behind the front legs. Horse calibrated weight tapes that estimate weight based on heart girth are available. This approximate estimate of weight is useful in calculating feed requirements. The equation is:

$$WT = \frac{(GRTH)^2 \, (LNTH)}{330}$$

Where:

WT   = estimated weight, pounds

GRTH = heart girth, inches

LNTH = length measured from the point of the shoulder to the point of buttocks, inches

Consider the size of a horse's hoof to avoid places where they can get caught in partitions, grillwork or between stall fixtures. A mature horse's hoof is about a 5-inch circle, but ranges from 4 to 6 inches in diameter. A foal's hoof can be as little as a 2½-inch diameter circle. Orient pipes vertically in grillwork over a partition, so a horse is more able to remove a caught hoof.

Table 1-3	Typical weights of riding horses.	
Horse	Weight range (lbs)	Design weight (lbs)
Foals	100 to 350	350
Weanlings	350 to 450	450
Yearlings	450 to 700	700
2 yr olds	700 to 1,000	1,000
Mature horses	900 to 1,400	1,400

Data Tables

Table 1-4	Common dimensions for horses in box stalls.	
Horse	Horse size	Box stall size ª(feet)
Mature animal (Mare or Gelding)		
	Small	10 x 10
	Medium	10 x 12
	Large	12 x 12
Broodmare		
	Minimum size	12 x 12
Foal to 2 year old		
	Average	10 x 10
	Large	12 x 12
Draft		
	Average	12 x 14
Maternity		
	Small	12 x 12
	Medium	14 x 14
	Large ᵇ	16 x 16
Stallionᶜ		
	Minimum size	12 x 12
Pony		
	Average	9 x 9 or 10 x 10

ª Sizes larger than listed are unnecessary, but can provide more comfort to the horse. Larger stalls will result in an increase in bedding and labor.
ᵇ A removable partition can turn two regular stalls into one large maternity stall.
ᶜ Work stallions daily or provide a 2- to 4-acre paddock for exercise.

Table 1-5	Space requirements for horses in tie stalls.	
Horse	Horse size	Tie stall size (feet)
Mature animal (mare or gelding)	Small	5 x 9
	Medium	5 x 12
	Large	5 x 12
Foal to 2 year old	Average	4½ x 9
	Large	5 x 9
Pony	Average	3 x 6

Table 1-6	Hay manger and grain box dimensions (dimensioning inside the stall).		
Animals	Dimensionsª	Hay manger (inches)ᵇ	Grain box (inches)
All mature animals (Mares, Geldings, Broodmares, Stallions)	Length	30 to 36	20 to 24
	Throat height	38 to 42	38 to 42
	Width	20 to 24	12 to 16
	Depth	24 to 30	8 to 12
Foals and 2-yr olds	Length	24 to 30	16 to 20
	Throat height	32 to 36	32 to 36
	Width	16 to 20	10 to 16
	Depth	20 to 24	6 to 8
Ponies	Length	24	18
	Throat height	32	32
	Width	18	10
	Depth	20	6 to 8

ª See Figure 3-19 for dimension locations.
ᵇ Wall corner hayracks are often used instead of mangers. Five feet is the usual distance between the floor and bottom of the rack. Or, feed hay on the stall floor in both box and tie stalls and use a wall-mounted grain box in the corner of the stall.

Table 1-7 — Door dimensions for horse housing

Use	Door width (feet)	Door height (feet)
Stalls	4 [a]	8
Stable doors for small wheeled equipment and loose horses	10 [b]	10
Horse and rider	12	12
Large equipment, horse and rider	16	14

[a] Typical width. Range of 4 to 6 feet wide.
[b] Minimum width for loose horses. Ideally for loose horses to avoid injury the door width should be wide enough to allow the horses to exit a building simultaneously if startled.

Table 1-8 — Alley dimensions.

Use	Minimum width (feet)	Recommended (feet)
Horse traffic	10	12
Horses, pickup truck, tractor and wagon	12	14
Litter alley behind single row of tie stalls	6	8
Feed alley for a person and feed cart	4	6

Table 1-9 — Recommended roofed area for open-front horse housing.

Animal type	Covered area (sq ft/animal)
Foals	100
Yearlings	120
Mature horses	150

Table 1-10 — Feeder or manger space requirements for group-housed horses.

Animal	Space at manger or feeder (per animal)
Foals	24"
Yearlings	30"
Mature horses	36"

Table 1-11 — Creep area for foals.

Number of Foals	Creep Area (feet)
1	8 x 8
2	10 x 10
3	12 x 12
4	14 x 14
5	16 x 16
6	18 x 18
7	20 x 20
8	24 x 24*

*With adequate number of openings, a 24 x 24 foot creep area will work for up to 18 foals. A 12-foot feeder needs to be placed in the middle of the pen.

Table 1-12 — Arena dimensions for competition training.

Arena type	Dimensions (feet)
Barrel racing	150 x 200
Calf roping	100 x 300
Dressage, small	66 x 132 [a]
Dressage, standard	66 x 198 [a]
Show, small	110 x 220 [b]
Show, standard	120 x 240 [b]
Steer wrestling	100 x 300
Team roping	150 x 300
Western pleasure	100 x 200

[a] United States Dressage Federation (USDF) regulation size.
[b] National Horse Show Association regulation size.

Table 1-13 — Minimum unobstructed dimensions for non-competitive use indoor arena.

Arena type	Dimensions (feet)
Width	
Exercise and training (absolute minimum)	36
Exercise and training (preferred minimum)	50
Exercise, training, and riding	60
Exercise, training, riding and driving	60-100
Group riding or driving	80-100
Length	
Minimum	130
Height	
Minimum	14
Hunter and jumper training	16

Table 1-14 — Round pen dimensions according to use.

Activity	Recommended wall design	Pen diameter (feet)	Pen diameter (meters)	Comments
Initial breaking, training riding of horse Initial training of the rider	Solid walls, 6 to 7 feet high	33	10	Allows for maximum control and of horse by trainer. Fewer visual distractions to horse
Mid to final routine training area	Open fence, 6 feet high	66	20	Most usable size for all functions
Multiple horse functions Final training	Open fence, 6 feet high	99	30	Allows for maximum training flexibility of horse by trainer

CHAPTER 2

Site Planning

Planning new equine facilities can be a complex process that involves setting goals, evaluating needs, mapping existing and future facilities, and making decisions. Planning objectives may include expansion, replacing existing facilities, improving efficiency of resources (money, labor, energy, time, etc.), or meeting environmental, energy, and safety concerns.

Careful planning requires reviewing the present, assessing the future, and providing flexibility for expansion. Obtaining competent professional advice can help to avoid costly mistakes on any size project.

Before selecting a site or designing and constructing a building, contact and work with an insurance agent and a consulting engineer familiar with equine operations. Be aware that insurance companies **will not** automatically insure every building they are asked to insure. Each building usually must meet some minimum guidelines before an insurance company will even consider insuring a building or set of buildings. Failure to meet some of these basic guidelines may mean that an insurance company loss control representative will not insure the building or set of buildings at all. Therefore, an insurance company should be contacted early in the planning process of any remodeling or new construction project.

Contacting an insurance company early in the planning process not only helps in developing a well-designed structure, but can also help in incorporating relatively simple and low cost safety features for the people who work in these buildings.

Depending on the location and zoning requirements, working with a consulting

Safety features can be as simple as providing:
- Emergency exits for people to escape a burning building.
- Supplemental lighting that turns on during power outages.
- Storage for flammable materials in a building well away from stables and hay storage.
- A generator that operates automatically during power outages.
- Fire and smoke alarm systems.

engineer or professional design firm may be necessary. A licensed engineer will be needed especially if engineering documents are required. Only a licensed engineer may prepare, sign, seal, and submit engineering plans to a public authority for approval.

Many people try to cut cost by developing their own designs. These people are often disappointed because they find out during the process that they need to spend a lot of their

Hiring a consulting engineer or professional design firm often is beneficial because they can provide:
- Direct personal service (technical advice, etc.).
- Preliminary investigations, feasibility studies, and economic comparison of alternatives.
- Planning studies.
- Design.
- Cost estimates.
- Engineering appraisals.
- Bid letting.
- Construction monitoring and inspection.

valuable time trying to address unforeseen problems. Securing the services of an experienced consulting engineer or design firm can result in saving time and money and minimizing problems during the entire process. In the end, consulting engineers or design firms more than make up for the cost of their fees.

Consulting engineers or design firms usually do a project in three phases: preliminary planning, engineering design, and construction monitoring. They may be retained to help with one or more of these phases.

To select a consulting engineer, consider:
- **Registration.** To protect the public welfare, states certify and license engineers of proven competence. Practicing consulting engineers must be registered Professional Engineers (PE) in their state of residence and qualify to obtain registration in other states where their services are required.
- **Technical qualifications with horse facility design.**
- **Reputation** with previous clients.
- **Experience** on similar projects.
- **Availability** for the project.

An insurance agent typically does not charge for advice. A consulting engineer typically does not charge for an initial consultation but will charge for services beyond the initial consultation. Before contacting the insurance company or consulting engineer, have an initial idea or basic plan. This initial idea or plan will help to set some design parameters before focusing on a more detailed design.

Some good initial ideas or, plans to have are:
- Possible site location(s).
- Possible future expansion.
- Operational goals.
- Initial floor plan (sketch).
- Needed equipment within the building.
- Aerial photos.
- Topography maps.

The remainder of this chapter will address issues and designs pertaining to:
- Site selection.
- Site layout.
- Operational goals.
- Vehicle access.
- Landscaping.

Site Selection

A site for a new building or even a manure storage should be selected based on several considerations including: odor, dust, water supply, drainage, wind speed and direction, activities and off-farm factors such as roads, traffic, neighbors, noise, water quantity and quality, zoning, climate, and electric power supply.

Select a site that is somewhat elevated above the local terrain to facilitate surface drainage and good airflow. Lowland sites may suffer from flooding, slow surface drainage, high ground water and still air on hot days.

A site's topography determines overall drainage patterns. It can restrict the space available for buildings and arenas, and can affect access routes and convenience to utilities and other site activity centers. Do not locate the site on a floodplain, swale, low ground, peat soil, shallow depth to bedrock, a karst area, or very rocky soil.

In choosing building orientation and location, consider sunlight exposure, seasonal wind effects, expansion space, fire spread, security, utilities, view screening, and accessibility. Avoid locations near property boundaries, public roads, rivers, lakes, wetlands, and rough topography or other land feature that limits space. If looking to expand an existing site that has many limitations, consider moving or expanding to a new location. Being aware of the site's effects on neighbors is a very important consideration, especially if the site will house many horses or will significantly increase vehicle traffic for the area.

Site appearance, such as paint, permanent building sheathing, paving, mowed lawns, fences in good condition, trees, and year-around landscaping, is important, but proper site layout is fundamental. Trees and shrubs can be used for screening, privacy, and some reduction of noise, and odor. Landscaping can enhance a site's appearance. Correct location and spacing of facilities minimizes visual, odor, dust, noise and expansion problems.

Local zoning regulations also may affect the site's appearance, manure handling, odor control, noise, dust, night lighting, orientation and spatial relationships with other buildings and facilities. A wetland designation, for example, can inhibit site development.

To assist surface drainage and a sanitary waste system, a well-drained relatively permeable soil is needed for the farmstead site. Too great a permeability may result in soil and underground water contamination. Soil that has low permeability (high clay content) is slow to drain. These soils will lead to ponded surface water that can result in mud, ruts, and a breeding area for mosquitoes and other insects. Some low permeable soils also shrink when dry and expand when wet, requiring removal of top layers of soil before constructing building foundations, floors, and paved areas. A county soil survey report available through the local Natural Resource Conservation Service (NRCS) or Extension Service office may assist with soil questions and management.

Surface and subsurface drainage are critically important features to the farmstead. Natural drainage is preferred, but some improvements are usually needed. Intercept and divert surface water away from the farmstead with upslope diversions. Construct diversions across the slope to carry runoff away. Diversions are usually grassed and maintained by mowing. Gutter buildings and divert otherwise clean water away from paddock areas to minimize the amount of mud.

Good slopes for surface drainage are 2% to 4%. If the site does not have 2% to 4% slopes, fill or additional soil will need to be added to elevate the grade for the buildings.

As a general rule, surface drainage is used to remove storm water quickly. Tile drainage may then be needed in some soils to remove the remaining water over a period of days or weeks.

Topographic maps showing lines of equal elevation can usually be obtained from the NRCS office or purchased from the U.S. Geological Survey (USGS). These maps can be used to determine existing slopes, drainage ways, hills, and wetlands and are useful when developing a plan for the site.

Site Layout

Many new sites start with the construction of just a house on an acreage with future plans to construct a shop, stable, and pasture for a few horses. These sites locate the house or family living area close to the public road serving the site. Having the family living area close to the public road is advantageous after other buildings are constructed because this location controls the amount of traffic that has access to the site. It also presents an anesthetically pleasing view to the public. When siting other buildings, chose locations that allow an unobstructed view from the family living area of road, vehicle, machinery, and people traffic. This is a consideration for theft, vandalism, fire and biosecurity.

Some sites do not include a family living area, such as may be the case for some large facilities where the overseer of the operation lives across the road or in a residence away from the daily activities of the operation. Some basic and similar planning procedures can be used for both situations. Common to both are separation distances and/or work zones that can be used as a guide to enhance efficiency and minimize aggravation while performing common and daily tasks. In addition to separation distances and work zones, having a good understanding of the

Questions that need to be answered are:
- Will semi-trailers trucks be on the site delivering hay or bedding, or remove manure?
- Will multiple trucks with trailers be on-site at the same time?
- How much parking is needed?

types of vehicles that will be on the site is needed.

Once the concepts of separation distances, work zones, and vehicular requirements are understood, placing buildings or activity areas on a map using information from a new or existing site can help one visualize how everything will fit together and identify problem areas. Even physically staking out the locations of buildings or activity areas will help to visualize the layout. When laying out the buildings or activity areas, be sure to plan for any landscaping that will help enhance the aesthetics of the site.

Separation Distances

When planning, assume that activities at the site will double in size over time. Provide space for new buildings, clearance between buildings, and expansion. Separate all buildings by at least 35 feet for access and snow storage. Naturally ventilated buildings require 50 feet or more clearance. Fire protection will require at least 75 feet of clearance. Consider space needs for vehicle access and parking. A good way to assure adequate space for future expansion is to develop a complete site plan that shows the location of all current facilities and area for future expansion.

Zone Planning

Buildings are located in one of four specific areas or zones on the site, Figure 2-1. Zones are in about 100-foot increments. Zone 1 is for family living, lawn, recreation, gardens, office and visitor parking. Protect Zone 1 from odor, dust, insects, and unwanted visitors by locating other centers of activity outside Zone 1. The home should be closer to public roads than other buildings, especially large ones that tend to dominate or obscure the view of the house. A family living area at a separate site is a consideration for larger farms.

Zone 2 is for machinery storage, a repair shop, and related activities that are relatively quiet, dry and odor free. Zone 2 typically includes much of the driveway, service yard, and temporary parking space. Fuel storage and other more hazardous activities may be located

Separation distances between buildings and neighboring features depend on management, operation size, pollution potential, and appearance.

- **Operation size.**
  Larger operations create more noise, odors, dust, and traffic requiring greater separation distances. For example, a bulk hay and grain storage area for a few horses has less impact on the living area than a site with many horses that requires frequent activity of tractors and large trucks.
- **Pollution hazards.**
  Odor, dust, noise, and manure disposal problems can be associated with larger sites with many horses. Odors from large-scale equine operations can often be detected one-half mile downwind.
- **Appearance.**
  A neat and attractive farmstead is very important. Consider landscaping that will enhance the site's appearance, especially near roadways, and locate less attractive facilities and activities farther away.
- **Management needs.**
  Locate horse facilities at least 200 feet from the family living area.

to the far side of Zone 2—away from the family living area.

Zone 3 may contain a small stable, hay, grain, and bedding—activities that have frequent noise, dust, and traffic and that need daily labor. The electric power distribution pole, propane storage, and wagon parking may fit in either Zone 2 or 3.

Zone 4 is the major area for horse activities and other areas needing expansion space, access, feed, and manure management. Activities that produce noise, dust, odors, and traffic are located in Zone 4.

The location of the public road with respect to the site affects the Zone 1 living area location and overall site layout. For example, in the upper Midwest, it is usually preferable to have the driveway enter the farmstead from the south. This allows for an undisturbed tree windbreak along the west and north to protect the farmstead from prevailing northwesterly winter winds—yet allow prevailing south winds in summer to reach into the farmstead. Figure 2-1 shows recommended farmstead area arrangements in relation to the driveway/public road access.

The direction of the site from the main road affects layout. Layout assumes prevailing winter winds are from the north and west, and prevailing summer winds are from the southwest, south, or east.

When a family living area does not or will not exist on a site, an office building, stable or arena may be the first building that is observed by people entering the site. Similar to zone planning for a family living area, the first building that is observed by people entering the site will become the focus area for the site and will be located in Zone 1. This

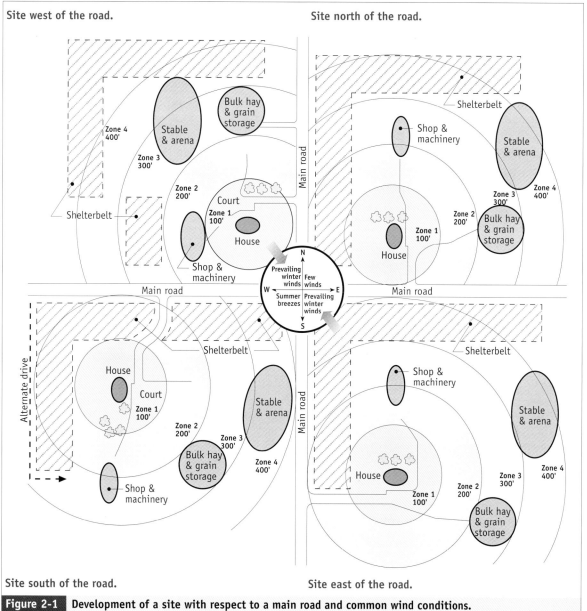

Figure 2-1	**Development of a site with respect to a main road and common wind conditions.**
	The direction of the site from the main road affects layout. Layout assumes prevailing winter winds are from the north and west and prevailing summer winds are from the southwest, south, or east.

building will be an area that people visit first on the site and will be treated similarly to the family living area. The main difference between a family living area and the new focus building is that the new focus building may need to be located further from the roadway because of the activities associated with the building. The other buildings need to be located in the appropriate zones away from the focus building in Zone 1. Because the focus building may need to be located further from a main roadway, pastures are often used as a means to fully utilize the area between the main roadway and the activities on the site.

Locating Buildings and Activity Areas

Initial building planning is needed before site options can fully be evaluated and planned. In the end, it is a back and forth decision making process between building design and site layout that is needed before the best option is selected. Laying out the site starts with developing a map of the site.

Using a professional land surveyor is certainly the most accurate method of mapping the site, buildings, and elevations. A surveyor can also establish setbacks needed from property lines for buildings and setbacks for livestock facilities to be in compliance with regulations. A good initial plan can often be developed with less sophisticated methods, especially if setback distances are not a concern. Professional land surveyors should be used if a more accurate plan is needed.

Maps can be sketched out by hand or with the use of a simple computer program. Whether using hand sketches or a computer program, make sure the drawings are to scale; otherwise, visualizing a plan can be very misleading. Hand drawings should be on grid paper, Figure 2-2, and sketched as accurately as possible using a straight-edge scaled ruler, or architectural/engineering scale.

Aerial photographs are also helpful with planning. The local Farm Service Agency (FSA) should have aerial photos at a 1:600-foot scale.

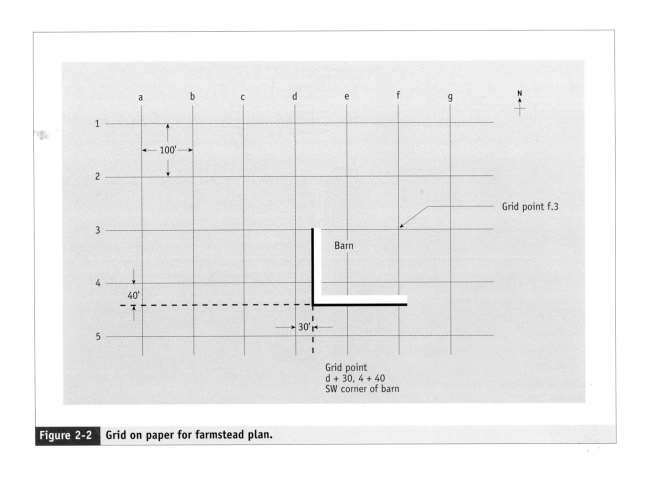

Figure 2-2 Grid on paper for farmstead plan.

The local NRCS or Zoning office may have other maps that show major landscape features. Some areas even have aerial photographs available for downloading from the World Wide Web.

In addition to buildings and activity areas, maps should include manure storage areas, septic systems, drainage ways, tile lines, underground utilities, overhead lines, drives, right-of-ways, property lines, and other key features that could affect future construction, Figure 2-3. One mapping approach is to make several photocopies of a base drawing and use those to sketch out different site ideas. Another method uses scale drawings of buildings that are cut out and moved around on this existing drawing to investigate the "what if" scenarios. Each arrangement will have advantages and disadvantages that must be considered as the final plan develops.

After mapping out the site on paper, review the site to obtain a better visualization of how the site will layout. Use stakes to identify the location of the corners of buildings and activity areas. A 100-foot tape or a handheld global positioning system (GPS) simplifies this process. The use of GPS technology is becoming common throughout the U.S. A handheld GPS

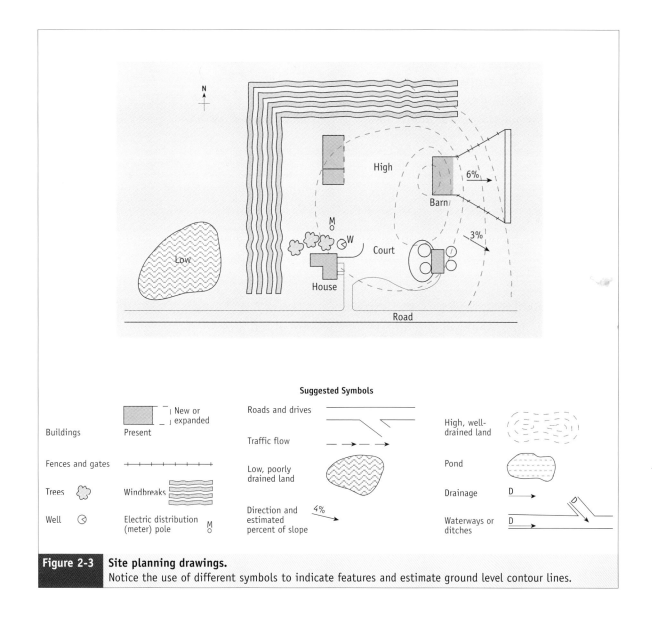

Figure 2-3 **Site planning drawings.**
Notice the use of different symbols to indicate features and estimate ground level contour lines.

employs strategically located signal-emitting satellites to provide location data through a special signal receiver for any place on the earths' surface. Even the most accurate GPS can still be off several feet unless very expensive equipment is used. Be sure accuracy of the equipment fits into planning expectations.

When staking a site, label each stake with a number and letter to show its position, Figure 2-4. Locate electric poles, water wells, buildings, roads, and other facilities for the site. Be sure to place the stakes as accurately as possible, and make use of identifiable and permanent benchmarks, such as fence posts or other existing buildings. The more accurate the placement of stakes, the better one can visualize the final design.

Use a 100-foot tape and stakes—wood or stiff wire with bright plastic flags—to mark corners and boundaries. Lay out a proposed road, building, or distance zone to help visualize the revised site.

Vehicle Access and Parking Areas

When planning access drives and parking areas consider:
- Surfacing for year-round access.
- Drainage to maintain the surface and control runoff.
- Area lighting for safety, convenience, and security.
- Space for maneuvering and parking.
- Space for snow storage.
- Safety and convenience.
- Moving or abandoning an existing drive to make the site more productive in the long term.

Entrance and branch drives

Provide a single entrance drive for better traffic control and security. Exceptions are a second drive to a large horse or public (show,

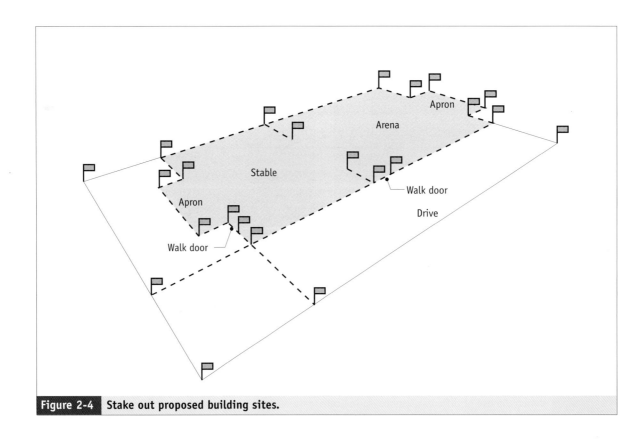

| **Figure 2-4** | **Stake out proposed building sites.** |

visiting mares, etc.) center or a second house near the site, Figure 2-5. Provide at least 100 feet of driveway from the family living area to an intermittently traveled public road. Some townships and counties are regulating the location of a new private access to township and county roads, and, in some cases, requiring the relocation of existing private roads.

When evaluating where to put an entrance drive, consider that fast moving vehicles need time and distance to avoid a slower moving horse trailer or farm vehicle exiting/entering the site. An important factor to consider is that vehicles moving at 60 mph cover 88 feet every second. Table 2-1 shows stopping distances. The stopping distances listed are the clear sight distance

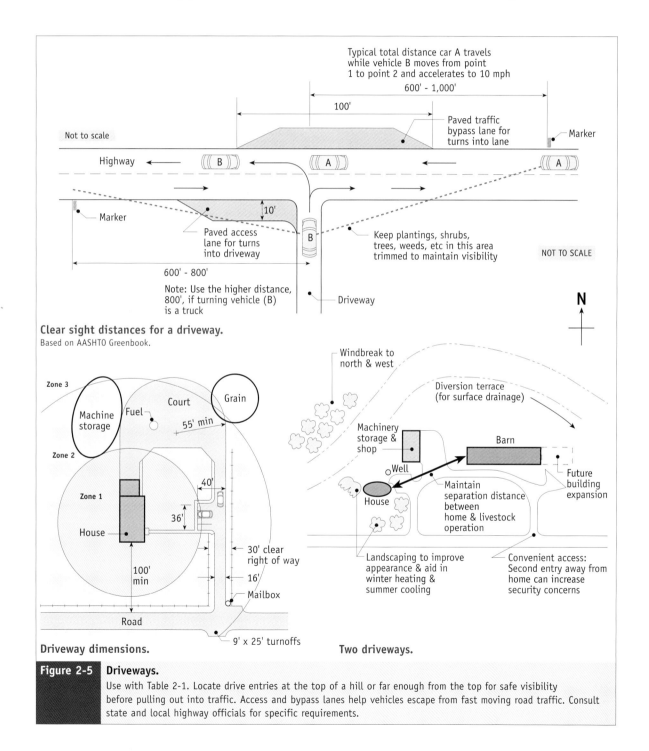

Clear sight distances for a driveway.
Based on AASHTO Greenbook.

Driveway dimensions.

Two driveways.

Figure 2-5 Driveways.
Use with Table 2-1. Locate drive entries at the top of a hill or far enough from the top for safe visibility before pulling out into traffic. Access and bypass lanes help vehicles escape from fast moving road traffic. Consult state and local highway officials for specific requirements.

needed for a person traveling on the road at the speed indicated to come to a full stop.

During the planning process, a practical way to evaluate the visibility of oncoming cars is to drive on the road and try to determine safe visibility, stopping, and acceleration distances. Use Tables 2-1 and 2-2 to help evaluate entrance drive locations so that vehicles can safely pull out of the site. In areas where there is more concern about driver's abilities, such as areas where there are frequent tourists or sightseers, increasing the clear sight distance for the entrance drive may be desirable. The general recommended distance to ensure safe visibility for slow moving vehicles entering and exiting a road with 60 mph traffic is 1,000 feet. If that is not possible, provide at least 800 feet of visibility. Locate drives either at the top of a hill or far enough from the top for safe visibility before pulling out into traffic. Provide turn-offs so someone entering the drive can wait safely out of traffic for large equipment or vehicles to clear the drive entrance. Provide a turning/acceleration lane for right-hand turns. Work with the county or state highway department to design

an acceptable entrance. As a test, park a vehicle at the proposed driveway site and then drive the public road noting the location from which the parked vehicle is first seen.

Branch drives provide access to guest, office, and visitor parking, the family garage and parking, and small buildings. Make the drive surface 16 to 18 feet wide, or 24 feet wide if the drive must accommodate two-way traffic. Include at least 8 feet of additional right-of-way on each side for overhanging equipment and snow storage. If security gates are installed to limit access to the site, locate gates into the entrance at least 40 feet (preferably 60 feet) from the road.

Drainage along the drive can be within this right-of-way. A gentle curve in the drive, along with plantings, provides better privacy and security from passing motorists.

Use hard, durable surfaces such as stone, brick, pavers, concrete, or asphalt surfaces for walks to parking areas and along drives.

Before constructing or modifying entrance drives, contact the local, county, or state transportation departments to approve plans.

Table 2-1 — Stopping and decision site distances.

Based on American Association of State Highways and Transportation Officials (AASHTO), *A Policy on Geometric Design of Highways and Streets* (The Green Book), 2001.

Vehicle travel speed (mph)	Emergency stopping distance[a]		Minimum stopping distance[a] (feet)	Decision site distance[b]	
	Wet pavement (feet)	Dry pavement (feet)		Rural road (feet)	Suburban road (feet)
45	284	179	360	395	600
50	357	212	425	465	705
55	417	249	495	535	865
60	495	288	570	610	990
65	581	330	645	695	1,100
70	686	375	730	780	1,215

[a] Minimum desirable stopping sight distance based on the vehicle traveling at the design speed on poor wet pavement when one clearly discernible object or obstacle is present in the roadway. The vehicle decelerates at a rate of 11.2 feet per second and the driver's perception-reaction time is 2.5 seconds.
[b] The decision sight distance is the distance required for a driver to detect an unexpected or otherwise difficult-to-perceive information source or hazard in a roadway environment that may be visually altered, recognize the hazard or its threat potential, select an appropriate speed and path, and initiate and complete the required maneuver safely and efficiently. Because more than one discernible object or obstacle is present in the roadway, more complex decisions need to be made. Use this distance to provide an added measure of safety and smoother operations.

Table 2-2 — Minimum stopping site distances on grades.

Based on American Association of State Highways and Transportation Officials (AASHTO), *A Policy on Geometric Design of Highways and Streets* (The Green Book), 2001.

Vehicle travel speed (mph)	Downgrades (feet)			Upgrades (feet)		
	3%	6%	9%	3%	6%	9%
45	380	400	430	345	335	320
50	450	475	510	405	390	375
55	520	555	595	470	450	435
60	600	640	690	540	515	495
65	685	730	785	615	585	565
70	775	825	895	690	660	635

Parking

The maximum allowable vehicle width to accommodate highway design width is 8 feet. Provide 3 to 5 parking spaces and a direct walk to the guest entrance for family visitors. Parking spaces for cars and trucks should be a minimum of 9 feet. Screen the route to the service entrance and farm buildings with plantings. Figure 2-6 shows some common parking arrangements.

Plan parking to encourage:
- Family guests to park near the house.
- Business visitors to park near the office or stable.
- Delivery and shipping traffic to proceed to the court.

Parking also should be made available for trailers, trucks and trailers, and semi-trailers. Table 2-3 shows some design guidelines for trucks and trailers and semi-trailers. When designing for large vehicle parking for group events, provide plenty of area to accommodate activities around the truck and trailer such as loading and unloading of horses and equipment, tying a horse up next to a trailer, and saddling, Figure 2-7. As a rule of thumb, provide about 10 feet of clear space on each side of and behind a truck and trailer. Using this criteria, an event that needs to accommodate parking for five

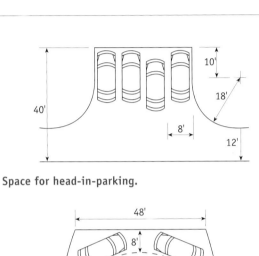

Space for head-in-parking.

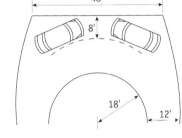

Parallel parking on circle drive.

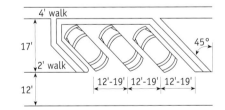

Space for diagonal parking.

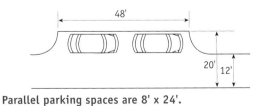

Parallel parking spaces are 8' x 24'.

Figure 2-6 Parking for trucks and cars.

Table 2-3 Vehicle lengths and turning radii.

Vehicle	Length (feet)	Turning radii (feet)
Truck and bumper trailer		
Average	32	25
Long	38	30
Truck and gooseneck trailer*		
Short	30	30
Average	42	35
Long	50	40
Very long	64	45
Semi-trailer		
Average	45	50-60
Long	60	60-80

* Similar for trucks that use a 5th wheel or mini-5th wheel trailer.

Figure 2-7 Trailer parking.

average size trucks and gooseneck trailers would need a parking space of 52 x 140 feet. This area does not include space needed for roadways or turn-arounds. If the large vehicle parking area will be used only for parking and no special activities, then only 2 feet of space are needed between vehicles. If five average size trucks and gooseneck trailers need only parking space, then the lot area needs to be only 52 x 50 feet.

Traffic loops

Provide traffic loops, also known as turn-arounds or courts, to minimize the need for vehicles to back up, to eliminate bottlenecks, and to avoid forcing all traffic back through a common point. Plan for parking, maneuvering, and temporary storage of machinery, trailers, and trucks, Figure 2-8.

A loop drive connecting the activity centers is common. Leave an open space in the center for overflow parking. Make traffic loops with a diameter of at least 110 feet, with a preferred diameter of 120 feet. Plan curves with an inside radius of 18 feet and an outside radius of 30 feet.

Backing up trailers is time consuming and dangerous because of the natural blind spots that exist around the trailer. Provide a parking area or traffic loop that will allow a truck and trailer to drive in and out without the need for backing up. Figure 2-8 shows two types of traffic loops that can be used for trucks and trailers and semi trailers.

All weather drives

Selecting a driveway surface depends on its desired appearance and intended use, available construction expertise and equipment, and desired investment. An all-weather gravel (macadam) driveway surface is practical, Figure 2-9. A concrete or asphalt surface minimizes surface maintenance and contributes to a neat appearance. Concrete is the most durable surface for heavy traffic areas and frequently scraped surfaces. Asphalt requires sealing every few years to prevent deterioration. Correct installation over a compacted base is essential for any all-weather driveway and heavy traffic drive surface.

Drainage ditches on each side of the roadway are important to keep the base under the road well drained and maintain its load-bearing strength. The subgrade (natural soil under the road, Figure 2-10) is important when developing an all-weather road. Most soils lose their bearing strength as moisture content increases. Therefore, measures must be taken to limit the amount of water that can reach the subgrade soil. There are several ways to keep water from reaching a road subbase, depending on the site.

Surface water can be kept away from the subgrade by constructing road ditches on either side of the road. The bottom of the ditch should be at least 1.5 feet below the surface of the subgrade, Figure 2-9. The cross section of the road ditch should be large enough to handle the expected flow of water without eroding the ditch bottom. The slope of the ditch and the ditch lining material should

12' to 16'
for cars and trucks
16' to 20'
for semi-tracter trailer

See Table 2-3

18'

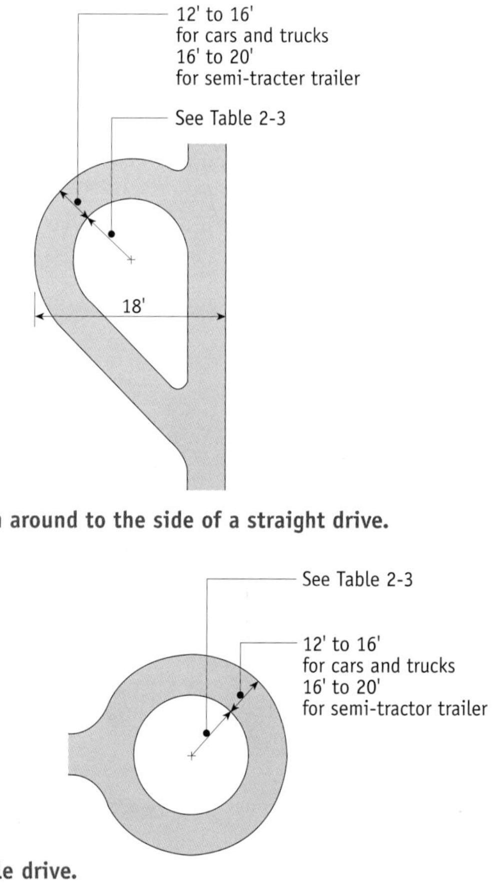

Turn around to the side of a straight drive.

See Table 2-3

12' to 16'
for cars and trucks
16' to 20'
for semi-tractor trailer

Circle drive.

Figure 2-8 | **Service yard turning spaces for trucks and trailers, and semi-trailers.**

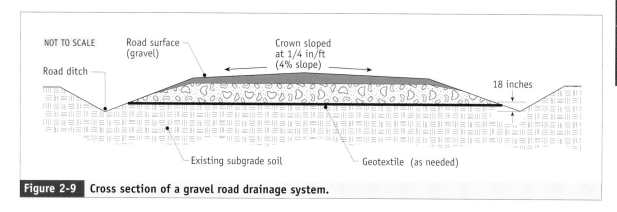

Figure 2-9 Cross section of a gravel road drainage system.

In figure: NOT TO SCALE — Road surface (gravel) — Crown sloped at 1/4 in/ft (4% slope) — Road ditch — 18 inches — Existing subgrade soil — Geotextile (as needed)

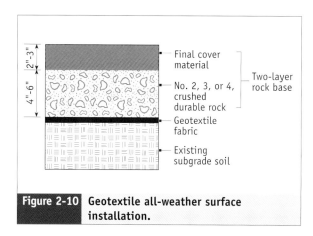

Figure 2-10 Geotextile all-weather surface installation.

In figure: Final cover material — No. 2, 3, or 4, crushed durable rock — Two-layer rock base — Geotextile fabric — Existing subgrade soil — 2"-3" — 4"-6"

be designed to avoid erosion as well. Banks of the road ditch should be no steeper than 4:1 (4 inches horizontal to 1 inch vertical) to avoid equipment rollovers.

If the water table moves into the subgrade, drainage tile with an unrestricted outlet will be needed to keep the subgrade as dry as possible. Runoff water from fields should not flow onto the road surface. Where flowing water must cross a road or driveway, use culverts to carry the water under the road subbase.

Precipitation falling on a road can reach the subgrade and reduce its strength. Crowning the gravel road surface in the center of the road with a surface slope of one fourth of an inch per foot (4%) encourages good surface drainage. Ruts, potholes, and gravel ridges or windrows at roadsides can trap water and encourage infiltration to the subgrade soil, requiring regular maintenance. The road surfacing material should contain some fine soil particles (binder) to encourage runoff. Wisconsin Transportation Bulletin No. 5 states

that a good road surfacing gravel has the following characteristics (percentages based on weight).

- 40 to 80% hard stone, uniformly graded from ¾ to 3 inches in diameter
- 20 to 60% sand smaller than ¼ inch
- 8 to 15% fines (silt and clay)

The road is constructed to spread the wheel load over a larger area of the subgrade and to allow water to move quickly to the road ditch. To accomplish this, the subbase must be sufficiently porous and must remain on top of the subgrade. Subbase materials can be well-graded gravel to breaker run (¾ to 3 inches) with 0 to 10% fines. The thicker the subbase, the lower the pressure exerted on the subgrade for a given wheel load. Therefore, thicker subbase layers are needed for larger loads. Subgrade soils containing a higher percentage of fines can increase water content in the subbase over time. Mixing soil with the subbase reduces the strength of the subbase and limits its ability to internally drain water to the road ditch. Geotextile materials are often used as a barrier between the subgrade and subbase to preclude the mixing of subgrade soils into the subbase.

In recent years, geotextile fabric has been developed for all-weather traffic surfaces on farmsteads, Figure 2-10. At a lower initial cost compared to concrete or asphalt pavement, the geotextile fabric provides an economical surface for keeping horses, less intense/lightweight traffic, stacked forage, and piled manure out of the mud. All-weather geotextile paved areas require maintenance and can quickly wear from heavy traffic or scraping. They require cleaned and compacted subbase preparation similar to that provided for asphalt or concrete pavement. A one- to two-layer rock base is spread over the carefully installed geotextile fabric. The fabric is porous so water passes through while gravel and rock that would otherwise be pushed down into the soil are held in place. Sub-surface draintile may be installed to assist drainage, maintain load-bearing strength of the subgrade soil, and prevent manure, urine, or mud seepage from contaminating ground water.

A fly-ash and Portland cement mix also can be used to pave well-drained, high-traffic farmstead areas. Fly-ash is a by-product of coal-fired, heat generation facilities and is available in different qualities. Higher grades with careful mix preparation, handling, and installation may replace a part of a concrete mix with little strength reduction. Simply mixing fly-ash with soil is sometimes used, but surface durability and effects from dry fly-ash blowing onto metal roofing can cause corrosion problems. Check with pollution control agencies or power suppliers to learn if unbound fly-ash is acceptable for use in your area.

More information on geotextiles surfaces can be found in *Using All-Weather Geotextile Lanes and Pads*, AED 45.

Culverts

Culverts are used in areas where rainwater can be transported only underneath an obstacle. In many cases the obstacle is a driveway or farm service road. Early systems often used concrete culverts. Problems with these systems have included absorption of liquid by extremely dry concrete and loss of liquid through leaking or misaligned joints. A minimum of a 12-inch diameter culvert should be used on farmsteads to minimize plugging. Culverts require periodic maintenance to remove sediment and debris that might clog them.

Smooth walled sewer pipe with joints capable of withstanding 40-psi internal pressure is recommended. Satisfactory pipes include PVC, high-density polyethylene sewer pipes, smooth walled steel pipes with welded joints, and smooth walled corrugated steel culverts. Storm

Pipe used for gravity flow system should meet the following criteria:
• Have a nonabsorbent, smooth interior.
• Have watertight joints.

drain culvert can be used if coupled properly to keep sections aligned to prevent leakage. Leakage throughout the joints can contaminate groundwater and decrease moisture content, thus preventing proper material flow. Install culverts following manufacturer's installation procedures. Short culverts (length no greater than 50 times culvert diameter) can be selected from Figure 2-11.

Snow Removal

In colder climates, removing snow from roadways and parking areas may be a necessity. Paddocks may also need to have snow removed so horses can get to feeding areas and to help facilitate drainage during snow melts.

The size of the area to pile snow depends on expected snowfall total and melting. A site that receives a 6-inch snowfall on a 16-foot wide road that is 350 feet long and has a 50 x 50 foot parking area will have a snow volume in these areas of about 4,000 cubic feet. If all this snow is piled in one location, an area about 32 feet in diameter will be needed. The height of this pile will be about 16 feet!

There are few ideal areas in which to locate a snow pile. Try to find areas where the snow pile is located:

- **Away from low areas and drainageways.** Snow piles can block water draining due to melting snow. This blockage can result in water accumulating around the pile and slowing down the melting of the snow pile. Accumulated water can also result in ice that inhibits horse and people traffic.
- **Away from wellheads, drinking water sources, and septic systems.** Snow can contain salts and manure. Snow melts can drain towards and into drinking water locations, which can result in a contaminated water supply. Locating piles

near or on wellheads and septic systems can make servicing these areas difficult. Also, the equipment used to move snow can damage wellheads and septic systems.
- **In a sunny area.** Thermal and solar radiation energy from the sun can facilitate snow melt. Snow piles located in shady areas can benefit only from thermal energy to melt snow.

- **Down wind from the site.** Snow from the pile can blow onto the just cleaned surfaces if they are not properly located. Locate the pile based on winter prevailing wind patterns.
- **In a large, open area.** Locate piles in a large open area that can allow snow to be piled from multiple snowfalls or a single heavy snowfall. It is not uncommon for people to realize that the large area they thought they had was not nearly large enough to contain the snow.
- **Near the area being cleaned.** Moving snow to a remote location can be expensive and time consuming. Locate piles at the end of roadways and parking lots, or in a corner of a paddock if possible.

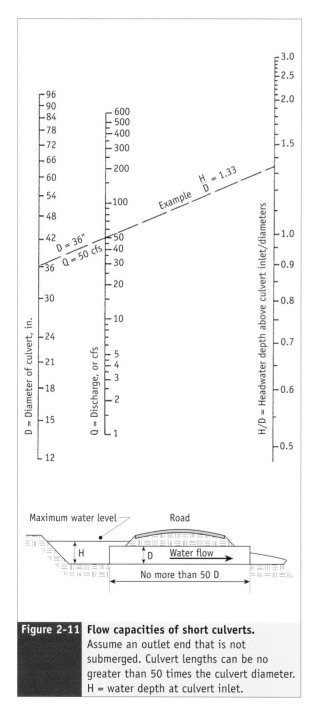

Figure 2-11 **Flow capacities of short culverts.** Assume an outlet end that is not submerged. Culvert lengths can be no greater than 50 times the culvert diameter. H = water depth at culvert inlet.

Landscaping

Landscaping can include proper site drainage and vegetation. Sites should be constructed and landscaped to facilitate *clean* water drainage away from buildings and manure storages. Water is considered clean when it has not or does not have the potential to be exposed to manure. Without proper drainage, water has the potential to pond or accumulate in low-lying areas. Ponded water areas can be exposed to dust particles from the site, which can be a source of odor as the water evaporates. Even if dust particles are not present, water can stagnate and produce odors as it evaporates. Insects be a problem.

Trees, shrubs, and flowers can be placed around a production site to improve site aesthetics. Maintain a good grass cover and reduce or eliminate weeds. Grass roots tend to weave together into a sod, holding soil particles together thereby minimizing erosion. Many types of weeds have roots that tend to grow straight down into the soil and do not hold soil particles together. A site with many weeds usually will have erosion problems, which can make mowing and maintaining a clean site more difficult. In addition, eroded areas can accumulate water. Areas where eroded soil particles have accumulated also will tend to be areas in which water ponds.

Wind and Snow Control

Shelterbelts or tree windbreaks are used to reduce wind velocities around building sites and to catch a major part of wind-driven snowfalls outside of the area. Some shelterbelts are grown to help control soil erosion, protect cropland in the summer, and to provide wildlife habitat. In areas where winters are less severe or where wind-blown snow is infrequent, planted shelterbelts are less common, but shelterbelt fences are often constructed around buildings and paddocks. Windbreak fences also can be used to control wind and snow in pastures and paddocks. Windbreak fences are discussed in detail in *Chapter 4. Pastures, Paddocks, Pens, and Shelters.*

When wind speed is reduced, snow, dust, leaves, and other wind-blown materials settle out. Therefore, efforts to control wind must allow space for snowdrifts and other deposits to build up where they will be out of the way of activity areas. Shelterbelts are most effective when oriented at right angles to the prevailing wind. Although wind may blow predominantly from one direction during winter, it rarely blows exclusively from that direction. As a result, protection is not equal for all areas on the leeward side of the shelterbelt. The use of north-south and east-west shelterbelts in combination will protect most sites.

Accounting for Prevailing Winds

Wind direction can be given in degrees measured clockwise (0 to 360°) from north. A wind direction of 0 or 360° is a North wind; an East wind is 90 degrees; a South wind is 180°, and a West wind is 270°, etc. Some wind rose diagrams, such as those displayed in Chapter 7, indicate average observed windspeed for each direction.

For Des Moines, Iowa, in January, about 7% of the time the wind blows from the south, about 8% from the north, about 12% from the northwest. The July map, on the other hand, shows the wind blowing more from southerly directions. So summer dust and odor problems will be minimized for a family living area or neighbors located southwest to west of a paddock or manure storage area.

Guidelines to minimize a site's snowdrift problems:

- Use trees, shrubs, fences, and other devices to catch drifting snow before it reaches the site's service area or buildings.
- Place drive lanes and roads parallel to—not perpendicular to—prevailing winter winds.
- Avoid locating roads directly upwind or downwind of large obstructions around which snow will drift; maintain a 100-foot clearance upwind and a 200-foot clearance downwind.
- Pile removed snow from parking areas downwind, not upwind, of the lot. Consider snowmelt drainage when locating piled snow.
- Provide adequate space between large buildings for snow removal and storage. This is particularly important for buildings that are perpendicular to the winter wind.
- Locate doorways to buildings to minimize the effects of wind and blowing snow.
- Doorways on the upwind end are difficult to seal; therefore, it is usually better to locate doors on the sides of a building toward the upwind end.

Shelterbelts

Shelterbelts are strategically planted rows of trees and shrubs used to diminish wind effects on humans, horses, plants, and property. Shelterbelts may take up to 10 years to grow to be an effective vegetative windbreak. Shelterbelts on the downwind side of buildings and manure storage create mixing and dilution of odorous air and lower wind speed at the structure. Shelterbelts on the upwind side deflect air over the buildings so the wind picks up less odorous air. Avoid placing dense windbreaks close to naturally ventilated stables so that cooling breezes and winds can help exchange air in these buildings. Locate shelterbelts a minimum distance of 100 feet, or 5 to 10 times the tree height, from a naturally ventilated building. On a property with a mature woods, that feature can be used as a windbreak during site layout.

The major steps in shelterbelt design include:

1. **Locating the shelterbelt.** Consider prevailing winds, site conditions, soil type, property lines, and shelterbelt positions. For wind protection only, locate the tallest tree row two to five mature tree heights from the area to be protected. For wind and snow protection, locate the windward row of trees about 125 feet from the area to be protected (Figure 2-12).

2. **Determine width and length.** The minimum shelterbelt width is two rows. Effective shelterbelts are generally no more than 10 rows. Provide adequate row length to give protection from expected wind changes and enough width to provide adequate density at the lower, middle, and upper levels of the shelterbelt.

3. **Select species.** Choose plantings that are adaptable to the site, and that will provide adequate density at the lower, middle, and upper levels of the shelterbelt.

4. **Arrange the shelterbelt.** Put shrubs, short trees, and slower growing trees in outer rows for adequate light and space between fast and slow growing trees to avoid suppressing

Shelterbelts provide many benefits including:
- Reduced snowdrift problems.
- Area beautification and privacy with color and landscape form.
- Reduced noise levels from nearby vehicles and other sources.
- Reduced energy use for heating and cooling buildings.
- Improved outdoor working conditions.
- Reduced wind damage to property.
- Potential provision of fruit, nuts, and firewood.
- Wildlife habitat.
- Filtering out blowing soil, dust, and other debris from nearby fields.

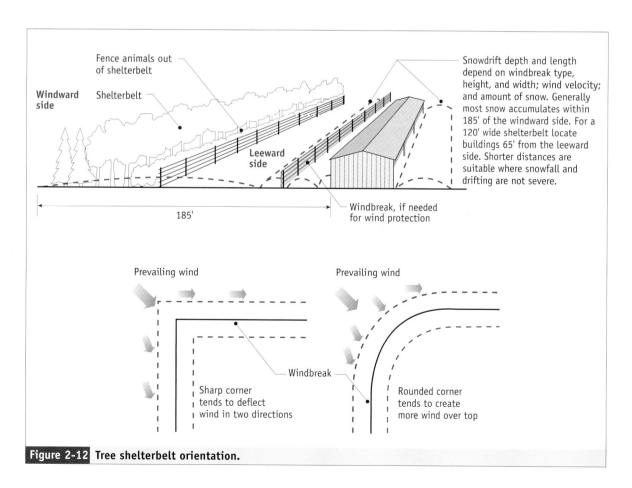

Figure 2-12 Tree shelterbelt orientation.

growth. Consider tree appearance use for outer rows.

5. **Determine spacing.** Between-the-row spacing of 8 feet to 30 feet and in-row spacing between plants of 3 feet for shrubs to 20 feet for tall trees are general recommendations. Make sure there is enough space between rows for tractor cultivation and tree maintenance equipment.

Tree and shrub variety selection appropriate to the site depends on local growing conditions. Each species has its own characteristics of winter hardiness, growth rate, height, width, density, longevity, and resistance to insects and disease. Contact and work with local nurseries and the NRCS office to develop an effective shelterbelt.

Locating buildings, paddocks, and service roads 125 feet downwind from the windward side of a shelterbelt minimizes snowdrift problems in these areas (Figure 2-12).

Exterior Lighting

Exterior lighting aids general safety and security. Along with lighted area coverage and intensity, lighting fixture selection, and location, one should consider the ease of bulb replacement; problems with bugs and birds, broken glass contamination, shadows, line-of-sight fixture glare, and unwanted light. Good lighting is a combination of light quantity, quality, and color. Quantity of light, measured in foot-candles, should be high enough for clear visibility to do needed work (Table 2-4).

The quality of light provided depends on glare, shadow control, and contrast between the light and its background. Color of lighting is determined by light source, the lighted surface, and aesthetics.

Lights—Provide at least one automatically controlled all-night light near the midpoint in the yard, on a pole or high on a building. Do not locate all-night lights over waterers or feeding areas. Bugs can be a problem when these lights are on. Also, birds will perch on these locations and leave droppings below. Use high efficiency lamps, such as high-pressure sodium or metal halide, and locate fixtures to provide lighting around the home, barns, and adjacent areas. Additional area lights, spots, or floods, may be needed on poles or principal buildings for specific areas visited after dark. One or more lights on principal buildings provide protection against prowlers or predators. Use motion detectors and photocells to conserve energy and activate lights only when needed. Check with your local electric power supplier to see if a lease program is available for outdoor security lighting.

Branch Circuit—Yard lights should be on separate circuits. This prevents other circuits from interfering with yard light control and keeps a failure of yard light wiring from interrupting service to other outlets.

See *Chapter 11. Utilities* for bulb selection, building lighting planning, and wiring information.

Table 2-4	Exterior lighting recommendations.		
	Source: Agricultural Wiring Handbook, 11th ed. 1996, National Food and Energy Council, Columbia, MO.		
Area or activity	Recommended light levels (foot-candles)	Typical installation*	Explanation
Security lighting and inactive areas	0.5 to 2	100- to 175-watt high-pressure sodium, 25 feet high, for 8,000 sq. ft.	Needed for an operator to move about safely
General work areas and paddocks	3 to 5	125- to 250-W watt high-pressure sodium, 25 feet high, for 8,000 sq. ft.	Recommended to discourage prowlers and predatory animals
Active work areas • fuel storage • building entrance • electrical load center • equipment, loading	5 to 10	250- to 400 watt high-pressure sodium, 25 feet high, for 2,000 sq. ft. supplement with fluorescent on specific areas as needed	Needed for servicing machinery

* Distance between lamps should not exceed five times mounting height. Less efficient incandescent lamps of proper wattage may be substituted.

CHAPTER 3

Stables

A stable protects horses from temperature extremes and keeps them dry and out of the wind, while preventing drafts, providing fresh air and light, and protecting against injury. Provide ample space for the well being of animals, convenience and safety of handlers, and the enjoyment of riders.

Stall barns typically allow animal access to paddocks or riding areas but house individual horses, or mares with foals, in individual stalls. Various types of structures for horse barns include post and beam, clear span, and masonry hoop structures or combination construction. Each type has advantages and disadvantages.

This chapter will present design details for a basic stable structure. Information on bedding is presented in *Chapter 8. Manure Management.*

Advantages of stables are that they:
- Provide shelter for horse care and handling.
- Allow closer observation and individual care of confined horses.
- Provide a better opportunity to regulate feed intake, and training or exercising programs.
- Allow a location for horses to be clipped for winter working and showing while maintaining condition.
- Keep horses warm, dry, and off pastures during wet, cold weather.
- Improve security.

Disadvantages of stables are:
- More manual labor and attention to horses is required for such things as cleaning stalls, bedding, grooming, feeding at least twice a day, watering, and exercising.
- Improper and inadequate care and exercise lead to poor health and/or vices.
- They are much more expensive to build and maintain than pasture shelters.
- A poorly designed or managed stable can be an unhealthy environment—excess moisture, hazardous construction.

Basic Planning

A stable, large or small, should be well planned, durable, and attractive. Its basic purpose is to provide an environment that protects horses from temperature extremes, keeps them dry and out of the wind, eliminates drafts through the stables, provides fresh air in both winter and summer, and protects them from injury. A secondary purpose of a stable is to provide an acceptable environment for the people who care for the horses.

The type of structure selected depends on the amount of land available, the type of operation, climate, amount of capital available, and the owner's preference. Consider general attractiveness and keep facilities well maintained. Locate buildings to take advantage of existing conditions and provide economical use of labor in feeding, cleaning, and maintenance. Build on high ground for adequate drainage year round.

For all stables and other horse buildings evaluate (list not necessarily in order of importance):
- **Safety.**
  Protect both humans and horses from unnecessary risk with good design and

construction. Eliminate sharp projections and slick footings. To minimize the risk of being kicked, feed and water horses without walking behind them. Provide enough space to allow safe passage of horse and handler through doors, gates, and alleys.

- **Environmental control.**
Barns minimize stress on horses and humans by modifying temperature extremes and protecting against rain, snow, sun, and wind. Summer wind cools, but winter wind chills and can drive snow and rain into the building. Obtain data on prevailing wind direction and velocity and use this information to properly orient buildings. More information on environmental control is discussed in *Chapter 7. Environmental Control.*

- **Space.**
Both horses and handlers need enough space, but too much unnecessarily increases expenses. Provide roofed space for stalls and indoor alleys and storage for tack, equipment, hay, bedding, and feed.

- **Good ventilation.**
Poor moisture, temperature, and draft control are major problems in stables. Ventilation minimizes moisture buildup and aids in odor removal while not allowing drafts. More details relating to good ventilation are discussed in *Chapter 7. Environmental Control.*

- **Fire risk.**
Precautions can prevent losses and may reduce insurance premiums. Special stable design features include installing fire alarm and suppression systems and using fire resistant materials and fire retarding paints and sprays. See *Chapter 12. Fire Protection* for more information on minimizing fire risks.

- **Construction and maintenance cost.**
Select materials and construction type for durability, ease of maintenance, cost, aesthetic value to help in advertising the facility, influence on family, and intangible values such as pride and satisfaction. Top quality may be the most economical in the long run.

- **Flexibility.**
Assume that remodeling will take place in the future to take advantage of technological advancements, meet changing needs, or convert cheaply and easily for other uses such as cabins, garages, or storage buildings. Remodeling will typically increase the property's resale value. Some people such as suburbanites and renters do not need or are not looking for fancy buildings. The answer for these people could be using a simple portable barn.

- **Attractiveness.**
Aesthetic value is achieved by a structure with good proportions in harmony with its surroundings and fulfilling its function. Good design is not achieved by fads, frills, or highly ornamental features. Good design enhances sale value.

- **Features.**
Special features may include a grooming area or wash rack, trailer storage, breeding area, exercise area, office, lounge, and living quarters. These facilities and others can be in one or several buildings.

- **Labor efficiency.**
Three quarters of horse chores are manual, so labor saving is desirable, especially for large operations. Design to minimize drudgery and reduce labor. Plan compact facilities that allow for efficient chore routines. Place highest priorities on daily chores: feeding, watering, cleaning and bedding stalls, grooming, exercising, turning out and bringing in. For many facilities, teasing, breeding, worming, veterinary procedures, foot care, halter breaking, etc. are secondary chores.

- **Clear distance from the floor to the ceiling.**
The minimum distance from the floor to the underside of roof or ceiling framing is 8 feet for a horse, and 14 feet for a horse and rider. Low ceilings interfere with ventilation, make the barn dark, and are a safety hazard for people and horses. Common ceiling heights are 9 to 10 feet for stall barns and 14 to 15 feet for riding areas. More information on the need for

high ceilings to enhance ventilation is discussed in *Chapter 7. Environmental Control.*

- **Suitable corrals and paddocks.**
Provide good drainage and safe, durable, and attractive fences. Review the topography of the land. Provide adequate space in lots and lanes. An efficient traffic plan reduces labor for turning out and bringing in horses. Fence the entire farmstead so loose horses cannot leave the property. *Chapter 10. Fencing* has more information on fencing.

- **Water.**
Sufficient quantity and quality of water must be available year round. Review placement of watering devices. Avoid using ponds and streams as direct water sources. See the section on *Water* in *Chapter 11. Utilities* for more information on water quality and quantity.

Floor Plan Options

When deciding on a floor plan, compare alternative housing arrangements and management methods and select those most suited to the situation. Collect ideas on horse facilities by reading books and magazine and by visiting as many existing farms as possible. Talk to people such as horse owners, agricultural engineers, and builders who have experience with facilities.

Stables floor plans are usually identified as single row, center alley, or island design, Figure 3-1. These identifications are based on the location of the stalls within the stable.

The single row configuration is attractive, but usually has the least amount of enclosed space compared to the other configurations. Horses are closer to their natural environment so each horse can have a desirable position within the stable. In most instances the handler is not protected from weather.

The central alley configuration can also be designed to provide horses with a door to the outside. This floor plan makes efficient use of interior space and protects people from the outside elements.

In the island floor plan, alleys can be used to cool horses, or if the ceilings are high

Attributes of a single row configuration are:
- Long single floor structure with side-by-side stalls.
- Each door opens into stable yard, individual runs, or communal paddock.
- Alley under roof overhang.

The central alley configuration commonly has:
- Stalls side-by-side along opposite stable walls and separated by wide alley.
- An alley that can be used for tying, grooming, saddling up, cooling out hot animals, cleaning stalls. The alley can be expanded to a small arena, although a very wide barn and excessive dust for horses in stalls may result.

Attributes of an island design are:
- Two rows of side-by-side and back-to-back stalls.
- Stall doors open into aisle, which encircles all the stalls.

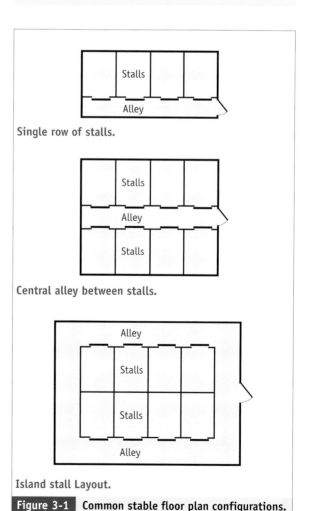

Single row of stalls.

Central alley between stalls.

Island stall Layout.

Figure 3-1 Common stable floor plan configurations.

enough, the alleys can be use to exercise animals during cold weather. If alleys are used to exercise animals, dust can be a problem. Because stalls are not located next to a wall, sunlight usually cannot reach stalls. Stalls can be more difficult to ventilate. This design also is the least efficient in its use of space.

The section on *Stalls* shows more specific layouts based on type and use of the stable and stalls.

Developing a sketch of the floor plan is an easy way to help visualize the building layout. When making a sketch allow for space to be taken up by walls and other structural members. Even though walls do not seem like they will take up much space, they will reduce the usable space inside the building. For example, two rows of 10- x 10-foot box stalls separated by a 10-foot wide alley do not fit in a 30-foot wide building, but do fit with very little room to spare in one that has a 32-foot outside dimension.

Building Framing Styles

Post and beam construction is common because posts support both the structure and the stall partitions. It is economical construction in many cases, but the drawback to this construction is a sacrifice of flexibility as compared to a clear span barn if remodeling becomes necessary.

Post or pole construction with a trussed roof provides a clear span barn and is a popular type of structure for stall barns or arenas. This type of construction avoids poured foundations. Rigid frames, arches, and gambrel frames are other alternatives that provide a post-free interior.

Figure 3-2 shows the basic roof frame types. Posts for stall partitions must be added in this type of construction. The shed is most often used for open-front barns or shelters. The gable roof style is used for both stables and open-front barns. The offset gable is most often used for stables that are designed as a standard gable style roof with the roof extended to provide a covered outside walkway. The gambrel and gothic styles are used for stall barns that have a large amount of hay storage above the stalls. The monitor roof style

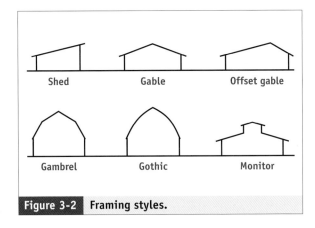

Figure 3-2 **Framing styles.**

is used for stables that want to enhance natural ventilation and want to bring in more natural light into the building. Whatever roof style is used, direct any roof runoff water away from paddocks and the manure handling area.

The building shell may use concrete block or poured concrete for the outer walls with interior clear span construction and wood stall partitions. An alternative is to use complete concrete block or poured concrete construction for both the outer walls and interior stall partitions. Poured concrete is more expensive than concrete block construction.

Shed roof

The shed style roof is widely used on open-front and enclosed permanent freestanding facilities, attached lean-to structures, and small movable buildings. This roof style is single sloped. It is relatively low in cost, provides good headroom, and is simple to build and insulate. It is adaptable to natural lighting with spaced translucent roof panels.

Most shed roofs employ a low pitch (slope) to keep the high side of the roof as low as possible unless room for overhead storage is desired. The minimum roof pitch is determined by the manufacturers' recommendation for the kind of roofing selected.

Figure 3-3 shows some common layouts for shed roof horse barns. Common rafters, beams, and trusses are used as framing members for shed roofs. The most common spans for wooden rafters range from 10 to 16 feet. In wider buildings, interior posts and beams are used in addition to the walls to support the rafters. Stall and pen partitions influence interior post location. To obtain a clear-span shed roof, one-slope trusses and long-span beams with purlins are often used. Clear-spans up to 48 feet or more may be constructed, although the longer trusses will be relatively more costly.

Gable roof

The gable roof shape is the most widely used for both open-front and closed buildings and for other horse housing facilities. It is applicable to both narrow and wide barns.

The gable is a triangular roof with two equal pitches that meet at a line in the center of the span. It has a pleasing appearance, is medium in cost, and is fairly simple to construct and insulate. It is adaptable for natural overhead lighting through fixed translucent roof panels, and for natural building ventilation through eave and ridge openings.

Side extensions for roof overhangs, covered ways, or greater barn width can be obtained by increasing the roof height of the basic building without changing the roof pitch, or by changing the roof pitch within the limits of good design. Headroom depends on wall height, roof pitch, and type of framing.

The ceiling may follow the slope of the roof or be dropped to wall height, with or without overhead storage.

Common wood rafters supported on walls, or interior posts and beams, may be used for buildings up to 72 feet wide. Rafter spans are influenced by stall size and service alley widths, and are most often 10 to 16 feet.

Clear span roof construction may be accomplished with wooden or steel trusses or with rigid frames of steel or wood. Wooden trusses are used extensively for clear spans to 60 feet. Pitches of less than 4:12 (rise:run) are seldom used on wooden truss roofs. Steel trusses may be extended further, but in many cases, rigid frame construction is used to obtain wider clear- space. Rigid frames, commercially produced of steel or laminated wood, are available for clear-span facilities of 100 feet or more wide. Figure 3-4 illustrates common gable roof horse housing options.

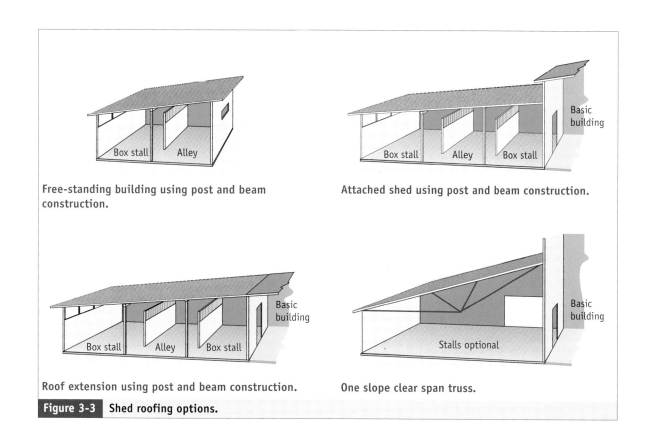

Free-standing building using post and beam construction.

Attached shed using post and beam construction.

Roof extension using post and beam construction.

One slope clear span truss.

Figure 3-3　Shed roofing options.

Offset gable roof

The offset gable is a triangular roof with two equal slopes of different lengths meeting at a ridge. It resembles the combination roof, which is two unequal slopes of different lengths. The offset gable roof is used on both narrow and wide structures for horse housing and associated activities.

Common framing methods involve rafters supported on walls, interior posts and beams, or a clear-span truss or rigid frame gable roof with a roof extension on one side. The roof extension may be either clear-span or supported on interior posts and beams. Both wood and metal construction are used.

Gambrel roof

The gambrel roof has two slopes on either side of a center ridge. The lower slope is steeper than the upper slope. It is used mainly on two-story barns up to 40 feet wide. This roof design is a more traditional barn look and allows for more overhead storage in the mow. If hay is going to be stored in the

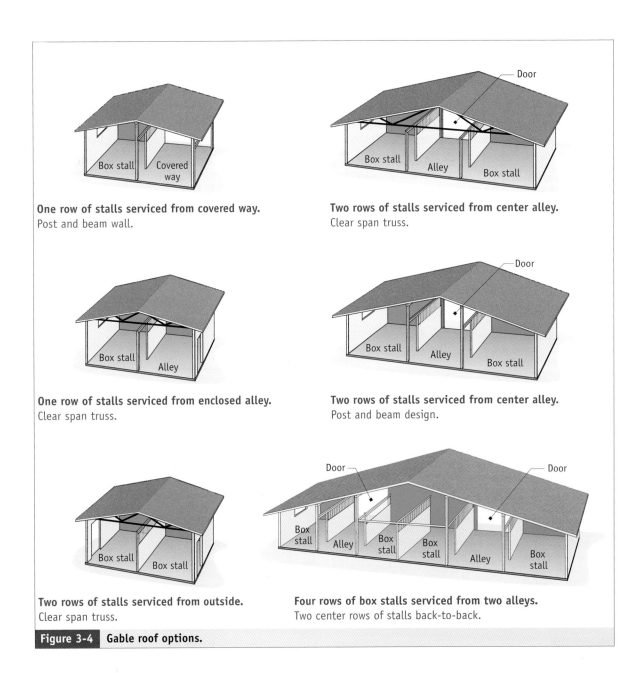

One row of stalls serviced from covered way.
Post and beam wall.

Two rows of stalls serviced from center alley.
Clear span truss.

One row of stalls serviced from enclosed alley.
Clear span truss.

Two rows of stalls serviced from center alley.
Post and beam design.

Two rows of stalls serviced from outside.
Clear span truss.

Four rows of box stalls serviced from two alleys.
Two center rows of stalls back-to-back.

Figure 3-4 | **Gable roof options.**

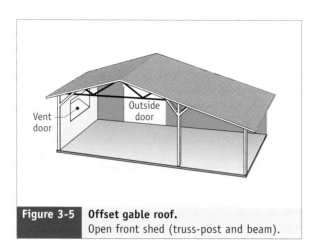

Figure 3-5 **Offset gable roof.**
Open front shed (truss-post and beam).

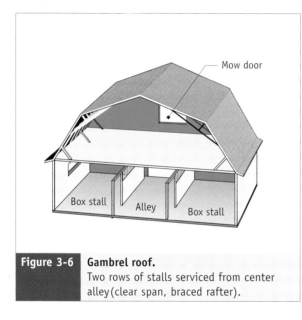

Figure 3-6 **Gambrel roof.**
Two rows of stalls serviced from center alley (clear span, braced rafter).

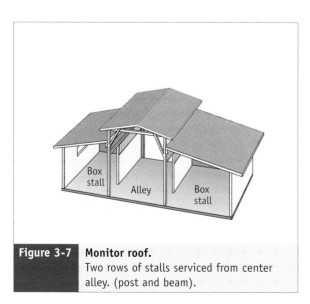

Figure 3-7 **Monitor roof.**
Two rows of stalls serviced from center alley. (post and beam).

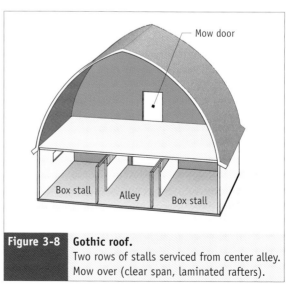

Figure 3-8 **Gothic roof.**
Two rows of stalls serviced from center alley. Mow over (clear span, laminated rafters).

mow, then be aware of the effect that this hay can have on ventilation and the fire hazard concerns. *Chapter 7. Environmental Control* and *Chapter 12. Fire Protection* address these issues.

The most common type of framing is light, clear-span braced rafters, supported on the barn wall and anchored to the mow floor joists to resist horizontal forces and uplift.

Monitor roof

The full monitor roof is made up of two shed sections and a gable section for the center portion of the roof. The vertical wall area separating the shed and gable roof provides natural light and ventilation. The monitor shape is seldom used for horse buildings less than 36 feet wide. The center section may be wider than the sheds or the reverse may be true. Its use matches that of clear-span buildings of similar size with side extensions. Framing is similar to that for shed and gable roofs.

Gothic roof

The Gothic roof is a pointed arch formed by two similar curved roof sections meeting at a center ridge. It is used on two-story barns and also for separate free-standing structures to provide shelter at ground level. It is adaptable to both narrow and wide structures. Similar to the gambrel style roof, this roof style has concerns with ventilation and fire when hay is stored in the mow. Read *Chapter 7. Environmental Control* and *Chapter 12. Fire Protection* for more details on these issues.

Clear-span laminated or segmented rafters are supported by and anchored to the walls and mow floor or to the foundation. Segmented wooden rafters usually are used for spans of 40 feet or less. Laminated wooden rafters are suitable for almost all spans.

Hoop structure

Hoop structures can also work well for some facilities, Figure 3-9. Hoop structures generally have posts and tongue and groove sidewalls with steel arches and a fiber reinforced tarp to form the roof. Since most simple designs do not provide them, sidewall curtains may be added to assist with ventilation. This style of structure works well for stalled facilities. Horses need to be placed in stalls to prevent them from damaging the tarp material. Hoop structures are affordable and can be well lit if the tarp is translucent. Conversely, solar heat gain can overheat a translucent building on hot, sunny days.

Roof Covering Options

Good roofing materials are essential to prevent water from leaking into the stable. Durability and aesthetics are usually the first qualities that people want in a roofing product, but cost is often times the deciding factor. The most commonly used roofing materials are metal, asphalt shingles, and wood shingles or shakes.

Metal. Insulation and a vapor barrier under the roof or ceiling minimize water condensation and dripping in the winter. Wetness creates unhealthy conditions and must be prevented. Metal is a good option in many circumstances.

Asphalt shingles. Asphalt shingles are the most popular roofing material in the U.S. More expensive than corrugated metal, they still have a relatively low cost and good life expectancy. Purchase shingles with a good fire rating. A Class A rating provides the greatest fire resistance. In high-wind locations, purchase shingles that carry a wind resistance

Figure 3-9   Hoop structure used to stable horses.

label indicating that they have been manufactured and tested to demonstrate acceptable resistance for the area.

Wood shingles and shakes. The difference between the two is that shingles are machine-sawn while shakes are hand-hewn and rougher looking. Wood shingles and shakes are popular on the West Coast and in parts of the Midwest. Fire preservative treatment is recommended, especially for buildings in areas prone to brush fires. Most wood roofs are covered by warranties, but some local codes limit their use because of fire concerns.

Table 3-1 summarizes the advantages and disadvantages of each of the roofing materials described.

Construction Materials

Select materials and construction type for durability, ease of maintenance, cost, marketing value, aesthetic appearance, and intangible values such as personal satisfaction in appearance. Higher quality materials may be more economical in the long run. Flexibility in construction, such as clear-span truss framing, allows alternative uses and the ability to remodel in response to changing needs of the operation.

The type of construction materials used in stables must be properly matched to building use, durability, and aesthetics. The most common construction materials used in stables are wood, plywood, concrete, masonry, and metal.

Wood. Most stalls are lined with wood even if outer walls and partitions are masonry or metal. Use hardwoods for strength and to discourage wood chewing. Use fire retardant and preservative treated wood to reduce fire hazards. For longer building life, wood in contact with the ground or bedding and where chewing and cribbing are not common should be preservative treated.

Plywood. Use exterior plywood sheathing on the interior or exterior of stable. Unless the plywood is over a solid backing, use ¾-inch thickness to reduce damage from kicking. Use treated plywood where appropriate. To discourage horses from chewing wood or plywood, fit boards or planks tightly together to reduce the number of chewable edges. Cover exposed wood edges with metal, such as angle or channel iron, that is smooth and blunt.

Concrete. Concrete works well in areas that require durability but have limited contact with horses. Wash areas, storage rooms, and office areas are locations that can make good use of concrete walls.

Masonry. Masonry costs more than a frame building, but its durability and low maintenance costs may make it more economical in the long run. Consider a masonry outer wall (shell) and wooden stalls. Have the foundation and walls reinforced with steel rods. Treat interior masonry walls with a fireproof paint sealer for a smooth, nonabrasive, and cleansable surface. Unless treated with sealer, masonry tends to allow moisture passage, especially with the more porous, lightweight types of blocks. Do not use combustible sealers because they will practically explode during a fire. An insurance agent should be able to assist in recommending fireproof paint sealers. Use only non-lead waterproof paint, inside and out. Very light colors increase stable brightness inside and reflect solar radiation outside.

Masonry is considered especially desirable for large horse operations. Blocks with a baked ceramic tile surface are desirable for laboratories, foaling stalls, and washing areas. In stalls, ceramic tile can be placed on the lower 5 feet of a wall with sealed block above the tile. A wood wainscoting can be used in locations where horses could crash into a wall.

Metal. As a primary building material steel is expensive, but minimized labor costs may make total building costs lower than wood. Steel frame with a composition, wood, or plastic exterior can combine some of the advantages of each system. The interior of a metal clad building must be wood lined for safety from sharp edges and to decrease kicking damage.

Table 3-2 summarizes the advantages and disadvantages of each of the construction materials described. Figures 3-10 and 3-11 show some basic stall wall designs and methods to anchor interior walls.

Table 3-1	Common roofing materials.	
Material	**Advantages**	**Disadvantages**
Metal	• Long life (20+ years) • Moderate cost. • Available. • Easily installed.	• Hot in summer and cold in winter. • May not be as attractive as other materials. • Noisy in rain and hail. • Hail or other objects can dent the roof
Asphalt shingles	• More pleasing in appearance to some people, and a more finished look. • Provide a little more insulation than metal.	• More expensive than metal. • Requires skilled labor to install and some upkeep. • Are combustible.
Wood shingles or shakes	• Have a natural appearance and rustic charm. • Provide a little more insulation than metal.	• More expensive than metal. • Requires skilled labor to install and some upkeep. • Some municipalities and insurance companies will not allow their use because of fire concerns.

Table 3-2	Common building construction materials.	
Material	Advantages	Disadvantages
Wood	• Attractive appearance. • Naturally good insulator. • Maintains a drier environment. • Easier on horse's feet and legs when kicked. • Resilient. • Easier to build for amateurs.	• Requires annual maintenance, less durable than masonry. • Can increase fire hazard unless treated with a fire retardant. • Porous material so it can harbor microorganisms. • Not vermin proof unless preservative treated. • Edges need to be well protected to prevent damage by chewing.
Plywood	• Can be stained and will not warp, shrink, or split. • Very strong. • Requires less maintenance than planking • Costs less than planking.	• May not be as attractive as planking. • Edges need to be well protected to prevent damage by chewing.
Poured concrete	• Very sturdy, durable, and requires little maintenance. • Easier to construct than masonry. • Nearly fireproof. • Vermin proof. • Horses may test concrete but usually will not persist in kicking or chewing it. • Steel reinforcing allows for flexible designs.	• Needs a poured foundation. • More difficult than wood- or steel-frame construction to insulate adequately for colder climates. • Possibility of injury with horses crashing into the walls.
Masonry	• Very sturdy, durable, and requires little maintenance. • Attractive. • Nearly fireproof. • Vermin proof. • Horses may test masonry but usually will not persist in kicking or chewing it.	• Material cost is often low but labor cost is high • Needs a poured foundation and concrete slab. • More difficult than wood- or steel-frame construction to insulate adequately for colder climates. • Possibility of injury with horses crashing into the walls.
Metal	• Construction is simple and relatively fast. • Requires little upkeep and is durable and vermin proof. • Can contain a fire until hot enough to melt.	• Some may not like the look of steel sided stables and arenas. • Metal allows some noise intensification with echoes and reverberations that can annoy or frighten horses. • Cold in winter and hot in summer—requires insulation in otherwise uninsulated buildings. • Must be lined with wood inside to prevent horses from kicking through.

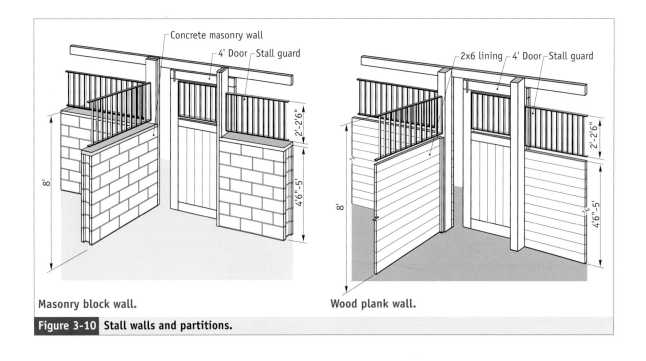

Masonry block wall.

Wood plank wall.

Figure 3-10 Stall walls and partitions.

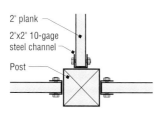

Wood post with steel channel.

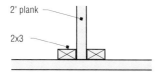

Wooden wall with 2-inch thick wood strips.

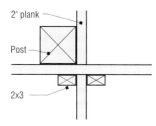

Wooden wall and post.

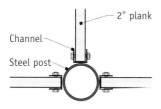

Round steel post with steel channels.

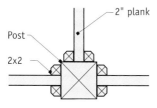

Wooden wall and post with 2-inch thick wood strips.

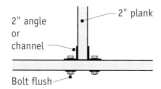

Wooden wall with steel channels.

Figure 3-11 **End anchors for stall partitions and walls.**

General Interior Design

Developing a safe and comfortable area to house horses is the main objective of a good stable design. In addition to comfortable stalls, it is important to design the building to be functional. Functionality can include interior construction features such as sturdy doors that do not hinder horse movement or alleys that allow for a makeshift exercise area during times of poor weather conditions. Functionality can also include specialty areas that allow for hay and feed storage, a tack room, or an employee meeting area.

The remainder of this chapter will review designs and design features that enhance horse comfort and the functionality of the stable.

Stalls

Horses housed inside fully enclosed barns or stables are almost always located in stalls. Because of concerns with fighting and injury, horses are often housed individually. To minimize hoof injuries and to add to the comfort of the horse, a good stall must have appropriate flooring and/or bedding. Because horses will typically spend a lot of time in the stall, food and water need to be provided.

When designing and constructing stalls, the absolute minimum distance from the floor to the underside of floor joists in a two-story barn, or to the underside of the lower chord of trusses or rafters in a one-story barn, is 8 feet for the horse only. Be aware that low ceilings interfere with ventilation, make the barn dark, and are a safety hazard for horse and handler. The absolute minimum distance for horse and rider is 14 feet. This distance also allows for better ventilation. Be sure that all upper surfaces are free of protruding nail points and other sharp objects that could injure a horse or rider.

The two types of stalls most commonly used are the box stall and the tie stall. A box stall is a confined area that allows the horse free movement within the area. A tie stall is an area in which the horse is tied. Housing horses in box stalls helps provide for individual care and reduce blemishes from biting, kicking, etc. In a tie stall the horse can stand

33

and lie down, but the horse does not have free movement to walk around the area. Tie stalls are used where horses are worked all day and need only a quiet place to rest, eat, and drink. Many barns or stables have only box stalls, Figure 3-12; some barns have both box and tie stalls, but seldom does a modern barn have only tie stalls. In most horse barns, some box stall space is necessary for sick animals, mares at foaling time, and colts.

Box stalls

The width of a barn or stable is usually determined by the box stall size and alley width. Typical building widths (outside measurement) for enclosed structures and for various box stall arrangements are illustrated in Figure 3-13. The most often-used width increment is 12 feet. Clear distances inside stalls and alleys will then be about 11 to 11½ feet. Select actual sizes to meet specific needs.

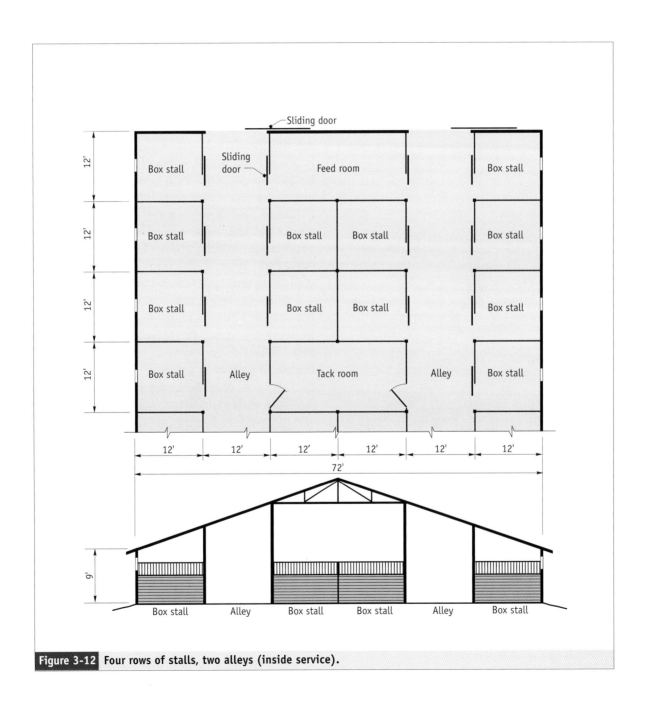

Figure 3-12 Four rows of stalls, two alleys (inside service).

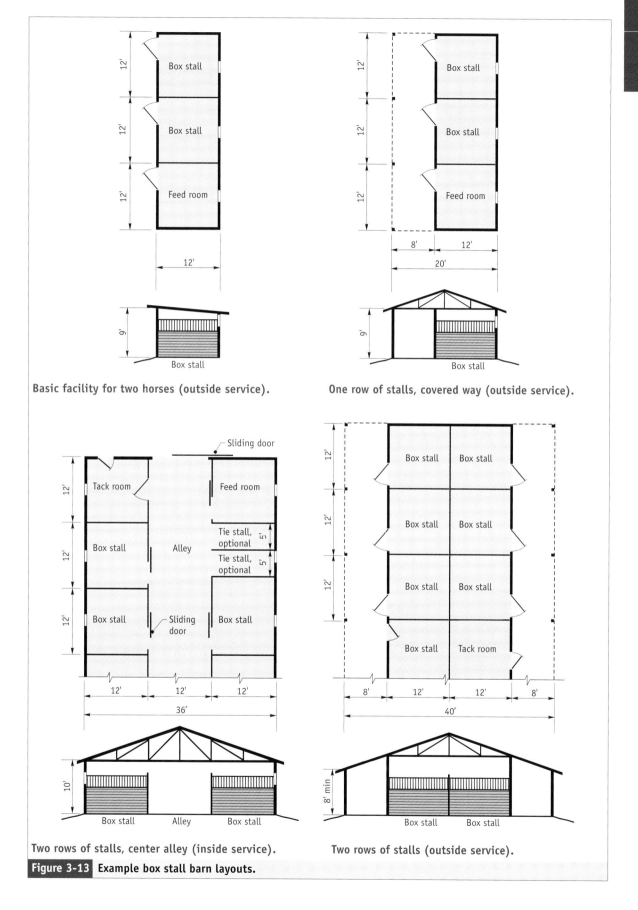

Basic facility for two horses (outside service).

One row of stalls, covered way (outside service).

Two rows of stalls, center alley (inside service).

Two rows of stalls (outside service).

Figure 3-13 Example box stall barn layouts.

Box stalls need to be large enough for the horse to move about freely. A horse needs space to lie down, roll over, and get up again without danger of casting itself. The more time a horse spends in a stall, the bigger the stall needs to be. For riding horses, the minimum box stall is 10 x 10 feet. The most common box stall size is 12 x 12 feet, but 16 x 16-foot stalls and larger are not uncommon. If the barn layout permits, a stall 16 x 20 feet or larger is useful for foaling. Box stalls for ponies may be smaller, depending on the breed. A larger stall can be obtained by removing the common partition between adjoining box stalls. Table 3-3 shows common box stall dimensions. Figure 3-14 shows some standard stall layouts.

Equip box stalls with rugged Dutch doors (hinged doors with top and bottom halves that operate independently), a full-length sliding door, or swinging gates hung with heavy hardware. Horses can open doors, so to be safe, install door fasteners that the attendant can operate from inside and outside the stall and that the horse cannot open. A stay roller or guide is required outside the bottom of sliding doors to hold them in place.

Provide a convenient and safe stall arrangement. Consider both the attendant and

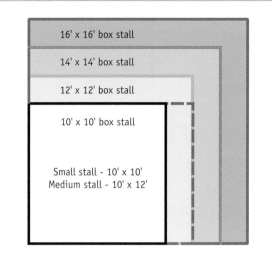

Box stall size comparison.

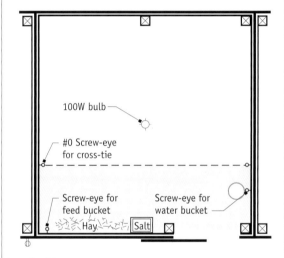

Standard layout.

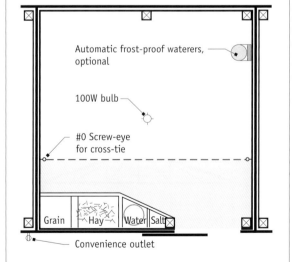

Layout with constructed feeding area.

Figure 3-14 Box stalls.

Table 3-3	Common dimensions for horses in box stalls.	

Horse	Horse size	Box stall size [a] (feet)
Mature animal (mare or gelding)	Small	10 x 10
	Medium	10 x 12
	Large	12 x 12
Broodmare	Minimum size	12 x 12
Foal to 2 year old	Average	10 x 10
Draft	Large	12 x 12
	Average	12 x 14
Maternity	Small	12 x 12
	Medium	14 x 14
	Large [b]	16 x 16
Stallion [c]	Minimum size	12 x 12
	Typical	14 x 14
Pony	Average	9 x 9 or 10 x 10

[a] Sizes larger than listed are unnecessary, but can provide more comfort to the horse. Larger stalls will result in an increase in bedding and labor.
[b] A removable partition can turn two regular stalls into one large maternity stall.
[c] Work stallions daily or provide a 2- to 4-acre paddock for exercise.

the horse. Include provisions for watering, feeding hay, grain, salt and minerals, and for cross-tying the animals.

The stall corner supports are usually pressure-treated posts or poles; steel pipe up to 5 inches in diameter is also used. In post and beam construction, the posts or poles serve as anchors for the end of the stall partitions, and their size is based on roof and mow design. Use pressure-treated wood for all wood materials in contact with the ground or foundation. Any area that could be subject to cribbing or chewing should be constructed of non-treated wood.

For pleasure horses, box stalls are preferred to tie stalls. If horses are housed in adjacent stalls, use a minimum 7-foot high partition between the stalls to prevent fighting. The bottom 54 to 60 inches of 7-foot stall partitions and inside walls is usually made tight in cold climates to prevent drafts and to protect the animals. Partition boards, spaced not more than 1½ inches apart, allow better ventilation but may require vertical center bracing to keep the wall from leaning due to abuse from horses. Concrete masonry partitions are popular because of ease of construction, durability, and low maintenance. The partition between the stall and the alley wall may be 5 to 6 feet high with no guard.

Stall fronts do not need to be as high as partitions. A 48-inch high front wall allows more air to enter the stall plus allows for easier observation. Some farms have totally open fronts.

The upper portion (24 to 30 inches) of the stall partition is often a rugged open panel or guard, Figure 3-15. This more-or-less open section aids ventilation and makes observation possible. Various materials are used for the open guards. The most common open guards are vertical ½-inch diameter steel rods, or ¾-inch pipe, or the equivalent. Bars must be sturdy enough not to bend on impact. This will prevent a horse from punching a hoof between the bars and getting stuck. The open space between slats, rods, pipe, or tubing should not be more than 4 inches. Other materials that are used for open guards are sections of #4 gage welded steel fence, flattened 1½-inch 9 gage expanded steel

Figure 3-15 Box stall with open panel that allows for easy observation.
Notice the grill is hinged to open out for the safety of the horse.

mesh, #6 gage welded wire 4- x 4-inch mesh, and chain link fencing.

A 1- x 4-inch cast rail is sometimes used in stalls to aid horses in righting themselves in the event that they lie down and cannot easily get back up. A ventilation slot inlet can be provided behind this rail to improve ventilation near the floor level. The slot inlet should be 2 inches wide by 7 feet long, and be protected by the cast rail. Install the slot inlet at a height of 20 inches above the stall floor

Tie stalls

The width of tie stall barns or stables is determined by stall length and alley width. If the building has both box stalls and tie stalls, the size of the box stalls usually determines barn width.

Tie stalls are not as widely used for pleasure horses as box stalls. However, they do provide an area for confining animals that are restless in box stalls. Tie stalls require about half the area of box stalls, less bedding, and are easier to clean than box stalls. They can often be constructed in existing buildings that are unsuitable for box stalls. Figures 3-16 and 3-17 show some basic tie stalls.

The typical tie stall is 5 x 9 feet (3 x 6 feet for ponies), although stall lengths up to 12 feet are often used for large horses and draft breeds. Table 3-4 and Figure 3-16 show common tie stall dimensions. The length of the stall is measured from the front of the

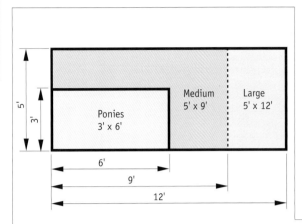

Table 3-4 Space requirements for horses in tie stalls.

Horse	Horse size	Tie stall size (feet)
Mature animal (mare or gelding)	Small	5 x 9
	Medium	5 x 12
	Large	5 x 12
Foal to 2 year old	Average	4.5 x 9
	Large	5 x 9
Pony	Average	3 x 6

Tie stall size comparison.

Common stall arrangement with tie stalls facing out. Serviced from the front feed alley. Built-in-manger.

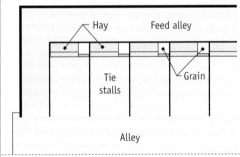

Common stall arrangement with tie stalls along wall. Serviced from the rear. Built-in-manger and minimum stall equipment.

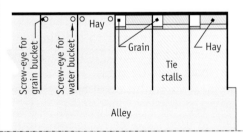

Figure 3-16 Tie stalls.

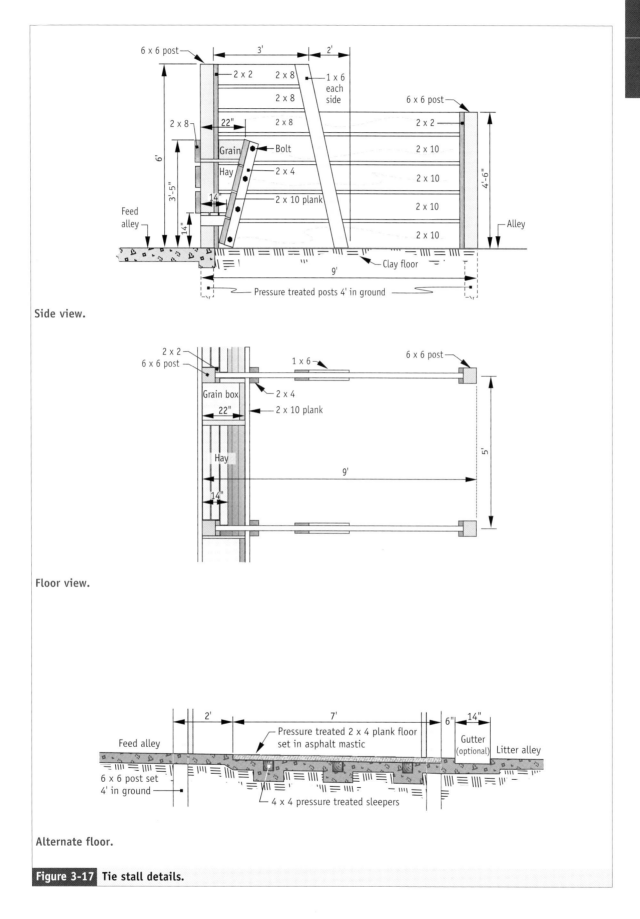

Side view.

Floor view.

Alternate floor.

Figure 3-17 Tie stall details.

manger or grain box to the rear of the stall partition. The top of a wooden built-in manger is about 2 feet wide. The standing platform is 7 feet long or longer. The built-in manger slopes forward at the bottom on the standing platform side to protect the animals' knees. Individual grain boxes and hayracks are sometimes used in tie stalls instead of built-in wood mangers. Avoid hay feeding on the floor because the hay may come into contact with manure, which can lead to parasite problems with the horse. Also, hay fed on the floor can be easily wasted because horses will often paw their bedding, including hay, backwards leaving no bedding or hay in the front. Horses are usually removed from the stalls for water and exercise, although watering in the stall is not uncommon.

A litter alley at least 6 feet wide and with a gutter is required behind a single row of tie stalls. A 10 to 12 foot litter alley with gutters separates two rows of stalls facing out. A 42- to 48-inch feed alley in front of each row of stalls is desirable. Feeding can be handled satisfactorily from the rear of a stall not serviced by a front feed alley.

Provide partitions between tie stalls high enough at the manger end to keep the animals from fighting. Use a height of at least 6 feet for the front or manger end of the partition, and 54 inches at the rear.

Typical building widths (outside measurements) for enclosed structures and various tie stall arrangements are illustrated in Figure 3-18. An actual tie stall arrangement is shown in Figure 3-19.

Mangers, Grain Boxes, and Hayracks

Mangers, grain boxes, and hay feeders can be purchased or constructed. Table 3-5 and Figure 3-20 show dimensions for constructing mangers and grain boxes using 2-inch wood, preferably a hardwood species or equivalent material. Corner or wall hayracks may be used instead of built-in wood mangers. Corner hayracks extend approximately 2 feet each way from the corner of the stall and usually have a circular front. Wall hayracks are approximately 4 feet wide with straight or circular fronts. Construct all mangers so they

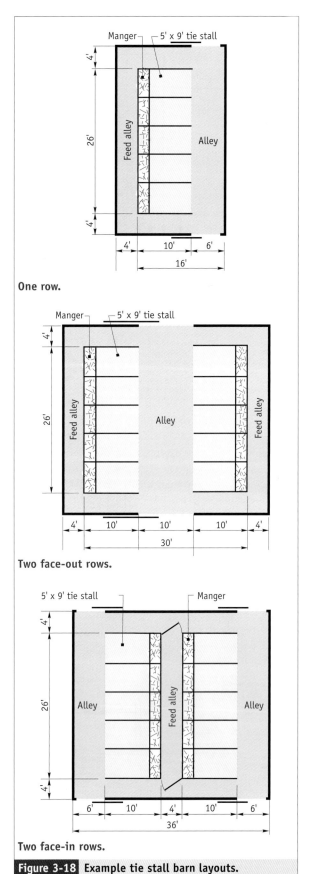

One row.

Two face-out rows.

Two face-in rows.

Figure 3-18 Example tie stall barn layouts.

Figure 3-19   Row of tie stalls.

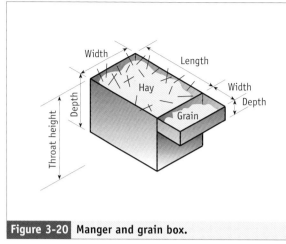

Figure 3-20   Manger and grain box.

Table 3-5   Hay manger and grain box dimensions (dimensioning inside the stall).

Animals	Dimensions[a]	Hay manger (inches)[b]	Grain box (inches)
All mature animals	Length	30 to 36	20 to 24
(Mares, Geldings, Broodmares,	Throat height	38 to 42	38 to 42
Stallions)	Width	20 to 24	12 to 16
	Depth	24 to 30	8 to 12
Foals and 2-yr olds	Length	24 to 30	16 to 20
	Throat height	32 to 36	32 to 36
	Width	16 to 20	10 to 16
	Depth	20 to 24	6 to 8
Ponies	Length	24	18
	Throat height	32	32
	Width	18	10
	Depth	20	6 to 8

[a] See Figure 3-20 for dimension locations
[b] Wall corner hayracks are often used instead of mangers. Five feet is the usual distance between the floor and bottom of the rack. Or, feed hay on the stall floor in both box and tie stalls and use a wall-mounted grain box in the corner of the stall.

are safe and convenient for horses to eat from and convenient for attendants to service.

Separate grain boxes, usually located in a stall corner for convenient feeding, are used in both box and tie stalls, especially when hay is fed in wall racks or on the stable floor. Grain boxes in box stalls are usually filled through a small opening in the front wall, and in tie stalls from the rear of the stall or from a front feed alley.

In box stalls, individual wall-mounted hayracks and grain boxes can also be used. A swing-out feeder is an easy way to feed horses without having to enter a stall, Figure 3-21. Many people like to feed hay on the floor. Some researchers and veterinarians believe

that it is healthier for a horse to eat hay in its natural grazing position than eating with its head at an abnormally high height (approximately wither height). The downside to feeding hay on the floor is that it contributes to feed waste, and horses can pick up diseases and parasites eating hay contaminated with manure. Some floor feeders have been designed to keep manure separate from hay. Figure 22 shows a protected corner hay feeding area at about floor level. Even this design cannot totally prevent a horse from pulling hay out onto the floor as is shown in the bottom photo of Figure 3-22. It is up to the horse owner to evaluate and decide on the advantages and disadvantages of each feed

Figure 3-21 | Swing-out feeder.

Protected feed area in a corner.
This design allows hay to be fed at floor level while being separate from stall manure.

Horses can still waste hay.
This design does not prevent feed wastage or keep the horse from defecating into the hay area.

Figure 3-22 | Floor level feeding.

method. Whichever method is used, it is important to clean up any feed or hay that falls to the floor on a daily basis.

Drinking Water Supply

A healthy horse needs an adequate supply of fresh water of the same quality as is used for human consumption. A mature horse of average activity level needs 8 to 12 gallons per day. The vast majority of horses are hand watered, but it is difficult to supply enough water by carrying it in pails, especially if caring for several horses.

Locate in-stall watering devices where spillage can drain directly from the stall—they may need filling more than once a day in a cold barn because of freezing. Locate stall waterers in a front corner of the stall, away from the feeder, and at a height of approximately 40 inches (or two-thirds the withers height) for mature riding horses. A stop and drain (frost proof) hydrant or an electrically heated watering bowl will supply fresh water in freezing weather.

One electrically heated watering unit can serve two stalls, or eight to ten horses in a lot. If horses are confined in tie stalls and a number are released at once, a small frost-free watering tank is desirable.

See *Chapter 11. Utilities* for a more detailed discussion of watering systems.

Interior Construction

Human and animal safety is a primary concern when designing or choosing construction materials for horse housing. Stall walls and partitions should be tight, smooth, and free of sharp corners, loose wires, protruding bolts and nails, and anything else that might

Excluding the stall, the main design areas of a barn or stable are:

- Acess doors.
- Alleys.
- Floor drainage.
- Windows.
- Ventilation.
- Lighting.

injure the horse as it moves about and lies down. The walls must be flush with the floor, so a horse cannot get its feet under the partition.

A common material used for stalls is 2-inch wood planks or tongue and groove lumber. Wood is a good material to use because it can withstand rough treatment, chewing, and kicking, while at the same time it flexes so striking it will not as easily result in injury to the horse. Concrete masonry walls are widely used in moderate climates where the outside stall walls are waterproof and block cores are filled with insulation material to reduce heat loss. Blocks are smooth and withstand rough treatment; chewing is not a problem. Concrete masonry partitions in horse barns are becoming more common.

Access doors

Three main types of doors are used for horse stalls: hinged, Dutch-style, and sliding. Hinged doors are usually one-piece doors. Typically, hinged doors should open out and not into a stall. The exception to the opening of a hinged door is when a screen door is used, Figure 3-23. In this case, the screen door opens inward unless a strong hinge and latch system used. A latch in the alley prevents this type of door from swinging closed or blocking an alley. Two locks should be installed for these doors to decrease rattling when it is pawed or kicked and to increase the door's strength. One lock should be installed 3 to 4 feet off the floor and one lock about 10 inches above the floor. The bottom lock should be foot-operated.

Dutch doors are one of the most popular types of doors for stables and are the type of

door most people associate with stables. Dutch doors are hinged, two-piece doors, split horizontally so the top portion can be opened separately from the bottom, see Figure 3-24. Dutch doors make a good exterior door to a paddock or run, where it is both a window and a door.

Dutch doors are less efficient along an alley, because it is awkward to have a door open into traffic. The bottom door should be about 4 to 5 feet high. This height makes the door tall enough to keep a horse from jumping over it, but low enough to allow the horse to put its head over easily. If allowed, horses will lean on the bottom door when the top is open as a window, which can lead to door and hinge damage. Also, horses will often nip at people who pass by. The upper door can be solid or a grill if it leads to an alley. Provide latches to secure top and/or bottom open to avoid accidental closings or blockage of alleys. Provide a latch to lock the two halves together to operate as one door.

Figure 3-23 **Hinged screen door.**
Hinged inside so horse does not push door off the hinges.

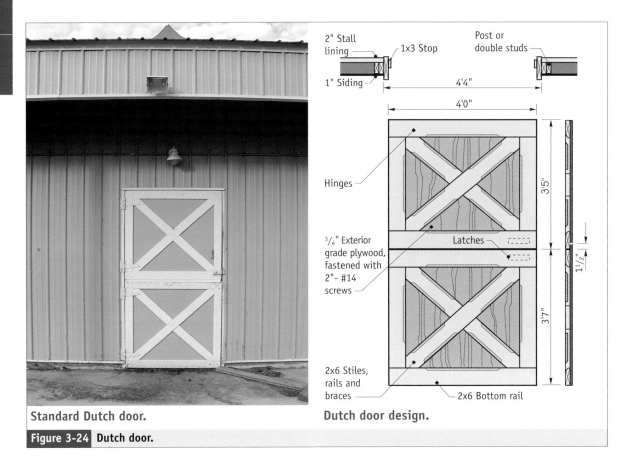

Standard Dutch door.

Dutch door design.

Figure 3-24 Dutch door.

Sliding doors are one piece, usually with a solid bottom and a grill at the top, Figures 3-15 and 3-25. These doors are mounted on the outside of the front stall wall or building on rollers and track. Often, sliding doors include a grill or vertical bars at least in the upper half of the door to improve ventilation. On some farms, the outside stall door is made up of two doors: one solid portion and one grilled door for improved ventilation. High quality hardware must be used to keep the door well balanced for easy opening. Choose heavy-duty track; a bottom guide is required to hold sliders in place. Installing guides at the lower corners can help prevent the bottom from being pushed out. Guides must be kept out of the doorway to avoid injuries. Sliding doors can be entirely screened. Doors that are entirely screened must use screens that do not allow a hoof to become stuck.

Because sliding doors are convenient to open, do not take up valuable alley space, and,

with appropriate hardware, can be secured part way open for a personnel pass, they are becoming very popular, especially for larger stables. The main disadvantages of sliding doors are they tend to be noisy, require more hardware, and are expensive.

Ideally, stalls should have two doors, one to the alley and one to the outside. This arrangement provides a fire exit, convenient access for cleaning, and cross ventilation for hot weather. Stall doors need to be at least 4 feet wide, with a preferred width of 4½ feet. Use 6-foot wide doors for broodmares, active animals, and mares with foals. Doors that are often used for horses with a handler should be even wider to avoid injury to horse and handler. Horses are known for throwing their heads and can injure themselves if the door frame does not have enough clearance. The minimum door height to reduce the potential for horse injury is 8 feet. Table 3-6 shows a summary of recommended stall door dimensions.

Good stall doors are important and this is one area that a horse owner needs to properly evaluate and spend money on wisely. Stall doors need to be constructed using rugged and durable materials and hardware. Durability depends primarily on quality of materials and construction, and on timely maintenance. All doors should operate easily. Mount them close enough to the floor so feet do not get caught. A door can be completely solid, completely grilled, mesh or screened, or a combination. Solid door sections need to use planed durable woods, preferably a hardwood such as oak. Normally, the doors are constructed of 2-inch planking. Doors can be completely solid to 8 feet high. When using a grill, place 2-inch

thick boards horizontally to at least 5 feet high. Two thicknesses of ¾-inch exterior plywood also make good doors.

To minimize the potential for injury, doors and latches cannot have sharp edges. Locks and latches must be very strong and horse proof. Heavy gauge steel is a must. Fasteners must withstand vigorous kicking. Horses open their own horse-proof locks quite regularly. Make the lock-accessible to a handler from inside as well as outside of the stall for safety. The latch should be simple to operate, but designed to be horse-proof, Figure 3-26. Minimize protruding edges. Recess hardware into the wall and door or add wood blocks above and below to cover the exposed metal. Hard rubber can be used to cap sharp edges, but rubber wears easily.

Screens are woven wire mesh (2 inch or less) that will not catch even a foal's foot. Some screens are 4½-foot high sections hinged up off the floor. Other screens are sliding doors, which extend from the floor up to 8 feet high. A heavy-duty partial screen inside the door frame allows increased summer ventilation, observation, and a better view for the horse without the horse leaning into the aisle. Set the 4½-foot partial screens 2 feet off the floor. The height can vary with individual horses. Hinge the door to open into the stall so horses do not push the door off its hinges,

Table 3-6	Door dimensions for horse housing.	
Use	Door width (feet)	Door height (feet)
Stalls	4.5[a]	8
Stable doors for small wheeled equipment and loose horses	10[b]	10
Horse and rider	12	12
Large equipment, horse and rider	16	14

[a] Typical width. Range of 4 to 6 feet wide.
[b] Minimum width for loose horses. Ideally for loose horses to avoid injury, the door width should be wide enough to allow the horses to exit a building simultaneously if startled.

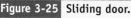
Figure 3-25 Sliding door.

Closed position.

Open position.

Figure 3-26 Example of a horse-proof latch.

Figure 3-23. Screens are not recommended where foals may escape underneath. Total screen doors, which slide, offer an easy view of horses, especially mares with foals. Allow ventilation where solid stall partitions have been used.

Sliding doors and Dutch doors are the most popular types of doors. When selecting a door type, be sure to evaluate the location and use of the door. One type of door may not be best in all locations. Exterior doorways should be protected with overhangs or eave troughs. The ground should be sloped to facilitate drainage away from the building.

Alleys

Alleys should allow enough room to maneuver manure handling equipment and should have a solid floor that can handle this equipment. Alleys also can allow horses to exercise or cool in them. Alleys should be wide enough for a horse to turn around easily and safely. Narrow alleys that allow only one-way traffic are inconvenient and can be blocked by open swinging doors.

Table 3-7 shows minimum alley widths. For convenience, safety, and animal traffic, alleys should be a minimum of 10 feet wide, preferably 12 feet wide. This minimum width allows room for moving horses, a small truck, or a tractor pulling a wagon or a manure spreader.

Alleys that do not have much or any horse activity do not need to be as wide as alleys with greater horse activity. Litter alleys or alleys located in the back of a single row of stalls should be at least 6 feet wide. Narrower alleys will increase hand labor and make moving horses through them more difficult. For convenient feeding, especially with baled hay, feed alleys should be a minimum of 4 feet wide. Cross alleys should also be a minimum of 4 feet wide. Paving alleys is optional. Any doors located at the ends of litter alleys should be either sliding or overhead type. Size doors for the kind of traffic anticipated. To save space in small barns, cross-ties can be provided for an informal grooming area in the alley. Some tack and equipment can be stored in the alley.

Alleys separating two rows of stalls in box stall barns are often used for handling and

Table 3-7	Alley dimensions.	
Use	Minimum width (feet)	Recommended (feet)
Horse traffic	10	12
Horses, pickup truck, tractor and wagon	12	14
Litter alley behind single row of tie stalls	6	8
Feed alley for a person and feed cart	4	6

resting animals and for limited exercise and training. Many times the building width will dictate the alley width. For example, a 50-foot wide barn or stable can have alleys as wide as 28 feet.

Alley heights should be 9 to 10 feet (8 feet minimum) for horse alone, 14 to 15 feet (12 feet minimum) for horse and rider, and 14 feet minimum, for horse and rider in arena.

Any water hydrants and electrical outlets should be located along the alley walls and near protective posts. Hooks are often located outside of each stall to store halters and lead ropes. These items should be hung well away from the grillwork so that a horse cannot chew this expensive equipment. Some facilities locate an extension telephone in the alleyway. Remember to always keep the alleys free from obstructions to avoid blocking traffic and to make the alleys easier to clean.

Windows

Windows can provide natural light and ventilation to a barn or stable even though they are not essential if other methods are used for lighting and ventilating the building. A small adjustable 2- x 2-foot window in each box stall will not only provide light and assist in ventilation, but can also provide visual stimulation to the horse by allowing the horse to look outside. However, windows do add to building costs.

Windows should be located near the top of the wall. Allow at least 6 feet between the window sill and the stall floor. Protect all windows that can be reached by horses with heavy 1- x 2-inch welded wire or a steel grating. Attach the protective guard to the window so it can be easily removed for window cleaning.

Translucent roof and wall panels can be used to admit daylight. However, they may become a heat source in the summer and are subject to severe moisture conditions and frosting in cold weather.

Summer ventilation can be provided by solid, adjustable-ventilation doors near the top of outside walls instead of, or in addition to, windows. Jalousie-type windows are widely used in horse barns because they admit air and light, exclude rain, and are easily adjusted,

Provide lighting for:
- General illumination of alleys and pathways
- Specific illumination of stalls, storage areas, and specialty areas
- Outside approach and service areas.

and window guards do not interfere with their operation.

More details about using windows for natural lighting and ventilation can be found in *Chapter 7. Environmental Control* and *Chapter 11. Utilities.*

Lighting

Good illumination is important for the convenience and safety of both the horse and the attendant.

Additionally, lighting can affect breeding efficiency and hair coat length of horses. Provide lighting receptacles to extend day length for higher breeding efficiency. Light can also be used to help to control coat length for show horses. Use enough lighting for efficient inspection and work. Provide at least two lighting circuits in each building. *Chapter 11, Utilities* provides more information on wiring for lighting and lighting recommendations. Electric wiring and fixtures must comply with applicable state and national electric codes.

Specialty Areas

Most barns and stables are not just areas to house horses, but also have space available for other areas that allows for easier horse care and management. These specialty areas include tack rooms, supply areas, feed and bedding storage, wash and grooming areas, offices, and restrooms. Some facilities even have an area to use portable stalls or isolate a horse in the event of illness or disease. In large barns, locating the tack, feed, and hay in the middle of a block of stalls is handier to all stalls, rather than housing it at one end of the building.

Tack room

Traditionally, in larger stables the tack room has been the horse owner's headquarters for essential equipment and activities. In smaller stables, a tack room can simply be an equipment storage area. Overall, the tack room can be a small area or room for riding equipment, or it can be large enough to serve as an office, a service shop for cleaning and maintaining tack, and a meeting and lounging place.

A small stable can have a combination feed-tack-grooming area, and good management can keep it useable for all purposes. Locate this multiple use area out of the way on a wall or in a separate room or building. Keep tack out of the horses' reach and out of traffic lanes. Tack trunks can be a practical solution.

Formal tack rooms at large show operations can include lounges, trophy rooms, show tack displays, office, and work rooms. Large stables may need a tack room for often-needed equipment close to the horses and a separate room for show equipment.

A well organized and maintained tack room needs to be enclosed, dry, free of dust, and secured from vandalism. Ideally, the tack room should be a totally enclosed area that is insulated, heated, and ventilated to keep it dry and comfortable in cold weather. Keep the room clean from dust, dirt and debris. A concrete floor helps housekeeping. Provide a drain, or slope the floor to a gutter or drain in the alley if you expect to use water in the room.

Keeping the room dry is a must because moisture and mildew rapidly deteriorate leather tack. Infrared heaters can help eliminate mildew and dampness and provide warmth. An overdry room's effect can be lessened by diligent oiling of leather. Some moisture is brought in by sweat on tack. Even though the tack room should be dry and dustless, ventilate it properly to remove odors and moisture.

The tack room needs to be rodent proof. Rodents chew on tack to obtain salt from sweat and can ruin a lot of expensive tack in little time. It is also important to control insects. Screened windows help keep insects out of the room.

Install at least 300 watts of incandescent lighting (100 watts fluorescent) per 100 square feet of floor area. Provide adequate convenience outlets with a minimum of two outlets.

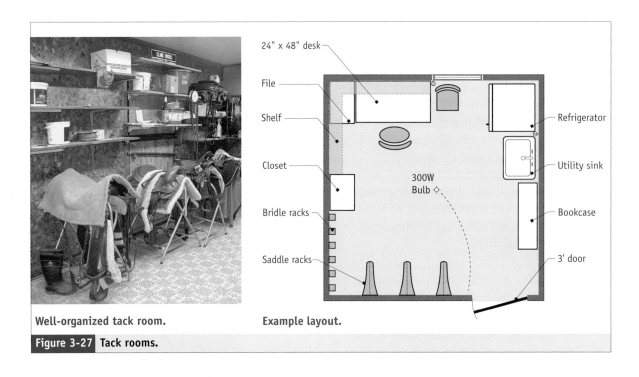

Well-organized tack room.

Example layout.

Figure 3-27 Tack rooms.

Build the tack room large enough for the activities associated with it. The tack room may contain all or some of the following equipment and facilities (Figure 3-27):

- Racks for saddles, bridles, halters, lead ropes, blankets, etc.
- Tack box.
- Grooming and shoeing supplies.
- First aid kit.
- Clothes closet.
- Storage cabinets, shelves, filing cabinets.
- Desk, chairs, miscellaneous furniture.
- Refrigerators, sink, cooking facilities.
- Working and loafing areas.
- Heating equipment, hot and cold running water.
- Toilet and shower facilities may be adjacent.
- Laundering facilities.
- Oven and refrigerator, stereo.

Vandals know that tack rooms are an area in which many valuables are stored. Install lockable doors and windows to provide security and guard against theft.

At a minimum, provide space for a rack for each saddle and bridle. A rack prevents the saddletree from being damaged and keeps saddles cleaner. Allow a 30- to 36-inch square area of wall space for each saddle, perhaps in more than one row. Western saddles weigh about 40 pounds, so install the rack at a convenient height, which is usually about hip height (32 to 42 inches). Hang bridles on 4-inch diameter rounded racks to keep the headstall in proper shape. Bridles and reins hung over nails tend to crack and break easily.

Supply, miscellaneous equipment, and tool storage area

On larger farms, plan a separate supply area. Include a refrigerator for medications, a sink and wash area, and storage for other veterinary supplies. This area may be incorporated with the tack room, but if the materials stored will be damaged by freezing, a separate heated room should be planned. This room might be incorporated with a utility room that includes the water heater.

A separate area or room for miscellaneous equipment and tools is not necessary, but consider where things will be stored. Keep brooms, manure forks, and shovels out of the way of horses and traffic. Keep wheelbarrows, carts, or baskets within easy reach to encourage prompt, continual clean-up. Keep disinfectant (lime) and fly repellent secure from children, horses and other animals. Have an area that has easy access for a first-aid kit and a secured area for horse medication, liniment, wormers, and hoof treatments. Some stables will need an area for storing farm equipment to mow lawns, haul manure, and remove snow.

Feed room

Even though horses can be quite large, they have a relatively small digestive system when compared to their size. The stomach of a 1,000-pound horse has only a 4-quart capacity; about 10% of it is intestinal tract. Therefore, horses need to be fed at least twice daily, three times preferred, so they can properly digest their food. Feed must be clean and free from mold. Horses do not tolerate spoiled feed as well as some other livestock species.

In the wild, horses graze all day long, so their natural inclination is to eat continuously (i.e., grazing to take in small but frequent amounts of forage). However, horses with free, or accidental, access to high-energy feed will have the potential to overeat and possibly develop laminitis (founder) and may die. Therefore, it is important to keep horses separated from feed, especially grains.

To keep horses away from having free access to grains, it is important to have a designated and secured feed area. Having a dedicated area or room in a stable also can help reduce problems with feed wastage, moisture, rodents, and messes due to torn bags and spilled feed. This is especially true for bagged ingredients. Install locks to keep horses out of the feed room. The door should be horse proof even if unlocked. In the long run, keeping the horse separated from the grains does more to protect the horse from harming itself than it does from keeping the horse from making a mess in the room.

The feed room design does not have to be elaborate. Some horse owners will use an unused box stall as their feed storage area. Even though the room does not have to be elaborate, some basic features help in making the area more useful. The feed room should be well lighted and equipped with convenience outlets. *Chapter 11, Utilities* shows the basic lighting and wiring recommendations. Usually, providing 150 watts of light and at least two convenience outlets in the feed room will be sufficient. The entrance door to the feed room should be at least 4 feet wide and equipped with a latch so that a loose horse cannot get into the feed.

Typically, only grains are kept in the feed room, but the feed room can store both grain and hay together. Keeping grains stored separately from hay also has its advantages, such as easier cleaning because materials will not mix together. Also, rodent control can be more effective because the rodent's food source (grain) is kept separate from a potential hiding area (hay).

The amount of space needed for feed storage depends on the number and size of the horses, activity level of the horses, how often the feed supply needs to be refreshed or replenished, amount of quality pasture provide, and amount of quality roughage provided. As a general rule, horses eat about 1% to 3% of their body weight in dry matter per day depending on their level of activity.

Tables 3-8 and 3-9 show some general guidelines for horse rations. Use these tables when reliable ration data for the operation is not available. Rolling or breaking kernels of grains such as wheat, corn, barley, and milo will help in digestibility. Processing larger grains (oats) does not seem to greatly improve the digestibility. Process all grain (cracked, crimped or rolled) for foals or horses with poor teeth.

As a general rule-of-thumb a 1,000-pound horse will consume about 15 pounds of hay and 5 pound of grain per day. Table 3-10 shows some feed density and volume properties that can be used to help estimate storage space requirements for hay and grain. Most bulk feed weighs 40 pounds per cubic foot or one ton per 50 cubic feet. See *Chapter 9, Bulk Feed and Bedding Storage* for information on storing large quantities of feed or hay.

Buy and store only what can be fed before it spoils. Parasites, insects, rodents, and birds must all be kept out of the feed. Provide only damp-proof and vermin-proof containers. Large (about 30 gallon) garbage cans that are about one-half to three-quarters full can hold about 100 pounds of corn or 50 pounds of crimped oats. Large stables may store feed in hopper-bottom bins, elevated for gravity unloading or equipped with inclined augers, to deliver grain to the feed room, Figure 3-28. Bins may be built on a roof or up high and connected to the feed room with a chute. Equipment is needed to load and unload these storage bins, which makes this system too expensive for a small stable.

Use containers that close tightly and/or can be locked if the feed storage is just a designated area in a very small stable. Metal-lined storage bins and hard plastic or galvanized cans are common. Eliminate sacks of feed to decrease rodent and bird problems. Store containers so they cannot be knocked over by even a very determined horse.

Organize the feed room for convenience and easy housekeeping, Figure 3-29. Plan storage for feed materials, equipment, and tools. Provide an uncluttered traffic pattern to reach the stored materials without interference. Keep the storage area as dust free as possible. Provide

Figure 3-28 Hopper-bottom bin for feed storage.

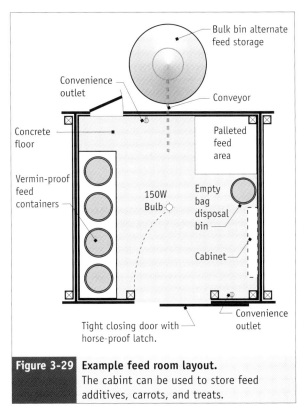

Figure 3-29 **Example feed room layout.**
The cabint can be used to store feed additives, carrots, and treats.

Labels in figure:
- Bulk bin alternate feed storage
- Convenience outlet
- Conveyor
- Concrete floor
- Palleted feed area
- Vermin-proof feed containers
- 150W Bulb
- Empty bag disposal bin
- Cabinet
- Tight closing door with horse-proof latch.
- Convenience outlet

Figure 3-30 **Scale used to measure rations.**

space for storing supplements, salt blocks, medications, minerals, vitamins, grain crimper, feed carts, scales, and any other items that are pertinent to the feeding program. Keep feed storage areas free of batteries, petroleum products, chemicals, and other non-feed items. A set of small scales (10 pounds) and a scoop are necessary for accurate daily feeding of concentrates and medicated feeds. Large scales (30 pounds) can allow for accurate measuring of total rations, Figure 3-30. The feed room can be combined with the tack room if feed is stored in containers to promote a clean room.

Store bagged feed in a rodent- and bird-proof area. Store bags on pallets that leave an air space under the bags to prevent moisture migration from the floor to the bags. In order to maintain rodent proofing and allow for cleaning up spilled feed, a concrete floor is desirable. Once bags are opened, it is desirable to empty a whole bag into a plastic or metal container with a tight fitting lid rather than feeding directly from an open sack each day, Figure 3-31. Measuring feed from an open bag

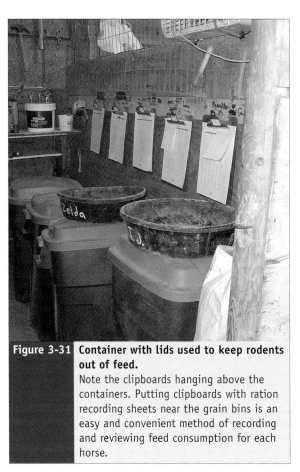

Figure 3-31 **Container with lids used to keep rodents out of feed.**
Note the clipboards hanging above the containers. Putting clipboards with ration recording sheets near the grain bins is an easy and convenient method of recording and reviewing feed consumption for each horse.

is difficult, and an open bag exposes the feed to moisture from the air. Label containers to preserve identification of feeds. In smaller operations, a large metal or wooden cabinet that can store several bags, and a container with a lid that will hold more than one bag of feed can be useful. Plan space for the disposal of empty bags.

A good rodent control program is essential. Feed grain must be stored in vermin-proof bins or containers. Metal containers such as large garbage cans and wood bins with tight lids are excellent for limited bulk feed storage. Hopper-bottom bins with mechanical unloading are also used either inside or outside the barn. Home-made and commercial grain bins are used for storing grain in large quantities. If necessary, use baits to control rodents. Contrary to common belief, cats are typically not effective in controlling rodents and should not be used as the only control for rodents. This is due, in

part, to many cats being fed food in the stable. This food is an attractant to rodents, and because cats are being fed, they are not as likely to prey on the rodents.

Many insurance companies have very strict requirements if hay is stored inside a barn or stable. Before storing hay inside a barn or stable, check insurance requirements regarding hay storage. Tables 3-8 to 3-10 can be used to help estimate the amount of storage needed for hay.

Hay may be stored in an overhead loft or on the ground floor. When storing hay in an overhead loft, be sure the hay does not affect any ventilation for the building. Also, if hay is stored overhead, some equipment, such as a conveyor, needs to be used to assist in moving the bales from ground level to the overhead loft; otherwise, a fair amount of physical labor will be needed to hoist bales. When storing hay at ground level, make sure enough space

Table 3-8   **Light horse rations.[a]**

Age, sex and use	Live weight (lbs)	Daily allowance (lb per 100 lb live weight)		
		Grain	Hay	Ration type[b]
Stallions in breeding season	900 to 1400	0.75 to 1.50	0.75 to 1.50	1, 2, 3
Pregnant mares	900 to 1400	0.75 to 1.50	0.75 to 1.50	4, 5, 6
Foals before weaning	100 to 350	0.50 to 0.75	0.50 to 0.75	4, 7, 8
Weanlings	350 to 450	1.00 to 1.50	1.50 to 2.00	8, 9, 10
Yearlings	450 to 700		——— Summer Pasture ———	
Yearlings, in training	450 to 700	0.75 to 1.25	0.75 to 1.25	3, 4, 8, 10
Yearlings, or rising 2 year olds	700 to 1000	0.50 to 1.00	1.00 to 1.50	3, 4, 11
Light horses at work				
•Hard use	900 to 1400	0.25 to 1.50	1.00 to 1.25	3, 12, 13
•Medium use	900 to 1400	0.75 to 1.00	1.00 to 1.25	3, 12, 13
•Light use	900 to 1400	0.50	1.00 to 1.25	3, 12, 13
Mature idle horses	900 to 1400	—	1.50 to 1.75	—

[a]From Light Horses, USDA Farmer's Bulletin 2127.
[b]Refer to Table 3-9.

Table 3-9   **Grain rations for light horses.***

Grain Type	Grain ration (lbs of feed material per 100 lbs of ration)												
	1	2	3	4	5	6	7	8	9	10	11	12	13
Barley	–	–	–	–	45	–	–	30	–	–	35	–	30
Corn	–	35	–	–	–	–	–	–	–	–	–	70	–
Oats	55	35	100	80	45	95	50	30	70	80	35	30	70
Wheat	20	15	–	–	–	–	–	30	–	–	–	–	–
Wheat bran	20	15	–	20	10	–	40	–	15	–	15	–	–
Linseed meal	5	–	–	–	–	5	10	10	15	20	15	–	–

* From Light Horse, USDA Farmer's Bulletin 2127.

Table 3-10 Bulk feed material properties.

Feed material	Density (lbs/cu ft)	Volume (cu ft/ton)
Baled hay	10	200
Barley, 15%	52	38
Bulk feed	40	50
Corn, 15.5%		
•Ear, husked	71	28
•Shelled	45	45
Ear corn	28	70
Flaxseed, 11%	45	45
Grain sorghum, 15%	45	45
Grain sorghum, 15%	50	40
Oat, 16%	78	26
Rye, 16%	44	45
Soybeans, 14%	42	48
Wheat, 14%	42	48
Whole oats	26	80

Figure 3-32 Feed room with shelves to store hay.

is available for storage and movement of bales. Hay stored at ground level should be located on a clean dry surface. Concrete floors are ideal for storing hay on the ground. Hay sitting on soil or a fine rock base, such as limestone, can pick up these fine materials making the hay less palatable. Hay can be stored on pallets, a sheet of plastic, or plywood to keep it clean. Small rooms and narrow doors are inconvenient for storing hay and add to the labor required to handle it when moving it into and out of storage. If hay is stored in the same room as grains, locate the hay at the opposite end of the room from the grains. Shelves can be used to store small quantities of hay, Figure 3-32. Having shelves is especially convenient if horses need a specific quantity of hay each day.

Grooming and wash area

The grooming area can be a separate room or stall or part of an alley outside of the stalls. Locate this area near the tack room, and provide cross-ties for horses. In busy alleys, locate the grooming area in a separate stall. Choose flooring that is firm, skid resistant, and easy to clean. Provide good lighting and ample electrical outlets for grooming equipment.

If the grooming area is also used for washing, provide a water faucet, preferably with hot water, Figure 3-33. Slope the floor

toward the drain, and ensure that the floor is skid resistant (e.g. install a rubber pad with a slip-proof pattern on a concrete floor). A 10- x 12-foot area is adequate size. A radiant heater in this area can dry horses in cold weather.

General design guidelines for grooming and working areas:
- Locate the area near the tack room for easy access to tools and tack.
- Avoid cross-tying horses in a busy alley for grooming.
- Provide cross-ties in the stalls or separate grooming area.
- Provide safe storage for supplies and a first-aid kit.
- Provide a firm and non-skid flooring.
- Use a high ceiling, 9-foot minimum.
- Provide good lighting and electrical outlets for grooming equipment.
- Provide a water faucet, preferably with hot water.
- Slope the wash area floor toward a drain.

Enclosed wash area.
Floor drain located below mat. Floor in this area
slopes toward the drain from all directions.

Wash area in a hoop structure.

Outdoor grooming and wash area.
Note the cross-ties that help position the horse.

Figure 3-33 Grooming and wash areas.

Office, supply, and restroom areas

An office or recordkeeping area, supply storage room, and restroom can all be useful additions to horse housing, particularly on larger farms. Often, one or two 12- x 12-foot box stall spaces can be enclosed for such use. Figure 3-34 illustrates examples of some potential layouts.

Often, a small office is useful for recordkeeping and for discussing tasks with employees or meeting with visitors. On some farms, larger offices are needed for employee conferences and as a communication headquarters. In those cases, a conference area may also be needed. A window is convenient in the office, and in or near each walk-in door. Heating may be desired in the office for colder climates. Electric resistance heat, a heat pump, or a gas space heater are options. Air conditioning also can be added to these areas.

Many facilities, especially those with off-farm labor, provide a small restroom in the main horse barn, usually near the office. Although the water heater and septic system for the lavatory and toilet are an added expense, a restroom improves working conditions, is a convenient clean-up area, and may be needed or required if horses are boarded. A shower, laundry facility, and clothes storage area are also desirable for farms with off-farm labor. At a minimum, a frost-free hydrant and drain are needed in the barn.

Portable stalls

Portable stalls can be used as an alternative to stationary, permanent stalls in cases where the building may be used for other purposes in the future. If the building is to be used only for horse housing, permanent stalls are preferred. The advantages of portable stalls include no permanent interior posts being required, stalls being movable to another site, and stalls being purchased as a package. However, they are generally not as sturdy as permanent stalls, often are more costly, and may require more repairs over time.

Isolation

If possible, isolate one stall from the others as a sick bay for contagious or

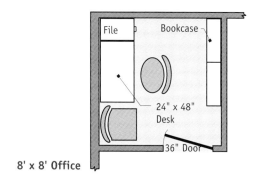

8' x 8' Office

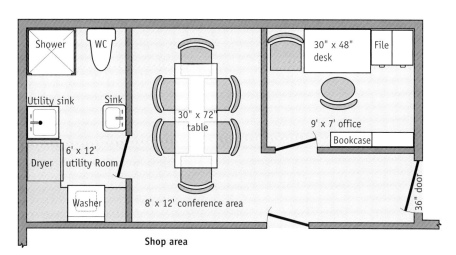

12' x 24' Attached office

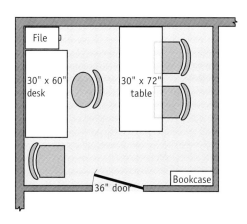

10' x 12' Office

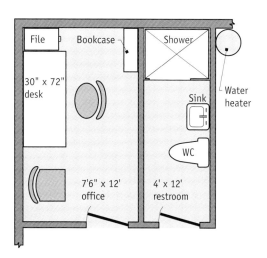

12' x 12' Office and restroom

Figure 3-34 Example office and supply room layouts.

infectious horses. Isolate new horses for a short quarantine period.

Isolation stalls are necessary when an outbreak of an infectious disease occurs on the farm. Locate isolation stalls in a separate barn, if possible. Isolate airflow from this area or stall to other areas of the stable. But on many farms, isolation must be accomplished within a single barn. Limit the traffic through isolation areas to prevent additional disease transmission. Isolation facilities related to breeding systems are further discussed in *Chapter 6. Breeding Facilities.*

The capability of cleaning and disinfecting conventional stalls is especially important in isolation stalls. Use smooth, easy-to-clean materials for stall surfaces, and limit the potential for animal-to-animal contact between stalls. In the event of a contagious disease outbreak, follow these procedures for cleanup:

1. Remove all bedding from the stall.
2. Soak the walls and floors with an anionic detergent or a disinfectant detergent solution to loosen caked organic matter.
3. Wash the surfaces with a steam washer or a high-pressure water spray.
4. Repeat the first three steps, if necessary, to thoroughly clean the stall.
5. Spray a disinfectant on the walls and floors. Allow it to air-dry.
6. Repeat the disinfectant application.
7. Allow the area to air-dry.
8. Place fresh bedding in the stall.
9. Contact a veterinarian to determine the best location to isolate horses.

Floors and Drainage

A good floor is important to a horse's well being. No one type of material seems to offer all the attributes of an ideal floor. The floor material selected, whether it's for the stall, alley, or another room in the stable, will depend on an evaluation of advantages and the willingness to accept certain disadvantages.

Characteristics of an ideal floor, ranked in importance from the horse's interest to the handler's interest:
- Easy on legs.
- Dry.
- Non-odor retentive.
- Good traction.
- Durable.
- Low maintenance.
- Easy to clean.
- Affordable.

A floor that is good for a horse has some give to decrease strain on tendons and feet. Flooring that stays dry is important in maintaining hoof health, although materials such as lime can over dry horse's hooves. Selecting a stall floor that does not retain odors or gases is important. High levels of some gases such as ammonia at the floor level can damage the lining of a horse's throat and lungs. Good traction properties are important, especially in the stall area, because a non-slippery surface will encourage the horse to lie down. Floor durability is important because it will help reduce maintenance costs over the long term.

To prevent frost damage to floors and foundation:
- Lower the water table with well drained subsoil and/or perimeter tile drains with suitable outlets.
- Provide granular fill, which has low capillary conductivity, under the flooring to break the water's upward travel. Large gravel or crushed rock, with the fines screened out, is best. In the worst case, subsoil will need to be excavated to the maximum frost penetration depth and replaced with the gravel.
- Raise the building floor to move away from the water table. Any building floor should be usually above the surrounding grade. A floor at least 12 inches above surrounding grade is acceptable. But even higher elevations that require additional fill may be needed if water damage is anticipated.

Avoid locating the stable in an area with a high water table, especially if fine soils are present. Fine soils, such as clay, draw water by capillary action from a water table resulting in saturated soil conditions under the building. A high water table causes similar problems. Saturated soil has less bearing strength than dry soil. Freezing of this water can result in frost action such as heaving and haphazard settlement of the floor and building foundation.

In addition to the negative effects that water can have on floors, the stable itself can have a negative effect on the groundwater. Many horse owners, especially owners of only a few horses, do not think about contaminating groundwater when they design their barn or stable. The type of stall flooring may determine the potential for groundwater pollution from the stable, especially in areas that have an aquifer close to the ground surface. Liquid manure can seep through to groundwater in some cases if an improper floor material or drainage system is selected and installed. Concrete, asphalt, and well-packed clay floors are considered relatively impermeable to seepage. In addition, bedding is almost always used with stall flooring. Bedding soaks up any liquids from the manure. If urine is allowed to accumulate and pond or if a permeable material is used, groundwater contamination can be a concern.

Floor Types

The type of floor material used in a stable can vary based on the floor's location in the stable. Floors are categorized as either being porous or impermeable. Impermeable floors are typically used in the alleys, wash areas, and the feed, tack, and break rooms.

Alley floors have diverse uses; select a material that is completely impervious to wetness, durable, easy to sweep clean, very slip resistant, and fireproof. Review and compare all the floor material properties listed in this section. Clay, for example, is not very durable and will not stay smooth in an alley. Concrete and asphalt floors are durable yet noisy when horses walk across them and can be slippery. Depending on type, soil-based floors can freeze hard and be dusty and muddy. Synthetic surfaces are resilient with good footing but are expensive. Alleys that are also used as exercise areas should be covered with sand or a material used in riding arenas.

Tack room floors are usually concrete. Feed room floors need to be easy to clean and sweep. A 4-inch thick layer of concrete that has been finished using a steel trowel typically provides a good floor.

Indoor/outdoor carpeting over concrete can be attractive in the tack room, feed room, lounge area, grooming areas, and some alley locations, but this material will not last long with a lot of horse traffic.

Stalls many times use porous flooring materials. Because almost all stalls are bedded, impermeable floors can also be used, but the amount of bedding used with impermeable floors needs to be increased for horse comfort. Discussion on bedding is located in *Chapter 8. Manure Management*. The type of flooring material selected will have an effect on the design of the drainage system. Drainage for stables is discussed later in this chapter.

Porous flooring materials

The most common porous flooring materials are topsoil, clay, sand, road base mix, wood, and grid mats. Table 3-11 lists a summary of the advantages and disadvantages of each.

Topsoil most resembles pasture footing, but its drainage and durability depend on the soil type. Some types resist drainage, resulting in mud or puddles, while others become dry and dusty. Sandy topsoil is often damp in cold climates and will shift with use, creating uneven footing and drainage problems. When used in stalls, a concrete or asphalt apron should be installed at the stall door to discourage pawing and digging.

Clay is traditionally the favorite among people who own or handle horses. The types of clay available will vary depending on location. Pure clay tends to pack too tightly and become impervious to drainage and slick when wet. Mixing the clay with other soils is best. A mix of one-third fine stone dust and two-thirds clay over a sub-layer of gravel to aid drainage is common. Areas of frequent urination are most likely to develop dips and holes. As with topsoil flooring, when clay is used in stalls, a concrete or asphalt apron should be installed at the stall door to discourage pawing and digging.

Sand is one of the most forgiving materials for a horse's legs and has excellent drainage. Fill sand or small-grain sand are the more common types used. Pure sand does not compact and will move easily, creating tracks

Table 3-11	Porous flooring comparison.	
Flooring type and use location	**Advantages**	**Disadvantages**
Topsoil		
Stalls, alleys	• Highly absorbent • Noiseless • Keeps hooves moist • Relatively warm • Affords a firm footing unless wet • Easy on legs • Inexpensive • Drainage variable	• Porosity can retain dampness and odor • Needs to be leveled and replaced often • Can be difficult to muck out • May freeze hard • Difficult to disinfect • Can pit
Clay		
Stalls, alleys	• Closest to a natural tread • Easy on legs • Noiseless • No dust • Keeps hooves moist • Highly absorbent • Relatively warm • Resists wear when dry and compacted • Affords a firm footing unless wet • Inexpensive • Good resiliency	• Can be difficult to keep clean and level • Needs to be re-leveled and repacked each year • Due to holes and pockets needs replacement every few years under constant pawing • Remains damp longer than desirable • May retain odor • Hard to clean • Can pit
Sand		
Exercise area, underlayment	• Highly absorbent • Soft surface • Noiseless • Good drainage • Non-slip	• Does not pack well • Damp in a cold climate • Dusty when dry • Drying effect on hooves • Mixes with bedding so harder to clean stall • Must frequently replace what is discarded during stall cleaning • Sand colic can be a problem as horses eat sand with dropped food or as a habit.
Road base mix		
Stalls, alleys	• Packs well; few problems after this • Good drainage • Easy to level	• Small rocks on surface are undesirable but they can be raked up once it is packed. • If not compacted well enough, holes develop and the material mixes with bedding.
Wood		
Stalls exercise area, breeding area	• Easy on the legs—springy • Warm to lie on • Rough wood has good traction • Low maintenance • Durable • Good exercise surface	• Porous—difficult to clean and disinfect • Retains odors • Slippery when wet • Needs to be checked often for signs of wear • With poor construction is prone to damage by insects and rodents • Has high initial expense • Needs frequent maintenance • Hard to clean
Grid mats		
Stalls	• Durable • Easy on horse's legs • Remains level • Can decrease bedding usage versus concrete • Low maintenance	• Expensive

and pockets with repeated use. The uneven surface should be raked smooth daily. Sand used in stalls can become mixed with bedding materials (especially shavings and sawdust), making cleaning difficult and creating a need for frequent replacement. When using sand, monitor horses for signs of intestinal impaction and colic because new horses and those fed off the floor may be especially prone to ingesting the sand. Sand dries out horse hooves, causing hoof wall cracks and splits.

Road base mix is known by many different names depending on the region of the country. In different locals, it is called limestone dust, washed sand, quarry waste, and stone dust. Different grades of road mix are available, ranging from coarse, large particles to very fine ones. Road mixes with the fewest and smallest rocks are best. This material is easily compacted, but if compacted too much, it can be as unforgiving to a horse's legs as concrete. On the other hand, if the floor is not compacted properly, a digging horse will easily dredge it and mix it with bedding. Because it is easy to level and offers some drainage, road base mix is often used as a sub-floor for rubber mats. Road base mix flooring materials should be 4 to 5 inches thick over a 6- to 8-inch base on sand or small gravel for drainage.

Wood provides a low maintenance, level floor that aids in stall mucking. A wood floor helps alleviate stiffness in the muscles and joints by insulating the horse from the cold ground. It offers a softer footing than concrete or asphalt, but may become slick when wet, and it is difficult to disinfect and keep odor free because of its porosity. Gaps between planks create holding spaces for spilled grain, inviting insects and rodent infestation. Correct construction and adequate bedding can minimize rodent and wetness problems. For best results use a minimum of 2-inch thick preservative treated hardwood planks such as oak. Gaps between boards allow urine drainage, but should be packed with sand, road base mix, or clay. Place planks over a level surface of 6 to 8 inches of sand or small gravel to aid drainage, or set them into asphalt or concrete.

Grid Mats offer an open grid pattern designed to support another type of flooring material or mat. Typically a rubber or plastic (polyethylene) mat is placed over a compacted, level sub-floor and topped with another flooring material such as clay, soil, or road base mix. The grid's open spaces aid in drainage, and the matrix prevents holes and damage from pawing. The characteristics of the stall floor match those of the topping material, but the grid mats decrease material movement from wetting and hoof action. A grid floor can be constructed by setting pressure-treated 2 x 4 lumber on edge across the width of the stall floor as an alternative to a grid matrix. Leave a 1½- to 3-inch gap between boards, then fill and top the lumber grid with a porous stall flooring material (clay, soil, or road base mix). The benefits of a grid floor will be similar to those of grid mats, though the longevity of the lumber grid will be less than that of rubber or plastic.

Impermeable flooring materials

An impermeable flooring material is one that does not allow liquids to flow through it like a porous material would. The most common impermeable flooring materials are concrete, asphalt, or solid rubber mats. Materials such as tartan surfaces and rubber-filled mattresses are becoming more popular. Impermeable surfaces require the use of bedding for horse comfort. Table 3-12 lists a summary of the advantages and disadvantages of each surface.

Concrete is popular because of its durability and low maintenance. Removing manure and cleaning a concrete floor stall is easier than with most other floors. Concrete is generally a good floor material for wash areas, feed rooms, feed alleys, and tack rooms. Concrete is very durable but hard on horses standing in the stall all day. Some horse handlers recommend that a horse be turned out at least four hours per day when housed on concrete flooring.

Steel troweling can make concrete overly smooth and slick. Steel-troweled floors can be used in feed, tack, and break rooms, but should be avoided in stall areas because the surface is too slippery, which makes horses reluctant to lie down and get up.

Wood float broom-finished surfaces provide better traction but tend to become smooth with wear. The brushed concrete, with its small ridges that give it the appearance of being swept with a broom, can be abrasive to lying horses without a deep bedding layer. Broomed concrete with a rough finish for traction and durability would be suitable in an alley.

Using a thick layer of bedding or solid rubber mats can minimize some of concrete's disadvantages. Provide a 4-inch minimum thickness for concrete floors under stalls and where vehicle use is limited. Provide 5 inches of concrete depth for drives and alleys with moderate vehicle traffic, such as heavy pickup trucks and manure spreaders. A well-drained sand or gravel base under the concrete is desirable, but not required. For durability use 4,000 psi concrete. See the *Farm and Home Concrete Handbook*, MWPS-35 for more information on concrete.

Asphalt is an alternative to concrete. It is easy to clean and long-lasting, while being more forgiving to the horse's legs and feet. Asphalt is a mixture of aggregate stone and sand held together with a tar compound. It needs to be applied thickly enough to prevent cracking and chipping. Provide a 2-inch minimum thickness in stalls when installing asphalt over a solid, level subsurface.

For alleys with vehicle traffic similar to driveway use, 3 or 4 inches is best. Under extra heavy use, asphalt may need to be replaced every several years. Asphalt can be either slightly porous or almost impervious. Unsealed asphalt is relatively porous compared to concrete. Porosity can be reduced by minimizing the amount of sand and small particles in the aggregate mixture.

New asphalt floors are not smooth and provide adequate traction. But repeated travel by horses will smooth out the floor, making it slick. Hot asphalt that has its surface raked rather than rolled will have more texture for traction. Likewise, asphalt with larger aggregate size will provide more traction. Asphalt retains heat, which could possibly lead to hoof problems during hot weather.

Solid rubber mats are typically used over another flooring, often to cover up faults like hardness or slipperiness. They are gaining popularity despite their expense. Mats will reduce the amount of bedding needed to provide cushioning; textured models can even be used alone, which saves money elsewhere. Install mats on top of an even, compact surface, such as 4 to 5 inches of road base mix or concrete. If the mat does not cover the entire area of the stall, then multiple mats should interlock or be anchored to the floor.

Without a secure connection between multiple-piece stall mats, keeping them in position can be difficult, as their smooth surface allows them to walk, and bedding chaff in the cracks eventually pries mats up and apart. Horses can lift up areas that are not properly secured.

Mats are heavy (a 4- x 6-foot mat weighs about 100 pounds) and cumbersome, but they are durable and can withstand a lot of abuse. Take care with horses wearing studded shoes since the studs may damage the mat surface. A range of mat thicknesses is available; the most common being ½- to ¾-inch. Top surfaces should be rippled or bumped to add traction, and the base of the mat should be grooved to aid in the removal of any urine that leaks

Table 3-12	Impervious flooring comparison.	
Flooring type and use location	**Advantages**	**Disadvantages**
Concrete		
Stalls, alleys, wash rack, all specialty rooms	• Durable, long life • Easy to clean • Possible to disinfect • Rodent proof • Difficult for horse to damage • Low maintenance	• Hard on legs, non-cushioning • Hard surface, foot problems, slick • May discourage normal behaviors, such as lying down • Cold and damp during cold weather • Needs more bedding or solid rubber mat to cover disadvantages • Relatively expensive

Table 3-12 Continued.

Flooring type and use location	Advantages	Disadvantages
Asphalt		
Stalls, alleys, wash rack, all specialty rooms)	• Less expensive than concrete to install • Easy to clean • Slightly more give than concrete • Long wearing • Provides traction • Good resiliency • Cleans fairly well • Maintains slope	• Hard and cold—but not as bad as concrete • Surface irregularities can trap urine and create sanitation problems • May crack and chip if not applied thickly enough • Relatively expensive • Not as durable as concrete
Brick		
Stalls, alleys	• Easy to patch • Good over sand • Cleans fairly well • Long wearing • Good resiliency	• Hard and cold • Can be slick
Solid rubber mats		
Stalls, breeding shed, foaling stalls, and recovery stalls	• Provides good footing • Long life • Easy to clean • Easy on legs • Low maintenance • Good resiliency • Cleans well	• Not as comfortable as traditional bedding • Expensive • Will move unless secured by walls, interlocking pieces, or anchored • May retain odor • Slippery unless textured
Rubber paving bricks		
Stalls	• Attractive • Durable • Safe • Comfortable • Low maintenance	• Expensive
Polyethylene interlocking blocks		
Stalls	• Durable • Drain well • Low maintenance	• Expensive
Tartan, artificial turf		
Stalls, alleys	• Provides good footing • Long life • Easy on legs • Low maintenance	• Expensive • Retains odor • Hard to clean
Mattress, multi-celled filled with rubber crumbs		
Stalls	• Tough • Flexible • Provides support and strength • Non-skid surface • Drains well • Absorbs shock • Easy to clean • Low maintenance	• Expensive • Can be damaged by horseshoes
Flexible, fiber grade polypropylene		
Stalls	• Tough • Flexible • Provides support and strength • Chemical resistance • Non-skid surface • Drains well • Reduces moisture • Absorbs shock • Easy to clean • Low maintenance	• Expensive

through joints from the surface. Untextured mats are slippery when wet. A mat surface makes stall cleaning easy, but forks cut the surface. Shop around for mats and delivery costs. There are many manufacturers with good warranties.

Tartan or *artificial turf* is used for stall floors and alleys by some innovators. This surface is similar to the surface on many track and field courses. This flooring is a non-slip surface that is easy on the horse's legs. It can be difficult to clean, and it retains odors. The surface can become slick over time. Overall, the maintenance is low for this material as long is it is checked periodically.

Mattresses are becoming more and more popular with horse owners, Figure 3-35. Most mattresses are durable, flexible, and absorb shock very well. Narrow, multi-celled mattresses hold up better to the daily wear and tear than wider-celled mattresses. The main disadvantage of mattresses is that they can be expensive and can be damaged from horseshoes.

Other alternative floorings include interlocking rubber paving bricks, fiber-reinforced polyethylene interlocking blocks, and a flexible, fiber grade of polypropylene. Rubber paving bricks are attractive, durable, safe, and comfortable. Polyethylene blocks are durable and drain well. Using a layer of stone dust, sand, or soil on top creates a forgiving surface for a horse's legs. The polypropylene product is tough yet flexible, provides support, strength, and chemical resistance, as well as a non-skid surface, and it drains well. It reduces moisture, absorbs shock, and is easy to clean. Most of these options are relatively expensive, though the maintenance is low.

Floor Construction and Drainage

All floors need to be designed and constructed so liquids are quickly removed whether by drainage or by bedding absorption. Good floor construction starts with a good base. Remove vegetation, roots, stone, and topsoil, and compact the subsoil below the stable site to prevent settling and cracking of the stable and flooring. Low and moderate clay content soils are adequate for compaction. In

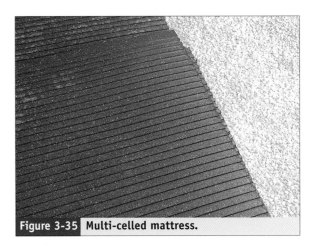

Figure 3-35 Multi-celled mattress.

lieu of compaction, allow subsoil to settle for several months before construction. Avoid high clay soils as sub-soils.

Water that accumulates inside and drains away from the stable is considered dirty water, which means it has had contact with manure or has a potential to have contact with manure. Dirty water needs to be treated before it can be released to a waterway. To ensure adequate drainage in the stable, the top of the floor surface should be elevated at least 12 inches above the outside ground level. Depending on the quantity, liquid draining from the stable can be treated with a septic system, directed to a runoff containment structure, or allowed to flow through a vegetative filter strip. Check with state and local officials regarding requirements for handling this liquid. Also, make sure that the drainage system is designed to not freeze. Freezing can lead to liquids backing up into the stable.

Stall

All stall floors need some way of handling fluids. Most often, bedding is used to soak up urine. In the absence of adequate amounts of dry bedding, the extra urine will have to drain somewhere. A water flow path is provided either along the floor surface or through the floor to sub-layers that allow the fluid to move away from the stable. Floor drains in horse stalls tend to clog with bedding and stall waste. Many horse stall floors function well with no accommodation for drainage other than careful bedding management for urine removal.

The two types of flooring systems are the porous and impermeable flooring systems. Figure 3-36 shows the basic design layout for the porous flooring system, and Figure 3-37 shows the basic design layout for the impermeable flooring system. Both systems have a compacted sub-soil, the difference is that the sub-soil for the porous system is used to direct water away from the stall area. The porous flooring system needs to have a layer of sand and clean rock or gravel to allow liquids to flow down to the sub-soil. The impermeable flooring system has an optional layer of sand or gravel that is used to level out the floor so that the impermeable flooring material can be laid on top. The top of the impermeable flooring material should be sloped to allow for liquids to drain away. The optional sand or gravel layer can to used to help position the impermeable flooring material to promote good drainage.

Drainage is important in stalls if a large amount of liquid could be present in the stalls. Liquids that are allowed to accumulate in stalls can lead to odors and promote disease. If stalls are to be washed or disinfected, some provisions must be made to direct this water out of the stalls. Sloping the floor toward a drainage channel or providing porous floor layers to allow liquids to flow from the stall can help facilitate drainage. Install a safe, open channel along the stall wall to catch surface wetness. Provide a 1% to 2% floor slope (1/8 to 1/4 inch per foot) towards the channel. Avoid noticeably sloped floors as this can strain a horse's tendons.

Do not use a drain in the middle of the stall as it will get clogged with bedding. Some horse owners use underground drains with inlets protected by heavy metal grates (which support horse and light vehicle traffic), but these increase the cost of construction and will almost surely clog with stall waste. A disadvantage of the open channel is the potential odor from stall waste accumulation. Proper sanitation management can minimize this. Open channels can be built with gradually sloping sides to reduce the injury potential for horses

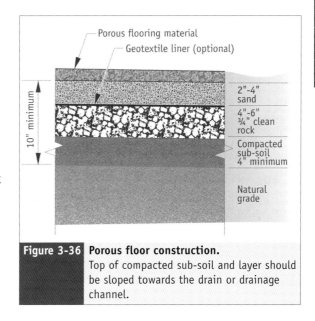

Figure 3-36 Porous floor construction.
Top of compacted sub-soil and layer should be sloped towards the drain or drainage channel.

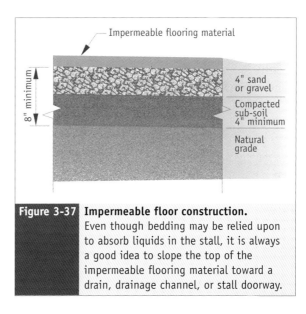

Figure 3-37 Impermeable floor construction.
Even though bedding may be relied upon to absorb liquids in the stall, it is always a good idea to slope the top of the impermeable flooring material toward a drain, drainage channel, or stall doorway.

and people stepping into them, or they may be filled with large gravel. A heavy open grill or solid grate may be placed over the channel in areas of horse and vehicle traffic, such as at doorways.

Shallow and safe open channeling is preferred to the complexity of an underground drainage system. Channeled water moves outside the stable, where a rock layer of large gravel or stones that extends well beyond the stable foundation assists drainage.

Non-stall area

Drains should be located in any area where washing or watering occurs. These areas include the wash area, foaling stalls where washing and disinfecting occurs periodically, and watering hydrants or faucets. Avoid drains near the middle of a traffic alley because much of the manure in this location is solid. This manure can and should be scraped.

Any water that comes into contact with manure is considered dirty, and this liquid should drain to a collection or treatment system. Use a 6-inch diameter or larger drain with a trap and access for cleaning. A trap is needed so that solids such as straw or sand do not plug drainage pipes. In stalls, drains should be located to one side of the stall to prevent uncomfortable conditions when the

Figure 3-38 shows three options of a floor-slope drainage system:

- **Single slope to alley.** Slope the stall floor toward a channel outside the front of the stall in the working alley. This single-slope floor is relatively easy to construct. Provide a way for water to escape from the stall into the alley channel along the bottom of the front stall wall. Keep any gap to less than 2 inches to minimize hoof entrapment.
- **Double slope to corner near alley.** Slope the stall floor toward one corner where a cutout in the wall allows fluid access to the channel or drain. One drain channel can serve two stalls. Construction of the double-slope floor is a bit more complex than the single-slope floor. This design offers the advantage of using an underground drainage system to collect stall wastewater.
- **Single slope to exterior wall trench.** Install a sloping gutter drain along the inside of the exterior stall wall; then slope the stall floor to the exterior wall. Provide a small trench two inches wide extending from the top stall flooring material down to the gravel sub-floor layer to collect runoff. Fill the trench with small stone or large gravel to enhance water movement.

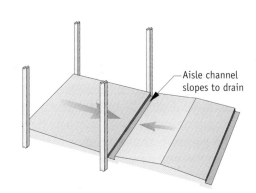

Single slope to alley.

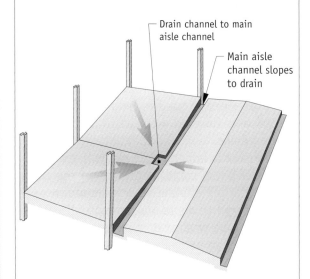

Double slope to corner near alley.

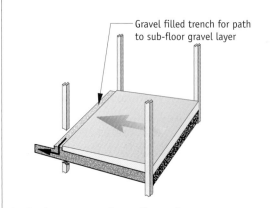

Single slope to exterior wall trench.

Figure 3-38 Stall drainage options.
Note: Slopes are exaggerated to show drainage.

horse lies down in the center of the stall. In a washing area, drains should be located in an area that does not obstruct the horse or person washing the horse.

Wash areas should have a non-slip floor impervious to water. Use rubber mats or carpeting over concrete, fine aggregate macadam, or very rough concrete. Locate the drain below a permeable mat or at the end of the wash area.

Floors should slope slightly towards a drain. Sloping the floor 1.5% towards the drain is adequate, which is about a 1-inch vertical drop over 6 feet of horizontal distance. An alternative is to slope the stall floor toward the front stall door where a shallow, narrow gutter (about 1 inch deep by 4 inches wide) is positioned along the front stall wall in the alley floor. This gutter would then slope along the alley toward drains. Figure 3-39 shows a drainage option to use near water hydrants. In this figure, floors can slope towards the hydrant. This design may not be acceptable for all areas. Check with state and local officials before using this design.

Exterior stable drainage

Proper drainage around and away from a stable is important. Surface water that drains toward and into a stable can have detrimental

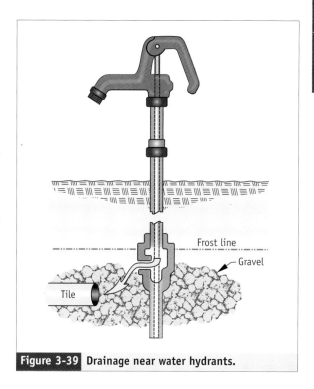

Figure 3-39 Drainage near water hydrants.

effects on stall floors. Slope the ground surface 5% away from the stable, and divert surface and groundwater away from the stable site. The top elevation of the floors should be a minimum of 12 inches above the exterior grade. Figure 3-40 shows some good exterior drainage designs.

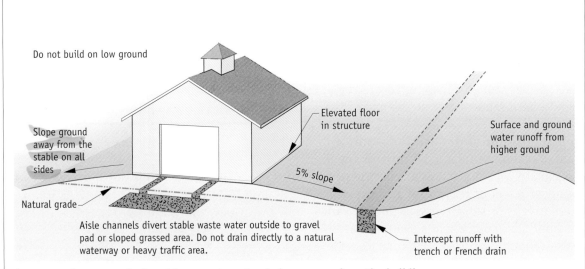

Do not build on low ground

Elevated floor in structure

Surface and ground water runoff from higher ground

Slope ground away from the stable on all sides

5% slope

Natural grade

Aisle channels divert stable waste water outside to gravel pad or sloped grassed area. Do not drain directly to a natural waterway or heavy traffic area.

Intercept runoff with trench or French drain

Area around an arena designed to promote water drainage away from the building.
Design based on Figure 8 in *Horse Stable Flooring Materials and Drainage*, G-96. E. Wheeler and J. Smith, The Pennsylvania State University Extension Service. April 2000.

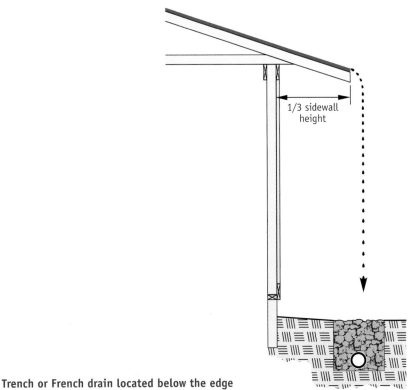

1/3 sidewall height

Trench or French drain located below the edge of the roof.

Figure 3-40 Designs that will promote water drainage away from the building.

CHAPTER 4

Pastures, Paddocks, Pens, and Shelters

Most horses and ponies are healthier and act more contented living outside. Outside living areas can be categorized as pastures, paddocks, or pens.

Pastures are well-maintained vegetative areas that are used primarily for grazing and have the added benefit of being an area in which the horse can exercise. Supplemental feeds, especially grain, may be required depending on the type of horse, exercise and work level of the horse, and the quality of the pasture.

A paddock is a vegetative area that allows the horse to graze and exercise. Paddocks are smaller than pastures and must be carefully monitored so they do not become overgrazed or overused. A pasture can sometimes be divided up into a series of paddocks so grazing can be more carefully controlled. Keeping horses in a single paddock will require providing supplemental feeds to the horses. A series of paddocks may or may not require the use of supplemental feeds.

Pens are usually areas of soil that have little or no vegetation. Typically, pens are areas designed to allow a horse to exercise and run around, or pens can be designed as training areas.

When horses are kept outside, provide free-choice shelter. A free-choice shelter is needed so horses can have an area to protect themselves from the severe weather elements such as strong winds, snowstorms, rain, and sun during hot weather.

This chapter will provide information about designing pastures, paddocks, pens, shelters, and wind and snow control devices. Information on fences for pastures, paddocks, and pens is provided in *Chapter 10. Fences,* and information on waterers for horses on pastures or paddocks is provided in *Chapter 11. Utilities.*

Pastures and Paddocks

The success of a pasture or paddock will depend on the forage types available and climate; on soil type, fertility, and slope; and on the number of horses on the pasture or paddock. A vegetative pasture with a good balance of grass and legumes can produce enough protein, vitamins, and minerals to supply the maintenance requirements of most mature, non-working horses and older yearlings without the need for grain supplementation, Figure 4-1. Even with good pastures, lactating mares, growing horses, and hard-working horses will usually need additional energy from grain

Figure 4-1   **Horses on pasture.**

supplementation. In a pasture or paddock, allow horses to have access to salt and mineral blocks at all times.

Selecting Grasses and Legumes

Kentucky bluegrass and common white clover are common species used in a pasture in the northern and eastern parts of the country, but these species can tend to dominate pastures because of their tolerance to grazing. Unfortunately, these species are not very drought resistant and can become dormant during the later summer months.

Common pastures in the Northeast, Midwest, and parts of the South are bluegrass and white clover. Common white clover is not to be confused with alsike clover, which also produces a white flower and looks very similar to common white clover. Alsike clover should not be used in horse pastures because it can cause severe photosensitivity and kidney damage in horses that consume it. Wheat-grasses are common in the subhumid and arid regions in the southwest and northern plains

of the country. In the extreme south, bermuda, bahia, and dallies grasses are common. A pasture management specialist can help develop a good pasture and help select grass and legume species based on the region. Contact the local extension service to help identify a pasture management specialist.

Sizing and Laying Out the Pasture

Horses will consume at least 1% of their body weight in hay or pasture dry matter per day, and more likely will consume about 1.5% of their body weight. Pastured areas used as a main food source for a horse need to be sized to accommodate forage consumption by the horse and to allow for a regrowth and recovery period. In non-arid regions of the country, the general rule of thumb for a managed pasture is to provide 2 to 4 acres per 1,000-pound horse for year-round grazing unless horses are provided supplemental feed. Unmanaged pastures should provide 5 to 10 acres per horse. A pasture using intensive rotational grazing should provide 1.0 to 1.5 acres for each mature, non-productive horse. Owners pasturing horses in arid regions should contact a pasture management specialist for recommendations on sizing a pasture.

Also important is pasture configuration, especially when more than one horse will be in the pasture at the same time. Horses will display a social order of dominance. Pastures should be configured to avoid right angles and areas in which a less dominant horse can be trapped or cornered by a more aggressive horse. More aggressive horses will kick and bite less aggressive horses. If possible, avoid using alleys or traffic lanes that allow horses to go from one pasture to another. Observe horses for aggression. If possible, put aggressive horses in different pastures from less aggressive horses.

In addition to minimizing areas in which less dominant horses can become trapped, provide spacious eating areas. For example, if a pasture has ten horses that are being fed, feed in a spacious area in which at least ten separate piles of hay, preferably fifteen piles, can be scattered about. Hay should be scattered so there is at least 20 feet between hay piles.

Managing the Pasture

Horses are notorious spot grazers. They will tend to overgraze some locations while undergrazing other locations. Overgrazing can lead to increased growth of weeds. Weeds typically are not nutritious, and some weeds can be poisonous to horses.

Good management will increase the productivity of a pasture or paddock and minimize health risks to the horse. From a management and maintenance viewpoint, it is better to have four or five smaller paddocks than one or two large pastures. Continuously grazed pastures usually have lower forage yields, and more weed and erosion problems. As a rule of thumb, do not allow the average pasture grass height to be less than 2 inches.

Undergrazing can lead to the vegetation becoming overly mature, which can lead to it being less palatable and nutritious. Another challenge with horses being spot grazers is that these areas can become infested with parasites from the horse manure. Weanlings and yearlings are the most susceptible to parasite problems.

Developing a rotational grazing program is one method that can be used to help minimize overgrazing and parasite problems. A rotational grazing program allows horses to graze in one paddock for a period, usually 3 to 7 days, before being moved to another paddock for grazing. The paddock is allowed a regrowth and recovery period before being grazed again. The rest period depends on stocking rate, type of grass and legume, rainfall and temperature, and soil conditions. The typical rest period for a pasture rotation is about 18 to 30 days. The result is typically higher forage yields. Figure 4-2 shows a sample layout with multiple paddocks. A pasture management specialist can assist in developing a rotational grazing program.

Grazing horses with more efficient grazers such as cattle or sheep has been used to combat undergrazing problems. This approach helps makes use of a feed that otherwise would be wasted. In a rotational grazing program, cattle or sheep can be brought into a paddock after horses are removed so that tall pasture grasses can be eaten. If tall pasture grasses are not eaten, the pastures need to be moved two or three times per season or after horses are removed from a paddock so the pasture can grow uniformly.

Drag a chain harrow, Figure 4-3, through the pasture a few times each season or after each paddock rotation to break up manure accumulations and to open hard spots on the ground surface. This procedure will help in parasite control by drying the parasite eggs,

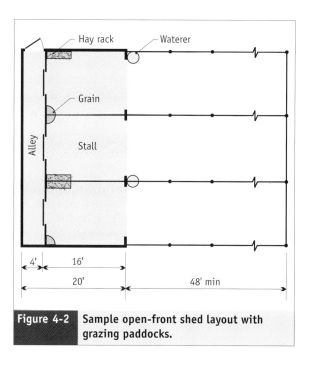

Figure 4-2 Sample open-front shed layout with grazing paddocks.

Figure 4-3 Drag chain harrow.

but this also increases the infected area if horses continue to graze the area. Deeper harrowing can help provide some aeration to roots. Note that if cattle are pastured with horses or immediately following horse grazing, transfer of parasites between species is not a concern. The parasites that affect horses do not affect cattle and vice versa.

Horses can physically damage a pasture much more than cattle. Horses run more and change directions while running much more than cattle. If possible, keep horses off pasture during periods of wet weather or when the ground is extremely wet; otherwise, they will tend to tear up and severely damage a pasture.

A good management tool for horse facilities on limited acreage is to provide at least one rainy day paddock for foul weather turn-out. The principle is to allow one paddock to take the worst wear during unfavorable weather conditions while attempting to preserve the grassy integrity of the remaining paddocks. The unfortunate paddock will not be expected to maintain grass. Because turf is easily destroyed during wet conditions, the rainy day paddock can take the abuse that would ruin grassed turnouts. This paddock is to be used for those horses that have to be turned out of their stalls despite the weather. The rainy day paddock can have a sand, stone dust, or wood fiber surface added to make it less muddy. This paddock should have safe and sturdy fencing and be located in an area accessible to the stable yet away from the main public viewing areas of the stable.

Pens

All horses need regular exercise to be healthy. When space is limited on a site, an exercise pen may be the only option for a horse owner. Exercise pens are also good to have during times that pastures or paddocks are too wet for horses to be in. A general rule of thumb for an exercise area is to provide at least 1,000 square feet per horse (e.g. 12- x 80-foot pen). A 10-stall barn would need roughly one-quarter acre of exercise area adjacent to the barn for intermittent exercise of the horses.

Similar to pastures and paddocks, pens should be configured to avoid right angles and areas in which a less dominant horse can be trapped or cornered by a more aggressive horse. Sod cover is preferable, but many pens are unvegetated. These lots need to be designed to promote good drainage from the lot and managed to reduce dust. Periodic removal of manure will be necessary to keep odors to a minimum and to discourage muck formation.

Free-Choice Shelter

Horses that are kept outside and do not have access to a stable need to be provided free-choice shelter.

Buildings and windbreaks are the most common types of free-choice shelters. Constructed sunshades are common with cattle but are less popular with horses. Natural barriers as the main means to protect horses should be avoided when at all possible because of their potential to create dangerous situations for the horse. For example, many times trees are susceptible to lightning strikes, which can lead to severely injuring or killing the horse. If trees are used as a windbreak, install a fence to keep horses out of the windbreak. Rock features such as caves and overhangs can actually put a horse in danger in the event rocks should fall or a horse should stumble and break a leg.

Buildings, sunshades, and windbreak fences must be constructed to prevent injury to horses. Properly cover corners, nails, metal, fences, and any other sharp objects to protect horses from injury.

The best options for free-choice shelter are:
- Buildings (Permanent or portable open-front sheds, building lean-to).
- Sunshades.
- Windbreak fences.

Buildings

The main types of buildings used for protection are open-front buildings and lean-to structures. Open-front sheds are the most common type of housing for horses kept outside. Open-front barns typically have no solid partitions and are located to allow access to an open pasture for groups of horses.

Open front buildings can be either permanent or portable sheds. The permanent shed is the most common type of structure, Figure 4-4. Permanent structures typically have a fence attached to them. Portable structures are smaller than permanent structures and usually are located away from the fences of pastures,

paddocks, or pens, Figure 4-5. As the name suggests, these structures can be moved to facilitate removal of manure or to make efficient use of a structure as pastures or paddocks are being rotated.

Figure 4-5 **Portable shed.**

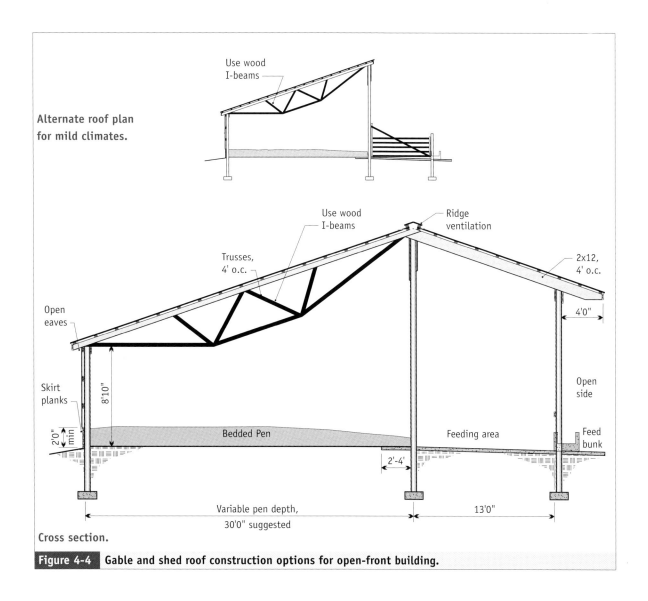

Figure 4-4 Gable and shed roof construction options for open-front building.

Design open-front barns to break the wind and provide shelter from rain and snow, while allowing free access by the horse. Face the open side of the building away from the prevailing winds, with the remaining three sides closed. Preferably, the structure will include the provision to open sidewalls for summer ventilation, Figure 4-6. The minimum clearance from the ground to the eave on the open side is 10 feet.

Depending upon the type of construction, the barn may be 14 to 40 feet wide. Open barns wider than 40 feet often do not ventilate well naturally. Depending on the number of horses, supply one or more single-slope shed barn or, for large groups of horses, a barn that is 32 feet wide (40 feet wide in cold climates) may be used. Provide a minimum of 80 square feet of floor space per 1,000 pounds of horse weight using the shelter. Preferred minimum areas are

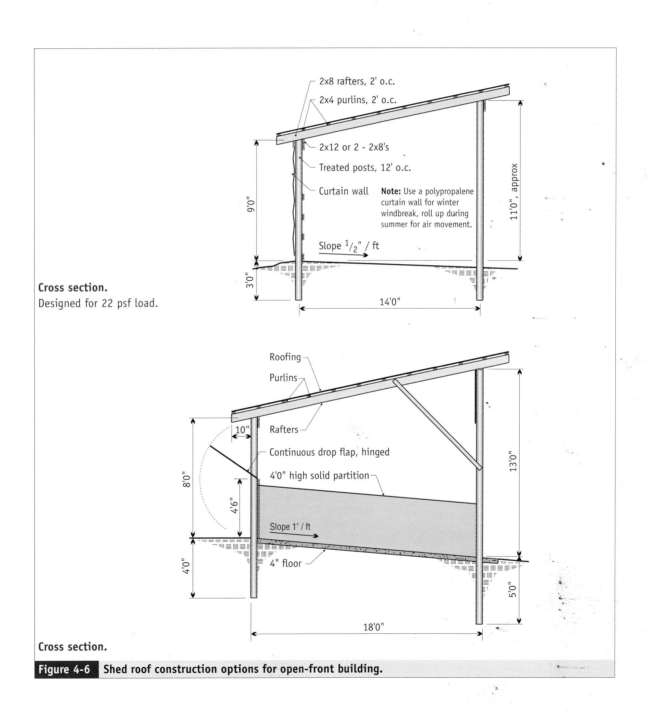

Cross section.
Designed for 22 psf load.

- 2x8 rafters, 2' o.c.
- 2x4 purlins, 2' o.c.
- 2x12 or 2 - 2x8's
- Treated posts, 12' o.c.
- Curtain wall

Note: Use a polypropalene curtain wall for winter windbreak, roll up during summer for air movement.

Slope ¹/₂" / ft

9'0"
11'0", approx
3'0"
14'0"

Cross section.

- Roofing
- Purlins
- Rafters
- Continuous drop flap, hinged
- 4'0" high solid partition

Slope 1" / ft
4" floor

10"
8'0"
4'6"
4'0"
13'0"
5'0"
18'0"

Figure 4-6 Shed roof construction options for open-front building.

given in Table 4-1. Provide at least 10 feet clear height to the eave on the open side, Figure 4-7. Some additional space may be allowed in the barn for pens, foal creep areas, a tack room, or for limited storage of hay and bedding. For fire safety and better ventilation, store most of the hay and bedding in a separate barn or building. See *Chapter 7, Environmental Control.*

When selecting a site for the shelter, consider its location in relation to other buildings and traffic lanes. Proper building location will make it more convenient to handle horses. Some artificial light is desirable in non-portable structures. Provide 100 watts of light

Table 4-1	Recommended roofed area for open-front horse housing.	
Animal type		Covered area (sq ft/animal)
Foals		100
Yearlings		120
Mature horses		150

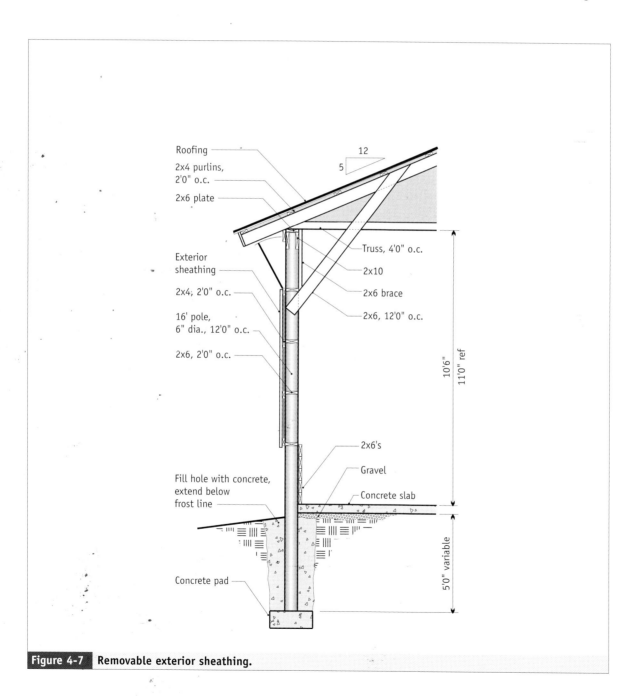

Figure 4-7 Removable exterior sheathing.

per 500 square feet of floor area. Install ridge devices, and adjustable panels in the back wall for summer and winter ventilation.

Provide an adequate supply of fresh clean water. A heated stock waterer may be required in the winter; a single heated water bowl serves eight to ten horses. Provide 12 inches of rim space for each ten horses. Locate the water bowl(s) or tank outside, and provide good drainage around the waterer(s). Plan for daily cleaning of the waterers and disposal of the wastewater.

Hay and bedding may be stored in the shelter, but a better alternative to cut down on dust and to conserve bedding is to store feed hay outside the building in racks. Table 4-2 lists suggested feeder space requirements for group-housed horses.

Creep feeders are used to provide specialized diets to help foals grow while they are still nursing. Creep feeders provide a location that mares cannot access, thereby reducing the possibility of the foals being injured. Locate these feeders near water, shade, or mare feeding areas. A corner feeder can be constructed by placing a post and two boards to create a sheltered area for the foals. The boards should be 4 feet above the ground and easily removable in case a mare crawls into the creep area. In an open pasture, a creep area may be created using four posts with railing. Provide a gate to allow removal of mares that manage to enter, Figure 4-8. The creep area should be sized based on the number of foals, Table 4-3.

Use a bunk suitable to the number of foals. Creep areas may also have two creep gates rather than continuous openings. These should be 4 to 5 feet high and 15 to 24 inches wide, depending on the foal size. Provide one more opening than the number of foals that will be fed.

Sunshade

Shades provide comfort and cooling for horses in pastures and large open pens. Benefits from an effective shade include improved growth and reproduction. Figures 4-9 and 4-10 show example sunshades.

If feed and water are provided under the shade, orient the long dimension east-west;

Table 4-2	Feeder or manger space requirements for group-housed horses.	
Animal		Space at manger or feeder (per animal)
Foals		24"
Yearlings		30"
Mature horses		36"

Table 4-3	Creep area for foals.
Number of foals	Creep Area (feet)
1	8 x 8
2	10 x 10
3	12 x 12
4	14 x 14
5	16 x 16
6	18 x 18
7	20 x 20
8	24 x 24

| Figure 4-8 | Creep feeding area for foals. |

otherwise, orient the long dimension north-south to promote drying under the shade.

Build shades at least 12 feet high. Increase the height to improve air movement if shades are wider than 40 feet. Allow at least 50 feet between shades and trees, buildings, or other obstructions.

Provide at least 40 square feet of shade per horse. For high rainfall areas, consider a paved area with a 1.5% to 2% slope to eliminate mud. Take into account shadow migration throughout the day when planning the shade area.

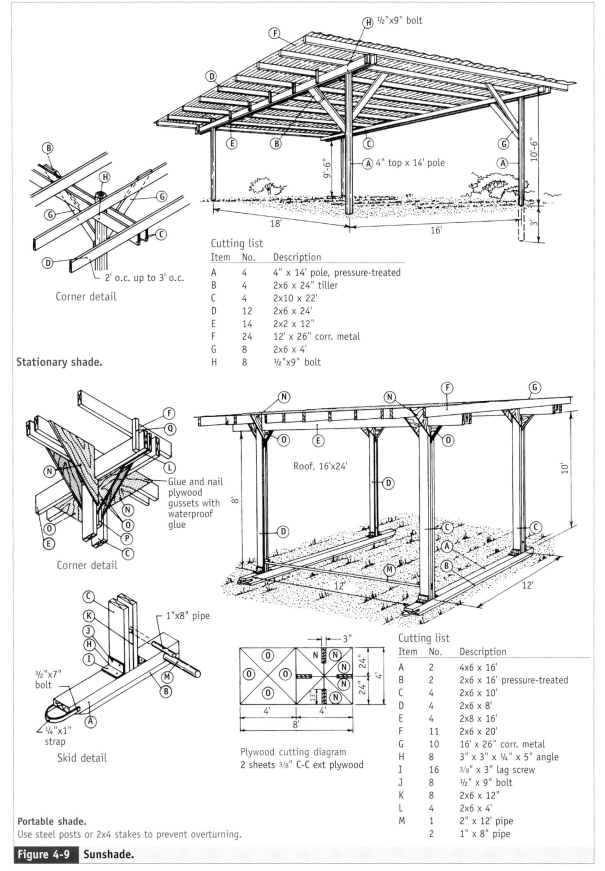

H ½"x9" bolt

4" top x 14' pole

9'-6"
10'-6"
3'
18'
16'

B

2' o.c. up to 3' o.c.

Corner detail

Stationary shade.

Cutting list

Item	No.	Description
A	4	4" x 14' pole, pressure-treated
B	4	2x6 x 24" tiller
C	4	2x10 x 22'
D	12	2x6 x 24'
E	14	2x2 x 12"
F	24	12' x 26" corr. metal
G	8	2x6 x 4'
H	8	½"x9" bolt

Glue and nail plywood gussets with waterproof glue

Corner detail

Roof, 16'x24'

8'
10'
12'
12'

1"x8" pipe

½"x7" bolt

¼"x1" strap

Skid detail

3"
24"
24"
4'
13"
4'
4'
8'

Plywood cutting diagram
2 sheets ⅜" C-C ext plywood

Cutting list

Item	No.	Description
A	2	4x6 x 16'
B	2	2x6 x 16' pressure-treated
C	4	2x6 x 10'
D	4	2x6 x 8'
E	4	2x8 x 16'
F	11	2x6 x 20'
G	10	16' x 26" corr. metal
H	8	3" x 3" x ¼" x 5" angle
I	16	⅜" x 3" lag screw
J	8	½" x 9" bolt
K	8	2x6 x 12"
L	4	2x6 x 4'
M	1	2" x 12' pipe
	2	1" x 8" pipe

Portable shade.
Use steel posts or 2x4 stakes to prevent overturning.

Figure 4-9 Sunshade.

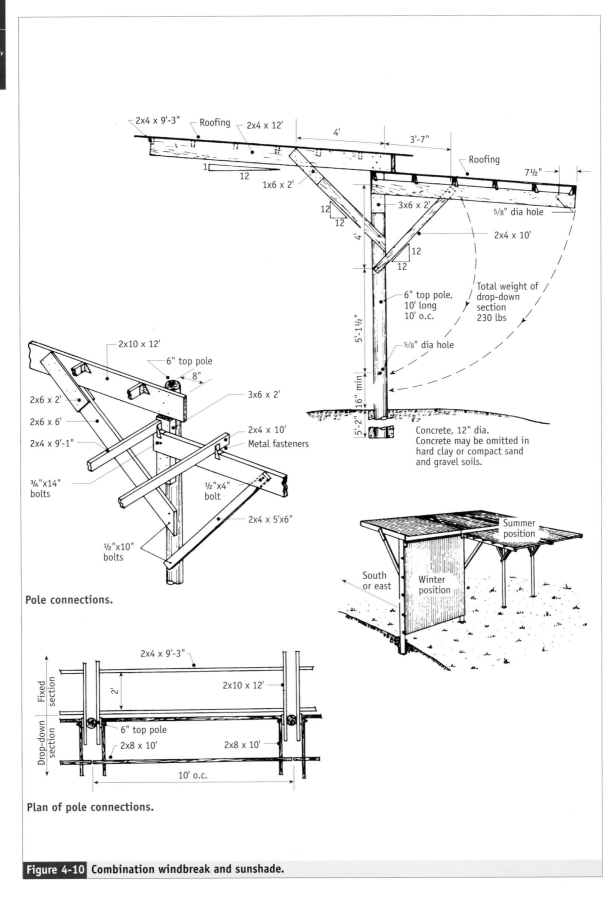

2x4 x 9'-3" Roofing 2x4 x 12'

4'

3'-7"

Roofing

7½"

1 12

1x6 x 2'

12 12

3x6 x 2'

5/8" dia hole

2x4 x 10'

4'

12 12

6" top pole, 10' long 10' o.c.

Total weight of drop-down section 230 lbs

5'-1½"

5/8" dia hole

16" min

5'-2"

Concrete, 12" dia. Concrete may be omitted in hard clay or compact sand and gravel soils.

2x10 x 12'

6" top pole

8"

2x6 x 2'

3x6 x 2'

2x6 x 6'

2x4 x 10'

2x4 x 9'-1"

Metal fasteners

¾"x14" bolts

½"x4" bolt

2x4 x 5'x6"

½"x10" bolts

Pole connections.

Summer position

South or east

Winter position

2x4 x 9'-3"

Fixed section

2x10 x 12'

2'

Drop-down section

6" top pole

2x8 x 10'

2x8 x 10'

10' o.c.

Plan of pole connections.

Figure 4-10 Combination windbreak and sunshade.

The most effective shade materials are reflective surfaces such as white galvanized metal or aluminum. Painting the upper surface white improves cooling. Shade cloth providing 30% to 90% shade is available. Shade cloth with greater than 80% shade tends to hold water after rainfalls, which can result in structural problems.

Windbreak Fences

Shelterbelts are often used to provide protection from wind and blowing snow, especially for buildings. (See *Chapter 2. Site Planning*.) Unfortunately, some areas such as open pastures cannot make use of shelterbelts. In these cases, windbreak fences may be the best option. Windbreak fences are barriers that are used to provide temporary relief from the negative effects of wind and blowing snow for horses that do not have access to an enclosed area.

The actual area protected by a windbreak fence depends on wind speed and direction, barrier height, and porosity. Wind is slowed for a longer area downwind if it strikes perpendicular to the barrier. A completely solid barrier provides wind and snow protection for only a short distance downwind (one or two barrier heights), Figure 4-11. A solid windbreak fence is more useful for increasing protection for small areas that already have general wind protection.

Compared to a solid windbreak fence barrier, a partly-open or porous, 80%-solid fence reduces wind speed for a greater distance downwind and spreads out drifted snow. A porous windbreak fence is useful for protecting larger areas such as a pasture and paddock. Horizontal or vertical slots in a fence perform about the same. Portable porous windbreak fence barriers built on skids may be towed for use at different sites from season to season, Figure 4-12.

Various configurations of windbreak fence barriers are used. A 10-foot high, part-open or slotted windbreak fence on a 4-foot high, built-up, earthen ridge (for improved drainage) may provide wind protection for 200 feet downwind, Figure 4-13. Another type of windbreak, designed for use in open western rangelands, is a large vee-shaped configuration, Figure 4-14.

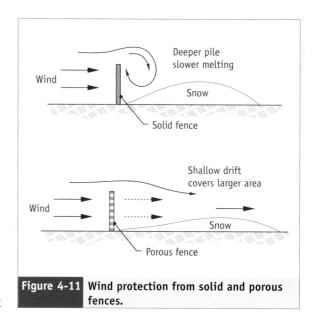

Figure 4-11 **Wind protection from solid and porous fences.**

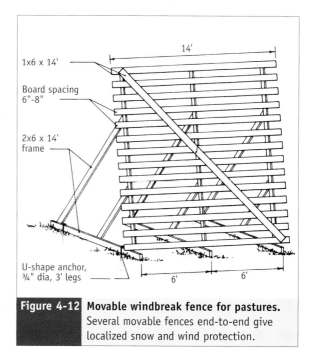

Figure 4-12 **Movable windbreak fence for pastures.** Several movable fences end-to-end give localized snow and wind protection.

Smaller versions of the vee-shaped fence can be used to protect smaller areas in pens, Figure 4-15. Temporary windbreak barriers can be made of stacked, large bales or used tires. Figure 4-16 shows the use of mounded earth as a means of controlling wind and snow. Note that a wind from a direction different from that designed

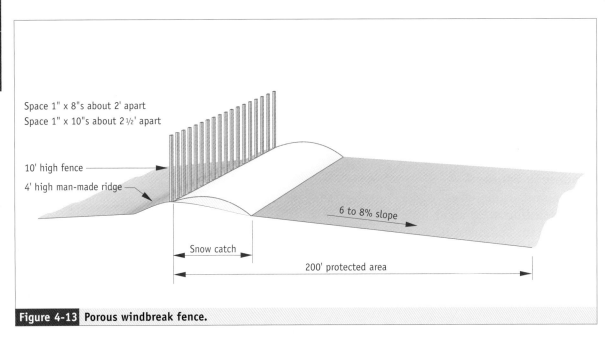

Space 1" x 8"s about 2' apart
Space 1" x 10"s about 2½' apart

10' high fence

4' high man-made ridge

6 to 8% slope

Snow catch

200' protected area

Figure 4-13 **Porous windbreak fence.**

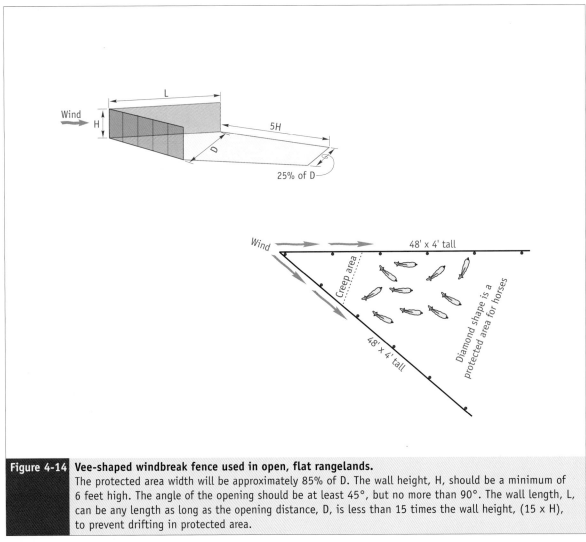

Wind

L

H

5H

D

25% of D

Wind

48' x 4' tall

Creep area

48' x 4' tall

Diamond shape is a
protected area for horses

Figure 4-14 **Vee-shaped windbreak fence used in open, flat rangelands.**
The protected area width will be approximately 85% of D. The wall height, H, should be a minimum of
6 feet high. The angle of the opening should be at least 45°, but no more than 90°. The wall length, L,
can be any length as long as the opening distance, D, is less than 15 times the wall height, (15 x H),
to prevent drifting in protected area.

Figure 4-15 Small vee-shaped windbreak fence used to protect horses and prevent hay from blowing away.

for may actually increase snowdrift or draft problems around a wind barrier.

Open-sided buildings or buildings that have large openings are vulnerable to snow drifting and drafts inside unless they are properly protected. Windbreak fences can also be used to help minimize the negative effects of blowing wind and snow around buildings. A misplaced windbreak fence can have a negative effect on an open-front building while a well placed fence can have a positive effect on snow and soil deposition around buildings, Figure 4-17.

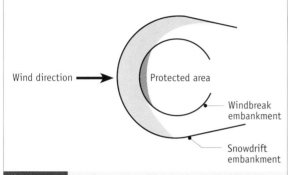

Figure 4-16 **Earthen mound horseshoe wind barrier.** This shows a large windbreak in the center, a smaller snowdrift embankment, and the borrow area and catchment basin between them. The wind velocity in the protected area may be reduced 50 percent as far as 20 to 30 feet inside the windbreak. A windbreak 400 feet long is large enough to provide protection.

Additional management practices that can help minimize the negative effects of blowing wind and snow on an open-sided building are the following:

- Provide a continuous eave inlet on the closed side. Locate inlets below roof overhangs (3-foot overhang minimum) to keep snow out during heavy snowstorms.
- Do not build near a large building or silo. Provide at least a 30 feet wind passage between buildings.
- Close part of the front wall at each end— up to one-half of the building length.
- Install solid cross partitions 50 feet apart in long buildings to reduce drafts.

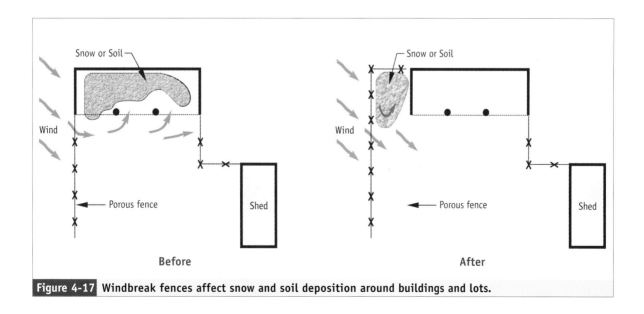

Figure 4-17 Windbreak fences affect snow and soil deposition around buildings and lots.

Installing a windbreak fence to form a swirl chamber at the west or north end of an open-front building can reduce the wind in front of and inside the building. Figure 4-18 shows more specific details in regard to locating an open-sided building and windbreak fence placement.

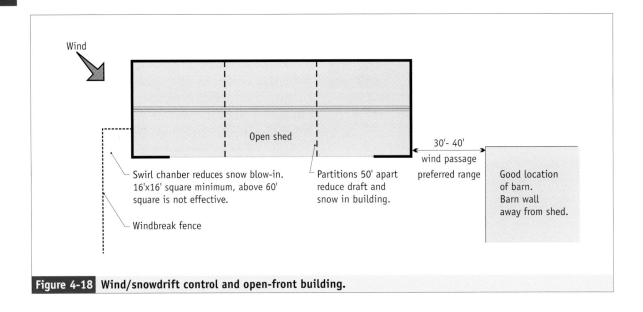

Wind

Open shed

Swirl chanber reduces snow blow-in.
16'x16' square minimum, above 60'
square is not effective.

Windbreak fence

Partitions 50' apart
reduce draft and
snow in building.

30'- 40'
wind passage
preferred range

Good location
of barn.
Barn wall
away from shed.

Figure 4-18 Wind/snowdrift control and open-front building.

CHAPTER 5

Arenas and Training Facilities

Many horse owners need an area in which to exercise their horses, but have limited land for their horse to run in a pasture. Other horse owners need a special area designated for training. A properly designed riding arena can benefit both cases. Specially designed arenas or training facilities do not have to be elaborate, but they do need to have a good surface and be designed and constructed so that they are safe for the horse and rider to use.

Arenas can be located outside where exercising or training can be done in the fresh open air, but an arena in a specially designed structure can allow for exercising and training to take place during inclement weather.

This chapter will present the basic recommendations for developing a successful arena in which to exercise and train horses.

Arena Design

The size of a riding arena depends on its intended use. Table 5-1 shows recommended arena sizes depending on training for different activities. The dressage and show arenas listed in Table 5-1 and illustrated by Figure 5-1 show a standard and small size. The standard size is the standard regulation size. The small size is the smallest that can be used for training for these events. This size is normally used for indoor facilities to minimize construction costs.

The remainder of this section will describe basic design guidelines for outdoor and indoor arenas. The last topic in this section details round pens used for training. Round pens are unique in that they use permanent or portable fencing or walls, and they can be located inside or outside.

Table 5-1	Arena dimensions for competition training.
Arena type	Dimensions (feet)
Barrel racing	150 x 200
Calf roping	100 x 300
Dressage, small	66 x 132[a]
Dressage, standard	66 x 198[a]
Show, small	110 x 220[b]
Show, standard	120 x 240[b]
Steer wrestling	100 x 300
Team roping	150 x 300
Western pleasure	100 x 200

[a] United States Dressage Federation (USDF) regulation size.
[b] National Horse Show Association regulation size.

Outdoor Training Areas

Arenas that will be used for varying activities may need to be larger than listed in Table 5-1. For example, if an arena will be used to train a team of horses to pull a wagon, a larger arena will probably be needed. One advantage of outdoor arenas is that larger sizes can be economically constructed. Building construction costs make large indoor arenas cost prohibitive for most private facilities. The limiting factor many times for outdoor arenas is availability of adequate and suitable land.

When making the decision to build a large arena, evaluate the overall requirements to properly perform needed functions within the ring. Check out other multi-use arenas. The Olympic games have dressage, jumping, and eventing. The 1996 Olympic Games in Atlanta had seven multi-use arenas constructed to accommodate these varying activities. Four

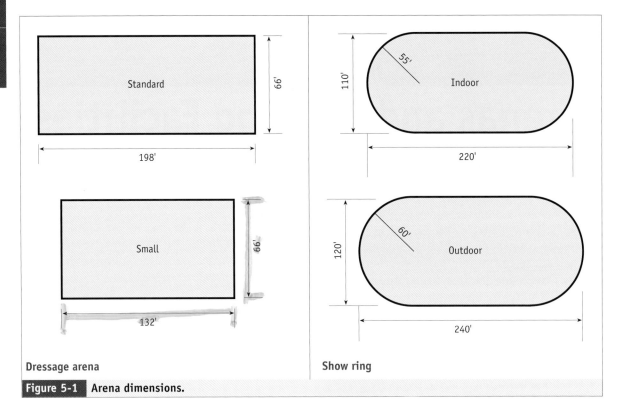

Standard

66'

198'

Small

66'

132'

Dressage arena

110'

55'

Indoor

220'

120'

60'

Outdoor

240'

Show ring

Figure 5-1 **Arena dimensions.**

arena sizes were used: 144 x 295 feet, 148 x 295 feet, 148 x 262 feet, and 148 x 312 feet.

For outdoor arenas, select a good site that has, or can be modified to obtain, proper drainage and surface conditions for the riding events, Figure 5-2. Having a few different site options is a good idea. Investigate the soil at each proposed site. Evaluate the cost to obtain the desired riding surface at each site in addition to its accessibility to other buildings and activities at the site. Sometimes a desirable location does not have good soil for constructing an arena. Making the site useful can be cost prohibitive.

Site grading, sub-base, and base materials for an outdoor arena should extend at least 10 feet beyond the perimeter of the planned final arena size. Because an outdoor arena needs to be able to shed water, sloping the base and top surface as shown in Figure 5-7c is important for good drainage. A 2% slope in the direction of the shortest dimension is the most cost effective, with options shown in Figure 5-7a and 5-7b.

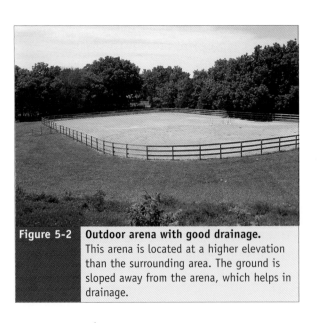

Figure 5-2 **Outdoor arena with good drainage.**
This arena is located at a higher elevation than the surrounding area. The ground is sloped away from the arena, which helps in drainage.

Indoor Arenas

Indoor arenas are basically clear span structures that are part of, attached to, or close to the main horse barn. When designing an indoor arena, a critical dimension to consider is ceiling height, which is the distance from floor to the lowest object that a rider could touch. This could be a light fixture, water sprinklers, or the bottom chord of a truss. A minimum ceiling height of 14 feet is needed for general riding or training; 16 feet is the minimum if training for hunters or jumpers.

Facilities need to be an absolute minimum of 36 feet wide for riding and training horses, but designing for a least 50 feet wide is preferred. The narrower the arena, the more stress and strain that will be placed on the horses' legs and joints as they perform in repetitious small circles. A 60-foot wide arena is common for mass-produced riding arena packages.

Facilities used to train, ride, and drive horses will need a clear span of 60- to 100-feet wide. An arena width of 80 to 100 feet is needed for group riding or driving of horses. The minimum length of an indoor arena should be 130 feet to allow a person to obtain some speed from his or her horse before negotiating corners.

Because indoor riding arenas cover a fairly large area of land, it is very important to develop a plan to divert rainwater and snow melt that drains off the roof away from the building. Water that is allowed to accumulate and pool next to the building can seep into the building and have a negative effect on the floor. As with stables, the elevation of the arena must be high enough so that water drains away from the building, or a drainage system must be installed that will allow water to drain away, Figure 3-41.

Adequate and quality lighting is important in an indoor arena. An arena that has poor lighting design or sharp contrast between shadow and sunlight on the floor can be disorienting and frightening to the horse. Provide enough overlapping light sources so shadows are not present on the floor.

If natural light is used, avoid using ceiling panels, which allow light to shine directly to the floor surface. Instead, allow natural light to shine through wall openings located at the top of the sidewalls. Sidewall openings should be continuous the entire length of the building. The roof overhang helps to prevent

Table 5-2	Minimum unobstructed dimensions for non-competitive use indoor arena.

Arena type	Dimensions (feet)
Width	
Exercise and training (absolute minimum)	36
Exercise and training (preferred minimum)	50
Exercise, training, and riding	60
Exercise, training, riding and driving	60-100
Group riding or driving	80-100
Length	
Minimum	130
Height	
Minimum	14
Hunting and jumping training	16

direct sunlight from shining into the arena, which could cause shadows. Translucent, rather than transparent, panels will further diffuse sunlight and glare.

If standard windows or doors are used, design these areas with safety in mind. Windows should be protected with metal bars so that a horse does not break the glass, Figure 5-3. Doors should slide or pivot so no part of the door extends into the arena where a horse or rider may be injured, Figure 5-4.

Design indoor arenas with proper wall protection. Arenas have support columns that can injure a horse or rider. Installing a plywood liner is a simple protection solution, Figure 5-5. Installing mirrors around the arena can help riders evaluate their form while riding, Figure 5-6.

Figure 5-3	Sliding window protected by metal bars.

Figure 5-4 Pivot door ventilation with the door opening outwards.

Figure 5-5 Plywood placed on the wall to protect horse and rider from wood columns.

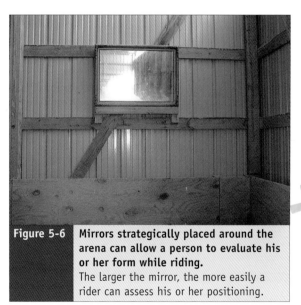

Figure 5-6 Mirrors strategically placed around the arena can allow a person to evaluate his or her form while riding.

The larger the mirror, the more easily a rider can assess his or her positioning.

Round Pens

Round pens are useful for a variety of purposes including exercise, training, show and demonstration, and sales. Round pens are often used outside but portable panels can be set up inside. The absence of corners make the round pen a safe area for the horse to have new training experiences. Pen size depends on its intended use, Table 5-3.

Select the site so that the horses can be controlled while traveling from their stall/pen to the round pen. Consider distractions (traffic noise and motion, dogs, shadows, etc.) and soil type variations when locating a pen. Choose a site that excludes adjacent drainage. Selecting a site with natural drainage can reduce the costs of shaping the pen floor. Drainage from the pen area gets larger as the pen encloses more area. The slope of the pens (about 2%) should be established before the addition of the footing surface layer. The final floor surface depends on the type of activity planned for the area. Provide an entrance to the round pen to accommodate a small tractor with equipment to add surface material and to groom/level the surface of the pen. The entrance to the pen normally has a 10-foot high cross rail to allow horse entrance and to add strength to the fence by making a complete circle. A galvanized or stainless steel cable on the exterior of the posts greatly adds to the stability of the pen.

Round pens are used to train young horses to be ridden by youngsters or to longe horses in training. Various diameters, from 30 to 150 feet, are acceptable depending on use. Smaller pens are preferred for limiting the horse's maneuverability such as during breaking. Rings of 60 feet and larger are more suitable for less stressful longeing and training. Horses may be penned in groups in the 60- to 100-foot diameter pens. A 45-foot diameter round ring may be successfully used for breaking and longeing.

A solid wall height of 7 feet will help deter horses from jumping out or from getting their head up over the wall to attempt to escape. To allow for airflow down in the bowl of the arena, leave 2 inches of space between boards

Table 5-3 Round pen dimensions according to use.

Activity	Recommended wall design	Pen diameter (feet)	Pen diameter (meters)	Comments
Initial breaking, training and riding of horse Initial training of the rider	Solid walls, 6 to 7 feet high	33	10	• Allows for maximum control of horse by trainer fewer visual distractions to horse. • Causes more strain on joints and legs as horses are asked to go at high speeds in small circles.
Mid to final routine training area	Open fence, 6 feet high	66	20	• Most usable size for all functions
Multiple horse functions Final training	Open fence, 6 feet high	99	30	• Allows for maximum training flexibility of horse by trainer

above 4 feet high. The bottom 3 feet of the wall should be solid and tightly constructed.

The wall should slope out from the center of the pen with a 5 to 7 degree lean from vertical. A greater slope can allow a horse to run up the wall. Walls made of wooden boards seem to cause fewer injuries than walls made of metal and other materials. Posts can be 6 x 6 inches and spaced every 8 feet. The solidity of the lower boards can be enhanced by positioning stout nailers on the outside of the fence between the main posts. This prevents the boards from bowing and exposing gaps over the 8-foot length.

Surfaces

Similar to other structures, arenas must be located in dry areas that have good drainage. The arena should not be located in an area in which rainwater draining from other areas of the site will flow across the surface of the arena. The arena should be located in an area that is relatively flat; otherwise, more costly work will need to be performed to move soil and possibly add a drainage system. That said, do not build in a low-lying, flood-prone area simply to reduce construction costs. The arena often will not be usable because of soggy conditions.

There are few overall differences in the footing (surface) design between an indoor and outdoor arena. The arena surface must be designed for proper drainage, sized to allow for proper training and exercise, and designed to protect both the horse and rider. The arena's surface is composed of three layers: sub-base, base, and footing material on top.

General Surface Design

A well-designed and constructed arena floor consists of specific layers. Each layer varies in its designed function within the system, but each layer has an important role in maintaining a successful and safe riding experience. The construction layers of the arena floor as shown in Figure 5-7 consist of:

• **Natural soil.** Often when constructing the floor, soil is over excavated so that it can be re-compacted and brought up evenly to its desired elevation. The elevation of the natural soil is usually level or flat across the entire area. The excavated area equals the arena's final size plus 10 feet on all sides as the final pad area.

• **Subbase.** The subbase is usually natural soil that is compacted and brought up to a predetermined elevation with a slight crown that directs water to the outer perimeter of the arena. The slope of the crown is usually about 2%. This layer must allow water to drain away and not pool below the top surface. A drainage system such as tiling may be installed at the perimeter of the arena to help direct water away. In a location with frequently saturated, poorly-drained soil, a drainage tile system under the arena will be needed if everyday use is necessary. Otherwise, under-arena drainage systems are not recommended due to the frequency of clogging and added expense. If soil types vary significantly over the entire area, it may be desirable to use a consistent soil type over the entire area. Soil can be brought in and compacted to provide a consistent subbase. If the natural soil type is consistent over the entire area and soil excavation is carefully performed, a flat and even natural soil level can be considered the subbase.

- **Geotextile liner.** A geotextile liner is an optional step in obtaining a satisfactory floor. Geotextile liners help keep granular material such as gravel separate from the soil subbase while at the same time allowing water to filter through the material to the soil below. A geotextile liner helps reduce the impact of localized loads that can occur in high traffic areas. Without a geotextile liner, granular material can be forced into the subbase, which can lead to ruts and poor drainage.

- **Base.** The base is usually a 4- to 6-inch layer of well-graded aggregate. Small to medium sized aggregate such as a sand-clay mix, or a fine limestone mix with aggregate no larger than 3/8 inch makes a good base. The base material needs to be compacted as densely as possible with at least an eight-ton roller. A 2% slope in all

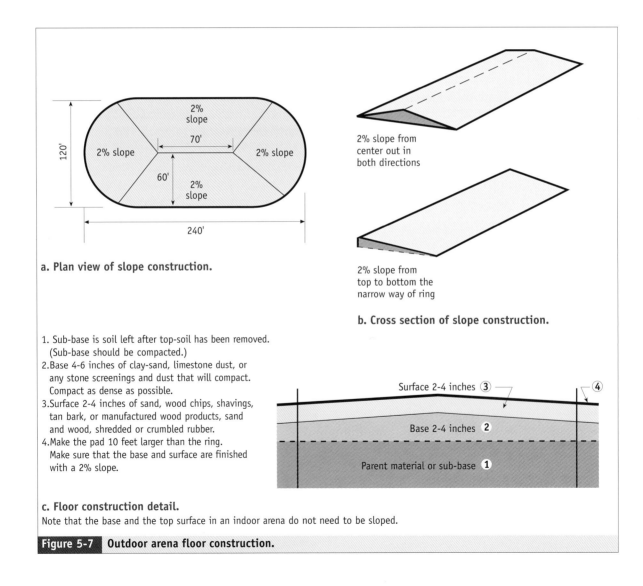

a. Plan view of slope construction.

2% slope from center out in both directions

2% slope from top to bottom the narrow way of ring

b. Cross section of slope construction.

1. Sub-base is soil left after top-soil has been removed. (Sub-base should be compacted.)
2. Base 4-6 inches of clay-sand, limestone dust, or any stone screenings and dust that will compact. Compact as dense as possible.
3. Surface 2-4 inches of sand, wood chips, shavings, tan bark, or manufactured wood products, sand and wood, shredded or crumbled rubber.
4. Make the pad 10 feet larger than the ring. Make sure that the base and surface are finished with a 2% slope.

Surface 2-4 inches ③

④

Base 2-4 inches ②

Parent material or sub-base ①

c. Floor construction detail.
Note that the base and the top surface in an indoor arena do not need to be sloped.

Figure 5-7 **Outdoor arena floor construction.**

directions is needed for drainage for an outdoor arena, Figure 5-7a. An indoor arena does not need to be sloped.

- **Floor surface.** The top footing surface is usually 2 to 6 inches thick. A good surface should help facilitate exercise and training while at the same time not affecting the horse's health and well-being. The surface materials applied over the base material may be different depending on climate, availability of local materials, and the type of surface material needed for the specific riding event.

Construction of the surface begins with removal of the topsoil (usually 6-inch depth) to expose the base material. After the topsoil is removed, the underlying soil will need to be evaluated for suitability as a base soil material. The base material needs to be able to be highly compacted to provide a stable material for hoof and tractor soil pressures. The most desirable natural soil for a base has a mostly clay content that is easily compacted. A clay-sand material is best for the base soil. If the existing base soil material is not suitable, an additional 4 to 6 inches of a suitable base material should be added to the site after topsoil is removed.

While all components have an impact on a successful arena floor, the floor surface layer or footing, has the largest impact in the long run on horse health and comfort. Having a good understanding of desirable and undesirable floor characteristics can aid in the evaluation and selection of footing materials.

Undesirable characteristics of arena surfaces are:

- **Hard surfaces.** Surface footing that is too hard can result in joint and ligament problems.
- **Soft surfaces.** A soft surface is usually the result of the footing layer being too thick or deep. This situation can lead to missteps that can result in strained tendons or other serious injuries.
- **Dusty surfaces.** An excessively dusty arena can lead to eye and nose irritations, and possibly respiratory problems in both horse and rider if the area is not properly managed.

- **Wet surfaces.** Excessively wet surfaces can lead to muddy conditions, which can lead to slips and falls or deep, sticky traction that results in muscle, joint, and ligament strains, and potentially serious injuries.
- **Uneven surfaces.** Can cause horses to stumble, which can lead to strained tendons or other serious injuries.
- **Frozen surface.** These surfaces can be both hard and uneven. Horses on these surfaces can have joint and ligament problems, strained tendons, or other serious injuries.
- **Slippery surface.** Lack of traction is a problem with materials that do not bind against hoof action. Some materials lose traction when dry (sand) while others do so when wet (stall waste, clay)

The compactability of a material can affect cushioning and drainage. Materials compact when the pores or spaces between particles are reduced. A material that has uniform particle sizes is less likely to compact than a material that has variable particle sizes. With variable size materials, smaller particles will distribute themselves in the pore spaces of the larger particles, which will decrease the overall materials pore space, Figure 5-8.

A good arena surface needs to:
- Provide a good cushion.
- Be compaction resistant.
- Provide good traction.
- Be non-abrasive to hooves.
- Not generate dust.
- Provide good drainage.
- Not be slippery when wet.
- Have minimal maintenance.
- Not be cost prohibitive.

Unfortunately, no material meets all these criteria.

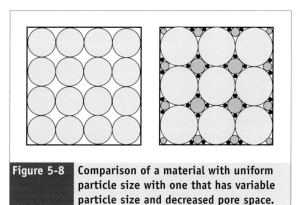

Figure 5-8 Comparison of a material with uniform particle size with one that has variable particle size and decreased pore space.

The most common surface materials are:
- Sand.
- Wood products.
- Road base mix.
- Rubber shavings mixture.
- Soil.

Since there is no one perfect surface material available, choose the negative attribute that will be easiest to manage with the available labor and equipment. Usually the more expensive the flooring surface material, the better results in cushioning, compaction, traction, abrasion, dust generation, drainage, slip resistance, and maintenance. Another thing to remember is that no matter how well an arena floor is constructed, most will need some maintenance and a major overhaul of footing materials every five to ten years.

Types of Floor Surfaces

Table 5-4 shows some common floor surfaces and their performance characteristics.

Sand

Sand is the most common material or ingredient used in arenas because it is relatively inexpensive. It is one of the most forgiving materials for a horse's legs and provides excellent drainage. Sand makes a good surface material if it has a good base and subbase underneath it. If the sand layer is too thick, it can have problems with being too "soft" (deep); therefore, do not use a sand layer thickness that is greater than 4 inches. When placing sand, start with a 2-inch layer and add ½ inch of sand as needed. Arenas used mainly for driving should start with only a 1-inch sand layer.

Clean sand that has been screened resists compaction because impurities like silt and clay have been washed away. Screened sand will have a more uniform particle size because the larger sand particles have been screened from the smaller particles.

The two types of sand particles are sharp or angular sand particles and round particles. Angular sand particles are obtained from quarries while river sand has more rounded particles. Angular sand particles provide better traction; therefore, it is more desirable as an arena floor material. Another type of angular sand particle is obtained from crushed rock. This manufactured product is not as hard as the natural particles and will degrade into smaller particles more easily; therefore, it is not as desirable as the natural particles.

Sand can be easily displaced during exercise and training activities making the surface uneven. A sand surface should be raked and smoothed after each day's use. Sand can wear out and erode overtime, and will need to be replaced once it starts to compact. Hard, angular sand like quartz can last up to 10 years or more.

Sand can dry out horse hooves, causing hoof wall cracks and splits. Sand is also very abrasive. Some sands have a tendency to be dusty and need constant maintenance. Dust associated with sand is caused by fine clay or silt particles mixed in the sand, or by very fine sand particles. Particle sizes less than 0.25 mm have the most potential to create dusty conditions. Keeping the sand floor moist and watering the floor before each use can help minimize the drying effects and dustiness of sand.

Coated sand materials have many of the same benefits of sand but have reduced problems with dust. They are water repellent and are not affected by temperature changes, water, or snow. They are very expensive, but

Table 5-4 Characteristics of common riding arena footing materials.

Adapted from *Horse Facilities 6: Riding Arena Footing Materials*, College of Agricultural Sciences Agricultural Research and Cooperative Extension, Pennsylvania State University, State College, Pennsylvania.

Material	Primary use	Cushion or compaction resistance	Traction improved	Dust	Drainage	Water reten- tion	Slippery when wet	Freezing potential	Durability	Abrasive	Mainten- ance	Appear- ance	Cost
Sand	Footing	H	M	Vᵃ	H	L	N	L	H	H	L	G	I
Stall manure	Footing	M	L	L	L	H	Y	V	L	L	H	V	I
Coated sand	Footing	H	H	L	H	L	N	L	M	L	L	G	E
Wood products	Footing or additive to increase moisture retention	H	M	Vᵇ	M	H	Y	V	L	L	M	G-V	I
Manufact- ured wood particles	Footing or additive to increase moisture retention	H	M	Vᶜ	M	H	Y	V	M	L	M	G	E
Road base mix	Footing or compacted for base	M	H	V	H	L	N	L	H	H	L	G	M
Mixture with rubber pieces	Additive to reduce compaction	H	M	L	H	L	N	L	M	L	L	G	V
Soil (not sandy)	Compacted as base	L	V	V	V	V	Y	H	L	M	H	G	I

ᵃ Needs regular watering.
ᵇ Needs watering or oiling on a regular basis
ᶜ Will break down over time

Legend

H = High	G = Good	I = Inexpensive	Y = Yes
M = Medium	V = Variable	E = Expensive	N = No
L = Low			

under normal use, they should last for many years with upkeep limited to releveling of traffic areas.

Wood products

Wood products such as saw dust and woodchips are often used to improve water retention in other surface materials. Wood product alone may also be used. Woodchips provide a cushion that can help alleviate stiffness in the horse's muscles and joints. Over a period of time, woodchips will break down and create a dusty condition that will require some type of dust control. Also, woodchips will eventually need to be replaced or replenished as they break down.

Do not use black walnut wood products because they are highly toxic to horses even when only in contact with the horse's skin. Avoid cherry wood products also because their wilted leaves can cause toxicity in horses.

Road base mix

Road base mix are known by many other names including screenings, limestone dust, quarry waste, and stone dust, depending on the region of the country. This material provides good traction with many properties similar to sand. Different grades of mix are available, ranging from coarse, large particles to very fine ones. Mixes without rocks are needed. Use one grade size so it does not compact as easily; otherwise, this material can be as unforgiving to a horse's legs as concrete. When the material is not compacted, it makes a good arena footing material. When compacted, it is used as stall floor and arena base; however, it has a tendency to dry out horse's hooves.

Rubber shavings mix

Rubber shavings or pieces are mixed with other footing materials to provide extra cushion and help minimize compaction. The rubber material adds a good, black color to a riding surface that helps to reduce glare in an outdoor arena. The material is easy to maintain because it does not require much raking and looks bright and black with a simple watering. Rubber won't decompose like wood product materials but will break into smaller pieces over time. Rubber additives in a footing mixture provide for a good surface that has some give and is not slippery when working horses. If the rubber additive material is cheaper than the main footing, using rubber additives can potentially reduce overall costs.

Rubber shavings or pieces are usually ground up recycled rubber material. Tires are probably the most common source of rubber, but recycled shoes and even golf club handle grips have been used, Figure 5-9. Two inches

Figure 5-9   Sand-rubber shaving mix.
Sand mixed with ground up golf club grips.

of rubber shavings mixed with the footing material usually provides a good surface.

Unlike recycled rubber, pure rubber can actually increase glare in outdoor arenas. Black rubber absorbs and retains heat, which can be a problem in outdoor arenas on warm sunny days. Indoor arenas may notice an odor generated from the rubber, and a darkened interior from less light reflection.

When purchasing rubber material, make sure that the material does not contain any metal such as steel belting from tires or other foreign objects. It is also a good idea to thoroughly inspect the material to make sure it does not contain any foreign objects before it is placed on the arena.

Less Desirable Footing Materials

Some materials used in arenas present challenges so their use is not very common. Soil and stall waste are some materials that present challenges.

Soil

Soil varies depending on the area of the country. Most soil types that do not contain a large amount of sand will tend to compact. Because of problems with compaction, many soils do not make a good arena footing material, but do make a good material for the subbase. Pure clay content soils tend to pack tightly and become impervious to drainage making them an especially good subbase.

Stall waste

Stall waste (manure with bedding) can be used as an arena footing material for a short-term basis (less than one year). It has acceptable cushioning qualities and is easily available. Stall waste breaks down easily. It can be dusty so it can have problems if not kept moist, and it can be slippery when wet. Maintaining a proper balance in moisture can be tricky. Flies can be a problem with arenas using this material. Stall waste consisting of manure and bedding will result in finer dust particles when it is too dry, and microbes and/or molds problems when the material is too wet.

Dust Management

Dust must be managed to minimize any negative health effects that it can have on horse and rider. Indoor arenas tend to have more problem with controlling dust than outdoor arenas. In addition to the negative health effects, dust in an indoor arena can coat the interior of the building making management even more difficult.

Small soil or sand particles less than 0.25 mm and other lightweight particles are the biggest contributors to dust problems. The main methods to control dust are to:

- **Eliminate fine particles.** The first line of defense in dust control is to minimize the amount of fine and lightweight particles that enter into the arena and minimize the use of materials that can generate dust.

- **Moisten particles to increase their weight and cohesion properties.** Watering down the surface is an easy and environmentally friendly way to control dust. The frequency of watering down a surface often depends on the amount of activity and water evaporation, which in turn is influenced by air movement, temperature, solar warming, and humidity levels.

- **Provide an additive to bind particles together.** Moisture retainers are one product that can help control dust. Wood chips are an example of an organic moisture retainer. Synthetic and natural fibers such as coconut can be used to intertwine particles to help in dust control. Crystal additives have been used to absorb relatively large quantities of water, which then releases the moisture slowly to surrounding footing materials. Water additives can also be used to slow evaporation, increase moisture penetration, and encourage microbes to grow on footing materials, each of which can help in dust control.

- **Use oil-based additives.** Oil based additives, that have a similar function to water, are an option in dust control. Products such as palm, coconut, and soybean oils adhere to footing particles, which increases the weight and cohesion properties of the particle. An advantage of oil is that it does not evaporate like water. The key to successfully using oil to control dust is to apply enough to keep dust levels down, but not so much that oil residue ends up sticking to the horse and people working in the arena. Additional oil is added periodically to the initial treatment to coat newly developed fine particles. Because of environmental concerns, do not apply petroleum products such as used motor oil to arena surfaces.

Surface Maintenance

Uneven and compacted surfaces result from normal exercise and training activities. Uneven surfaces can lead to injuries of the horse and damage the layers below the footing surface. High-traffic areas such as along perimeter rails or jumps are most susceptible to unevenness. Unevenness along perimeter rails for outdoor arenas can inhibit surface water drainage.

Using a dragging device is the best method to smooth out uneven areas and break up compacted areas. Frequent dragging will minimize the negative effects of exercise and training activities, especially near the perimeter rail. A tractor-pulled harrow with short spikes is used for heavier footing materials such as sand and screenings. Be careful that the harrow spikes are not so long that they penetrate and damage the subbase. Lighter drags may be suitable for lighter materials such as wood products.

CHAPTER 6

Breeding and Foaling Facilities

Before beginning to design horse breeding facilities, thoroughly observe facilities on existing breeding farms, and consult with breeding farm managers about the strengths and weaknesses of facility layout and design. There are several reasons why the type and design of breeding, maternity, and foaling facilities may vary between horse farms. The type of breeding system used on the farm, i.e., artificial breeding or natural mating, requires specific facilities. Breeding farm managers have individual management preferences about the layout and design of specific facilities. Also, recommendations on dimensions of facilities relate to horse size and temperament. The following recommendations are for horses with wither heights between 14 and 16 hands.

Design Considerations

Operational objectives of the farm dictate the size and type of breeding facilities, so accurate planning is necessary to integrate facilities with the goals of the operation. Items such as available land area, owner preferences for mare housing while at the farm, and the number of stallions and mares to be managed per year affect how horses will be managed. Also, several facility constraints relate to efficiently integrating the breeding system with other farm activities such as training. Other design considerations include allowing space for future expansion and providing an area for visitors to observe breeding and mares.

There are two major types of breeding systems: natural breeding and artificial insemination (AI). AI has several advantages over natural mating. AI maximizes the use of superior stallions and requires fewer stallions to be on hand. AI allows for a safer environment for the animals. During natural breeding, horses risk injury when mares kick or strike stallions, or stallions bite or strike mares. Employees work in a safer environment because they do not have to handle sexually stimulated and aggressive animals.

Breeding facility construction and maintenance are large expense items in farm budgets. These costs must be considered when budgets are developed for evaluation of economic feasibility. Additionally, the design and layout of breeding farm facilities must consider labor and horse handling needs for breeding and foaling. Labor costs are a major part of the daily operational budget, and breeding and foaling can require intense management of horses.

Moreover, personnel turnover can be large, and those involved with horse handling may be minimally trained. Therefore, use facility layout and design to promote safe and efficient movement and handling of horses.

Teasing Systems

The key to a successful breeding program is proper estrus detection. Estrus detection in mares can easily be missed if mares are not closely monitored. *Teasing* a mare by allowing a stallion to come into close proximity of the mare without allowing the stallion to mount the mare is an effective method of estrus detection. The visual and olfactory stimulation that occurs by allowing a stallion close to a mare provides for effective estrus detection. Generally, mares are teased for estrus detection at least every other day during the breeding season. Ideally, mares are teased daily.

Hand and group teasing systems have been used successfully on farms, but each method requires specific facilities. Contacting sources such as the state cooperative extension service, horse breeding farms, and commercial companies can help in developing facilities.

Hand Teasing

One method of hand teasing involves leading a stallion in front of the stalls housing the mares. Stall fronts should be solid construction to a height of 42 to 60 inches, above which are metal bars or wire mesh; see *Chapter 3, Stables*, for details on stalls. The stall-wall design should be sturdy and allow visual and olfactory contact but minimal physical contact between the mares and stallion.

Similarly, mares can be led to a stallion housed in a teasing stall. One design for a stallion-teasing stall is a 10- x 10-foot stall constructed with solid sides 7 to 8 feet high. Provide one or more windows in the sidewalls to allow the stallion to extend his head and neck out of the stall. Window height should be approximately 4 feet from the floor at the base of the window, or a height that approximates the height of the base of a stallion's neck.

Various window sizes have been used successfully. A common recommendation is a window 3 feet tall and 4 feet wide. Cover the window opening with a sliding or hinged door when not in use. Rubber matting and/or foam pads covered with nylon reinforced vinyl can be used on stall walls and on the edges of the window opening to reduce the chance of stallion injury.

Another method of hand teasing involves a teasing wall, Figure 6-1. Teasing walls are characteristically 10 to 12 feet long, 4 feet high, and made of solid construction. Padding the wall reduces the chance of injury. The mare is positioned along one side of the wall, and a handler leads the stallion along the other side. Handlers can be protected by adding perpendicular walls that are 3 to 4 feet long and 4 feet high.

Group Teasing Methods

Teasing pens, rails, and mills are examples of successful teasing methods for handling a group of mares at one time. Teasing pens are constructed to place a stallion inside a paddock of mares. Locate teasing pens in the center of the paddock so the stallion can extend his head and neck to the mares. A variation to the placement is positioning the pen so that several mare paddocks have access to one teasing pen.

A commonly used teasing pen design uses 3- to 4-inch pipe construction with three pipe rails, Figure 6-2. The larger diameter pipe is recommended if a bottom skid rail is used for ease of pen movement if the teasing pen is to be portable. Side rails are positioned at approximately 30, 42, and 78 inches above the ground on railed pens. Another variation is construction of a 42-inch solid side with a 78-inch top rail. Teasing pen dimensions vary; however, a 12- x 12-foot size is common. A 3- to 4-foot wide gate can help facilitate access into and out of the teasing pen. A teasing mill is a variation of the teasing pen in which the pen is surrounded with stalls housing individual mares.

A teasing mill consists of one central pen surrounded by smaller pens, Figure 6-3. The stallion is located in the center pen and mares in the outer pens, one mare per pen. The stallion will typically move from pen to pen to tease the mares. After all the mares have been teased, they are either removed all at the same time and replaced with a new group, or removed and replaced one at a time.

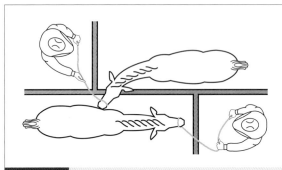

Figure 6-1 **Teasing wall.**
The stallion is located across the wall from the mare. Handlers are protected from kicking or striking.

Figure 6-2	**Teasing pen.**

A stallion is situated in the teasing pen. The teasing pen can be located in the middle of a paddock of mares or positioned so that several mare paddocks have access to the teasing pen. This pen is 12 x 12 feet and is constructed with 6-inch pipe. The bottom pipe allows for the pen to be moved. Side rail heights in this example are 28, 43, and 71 inches. Gate is 38 inches wide.

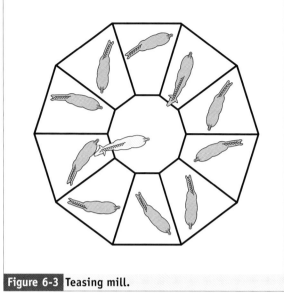

Figure 6-3 Teasing mill.

A teasing rail or chute allows for groups of dry mares to be hand teased. Mares are placed in a head-to-tail line while a stallion handler leads a stallion along the outside of the rail, Figure 6-4. Lengths vary depending on the desired number of mares in the rail at one time; 50 feet will allow for as many as six mares. Solid sides to a height of 36 to 42 inches topped with side bars spaced 12 to 18 inches above will allow for stallion contact with mares while protecting horse's legs from injury. The internal dimension of the chute should be 29 to 32 inches, or enough width for mares to move forward without being able to turn around. The entrance and exit should have flared gates, Figure 6-4b.

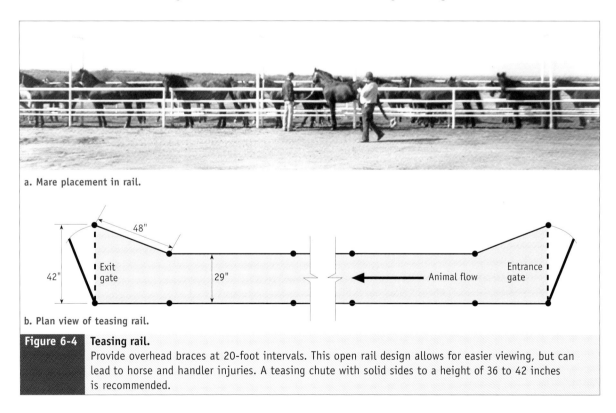

a. Mare placement in rail.

b. Plan view of teasing rail.

Figure 6-4	**Teasing rail.**

Provide overhead braces at 20-foot intervals. This open rail design allows for easier viewing, but can lead to horse and handler injuries. A teasing chute with solid sides to a height of 36 to 42 inches is recommended.

Breeding Shed

An enclosed area is needed for semen collection or breeding, and a well-designed breeding shed can facilitate these activities. The type and design of breeding sheds vary widely between farms. The dimensions depend on the type and amount of equipment housed in the shed. Breeding sheds may have teasing stalls or stocks that house a tease mare, wash areas for stallions, and a phantom mare for semen collection. Others, especially those designed exclusively for live-cover mating, have little to no equipment in the shed.

A 24- x 24-foot shed, Figure 6-5, is adequate when housing only a phantom mare, whereas sheds containing additional equipment may necessitate an area twice that size. Usually, breeding or collection requires several people in addition to the horses, so it is important that the area is large enough to provide a safe environment for handlers and horses. Also, placement of the equipment inside the shed and mare and stallion entrances and exits must be carefully planned to provide safe, efficient horse handling. Entrance and exit doors used by handlers with horses should be a minimum of 8 feet wide.

The breeding shed should be well lighted, dust free, and environmentally controlled from weather extremes; see *Chapter 7, Environmental Control*. Several different materials have been used successfully for breeding shed flooring. Flooring materials should provide a secure footing for horses and handlers and be easy to clean. River sand, caliche screenings, small grades of gravel, wood products such as tan bark and shavings, and rubber mats have

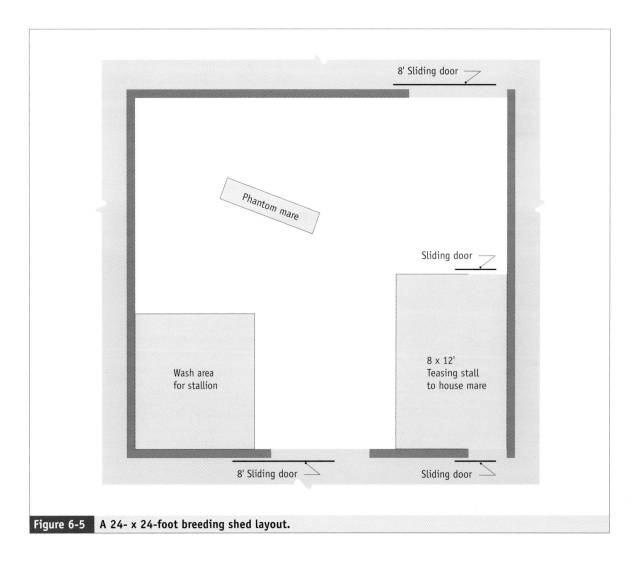

Figure 6-5   **A 24- x 24-foot breeding shed layout.**

Most farms using artificial insemination will house one or more of the following pieces of equipment in the breeding shed:

- Phantom mare.
- Stocks used for examination or teasing.
- Stallion wash area.

been used. Each has different strengths and weaknesses. Avoid surfaces that are dusty, hard to clean, slick when dry or wet, or difficult to maintain at a level grade.

Phantom Mare

A phantom mare, also referred to as a collection dummy, can be a very effective tool to collect semen. It eliminates the need for a cover mare. Phantom mares are padded cylindrical cores positioned on top of one or two pipe legs, Figure 6-6. Once trained, stallions will serve an artificial vagina (AV), also known as a breeding boot, while mounted on the phantom.

Phantom dimensions vary from farm-to-farm; however, most phantom mares are 5 to 8 feet long and between 54 to 72 inches in circumference. Phantom cylinder construction commonly uses an 8- to 10-inch diameter metal core constructed from pipe, heavy gauge

Figure 6-6 | **Typical phantom mare.**
Note: Padding on front leg removed to show adjustment set screw.

sheet metal, or pipe and sheet metal frames that are covered. The phantom core sits on top of 3- to 4-inch diameter pipes anchored securely in the ground. Metal cores and legs are covered with 4 to 6 inches of foam padding and covered in nylon-reinforced vinyl. However, other material such as leather has been used successfully. The covering must be nonabrasive and easily cleaned with water and disinfectant. Adding a leather simulated mane to the front one-third of the phantom allows the stallion to further stabilize by gripping the mane with his teeth.

The leg construction should allow for height adjustment on rear and front. Optimal phantom core heights above the ground vary with the stallion. Front heights from the ground to the top of the phantom are usually about 60 to 66 inches. Typically, rear heights are lower than the front heights, 48 to 56 inches. One common design uses two pipes per leg: an upper pipe of small diameter designed to slide inside the lower pipe. To secure heights, aligned holes are drilled in each pipe every 3 to 6 inches to allow for metal pin insertion through both pipes. A ½- to 1-inch set screw housed on the lower portion of the lower leg further stabilizes the legs.

The diameter of the phantom cylinder can have a major influence on performance. A small circumference cylinder can make it difficult for stallions to stabilize themselves on the phantom when serving the AV. However, a large circumference cylinder may make it difficult for the stallion to grasp without causing physical abrasion on the inside of the legs. One option that can enhance the performance of the phantom cylinder is to have a small diameter cylinder for the front of the phantom and a large diameter cylinder at the rear of the phantom. A design using a 48-inch diameter in the front and 60-inch diameter at the rear two feet of the cylinder has been used successfully, Figure 6-7. This design allows the stallion's front legs to grasp a small diameter cylinder while allowing his body to rest on the larger portion. Another modification of the cylindrical design involves a cutaway along the side or under the rear of the cylinder to allow for positioning of an AV.

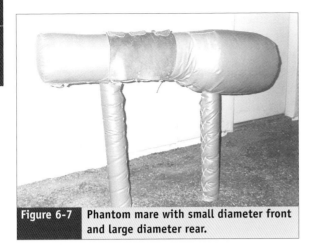

Figure 6-7 Phantom mare with small diameter front and large diameter rear.

Breeding Stocks

Breeding stocks are used for many purposes on horse farms. Relative to the breeding program, stocks are used for teasing, washing, palpation, and examination procedures of the stallion and mare. Stock construction must minimize the potential for horse and handler injury by avoiding sharp edges and projecting structures in and around the stock.

Typically, mature horses use stock frames constructed with 3- to 4-inch diameter pipe, Figure 6-8. The stock length typically is 63 to 72 inches, with internal clear widths of 26 to 32 inches. Sides are constructed with one or more side rails of solid metal or wood. Stocks with single side rails should have side bar heights at approximately 42 inches above the stock floor. Solid sides of 39 inches are suitable for mature horses. Sides that are hinged to swing out at the front or rear, or that have sliding or hinged windows allow access to specific areas of the horse's body for examination.

Some mares become upset if they are separated from their foals. Having specially designed stocks that allow the foal to be close to the mare can provide a safer situation for both the mare and the handler. Stocks designed to house foals alongside mares typically have solid sides and front and rear doors that should be at least 42 inches high. Foal stocks with taller sides may further deter attempts of a foal to jump over the sides, Figure 6-9.

When stocks are used for palpation and insemination, the rear door heights should allow for easy access to the mare but deter the mare from kicking above the top of the door. The preference for the amount of clearance beneath the door and actual door height varies among farms. Rear door and clearance heights should allow for the top of the door to be placed 32 to 39 inches above the floor, and the bottom 1 to 6 inches off the floor.

Additionally, stocks used for palpation and insemination will need an accessible water source at the rear of the stocks. Protect faucets and plumbing from horse contact. Some stocks are designed with plumbing along the top rail of the rear of the stock, with faucet placement on the side of the rear frame located 6 to 7 feet above the floor level. Also, small brackets or shelves can be constructed on the rear of the stocks to house soaps, paper towels, and other supplies for ease of access by the examiner. Position all of these structures away from horses as they are led or housed in the stocks.

A front gate placed to a top height of 42 inches may assist in containing unruly mares. Many farms use a cotton chest rope instead of a front door. The use of a rope allows for

Figure 6-8 **Common stock design.**
Stock length is 72 inches. Inner width is 32 inches. Front door and solid side are 43 inches tall. Rear door is 30 inches tall and located 6 inches (clear distance) above the floor. Top of frame is 96 inches above the ground.

Front view.
Foal stock clear width is 24 inches (left side) with a
24 x 61-inch door. Door is located 3 inches (clear distance)
off the ground. Mare stock clear width is 31 inches
with a 20 x 31-inch door. Door is located 30 inches off
the ground.

Side view.
Mare side in foreground. Top bar is 90 inches off the ground. The
stall length is 63 inches. The 20-inch sidewall is positioned 30
inches off the ground. The solid wall between mare and foal is 50
inches tall and touches the ground. The outside wall for the foal
is 61 inches tall and touches the ground.

Figure 6-9 **Foaling stock that allows for a foal to be placed next to the mare.**
In the rear, the foal stock door is 24 x 49 inches and is located 3 inches off the ground. The mare
stock door is 31 x 39 inches and is located 12 inches off the ground.

adjustment forward and backward thus allowing
the mare's hindquarters to be positioned
against the rear gate.

Teasing stalls or walls inside breeding
sheds can provide a safe environment for
estrus detection. Position the teasing stocks,
stalls, or walls inside breeding sheds to allow
for the presence of a tease mare, Figure 6-10.
The structures must be constructed and
located to prevent injury to the handler,
stallion, or mare as the stallion and mare
exhibit courtship behavior. Typically, all
structures are padded with foam pads or
rubber mats.

Wash Area

A stallion wash area is also included in
many sheds, Figure 6-11. A wash area is
important for washing the stallion's genitalia
before or after collection. Locate the wash area
in the corner of the shed to keep from wetting
the entire shed floor. Provide warm water, and
use durable, non-slip tile or floor coating as
the base floor. *Chapter 3, Stables* provides some

Figure 6-10 **Teasing stall.**
Stall is 30 inches wide, 48 inches tall, and
68 inches long.

additional recommendations for non-slip
flooring. Locate the drain inside this area to
catch wash water and transport it to a properly
designed wastewater treatment system.

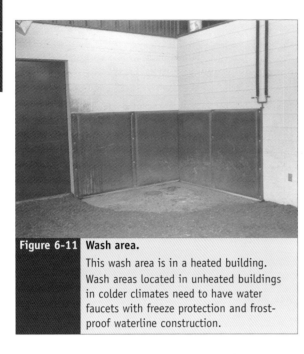

| Figure 6-11 | Wash area. |

This wash area is in a heated building. Wash areas located in unheated buildings in colder climates need to have water faucets with freeze protection and frost-proof waterline construction.

Breeding Laboratory

The on-farm laboratory is used to prepare semen collection equipment, examine semen, and prepare semen for insemination, shipping, or freezing. It is also used to clean and store artificial insemination (AI) equipment, Figure 6-12. The location of the laboratory is important. If possible, it should be directly adjacent to the semen collection pen to minimize delay in semen delivery and processing. A sliding window adjoining the laboratory and collection area helps coordination of collection and insemination procedures with the laboratory, and increases bio-security by preventing workers from tracking pathogens (e.g. manure) from the collection area and laboratory, Figure 6-13.

Water is very unfriendly to semen; therefore, care must be taken when processing semen near a sink. A sink does provide a good barrier between the semen processing area and the designed wet area.

A dependable source of hot water is needed. A utility room with a good hot water heater is needed, or the designs shown must be modified and rooms enlarged to include a hot water heater.

The size of the laboratory will depend on:
- Providing enough space for the number of people needed to collect and process semen.
- Whether an existing area is being remodeled or a new area is being constructed for a laboratory.
- Whether a hot water heater is located in the lab or nearby.

The items needed to set up a laboratory will vary according to the procedure used to process semen; however, the following equipment is typical:
- Microscope, slide warmer, slides, cover slips, etc.
- Temperature-controlled storage unit for items used in insemination and semen evaluation.
- Temperature-controlled semen incubator for short-term storage of semen.
- Densimeter or hemocytometer.
- Artificial vagina (AV), collection bottles, filters.
- Glassware, pipettes for processing and extending semen.
- Semen extender.
- Insemination catheters, sterile non-spermidal lubricant (KY gel), palpation/insemination sleeves.
- Refrigerator.
- Thermometers.

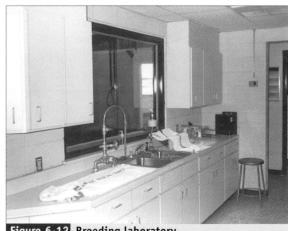

| Figure 6-12 | Breeding laboratory. |

Window shown is an observation window, not a pass through window.

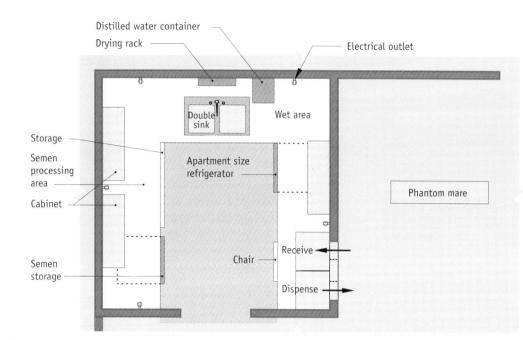

Distilled water container
Drying rack
Electrical outlet
Double sink
Wet area
Storage
Semen processing area
Cabinet
Apartment size refrigerator
Phantom mare
Semen storage
Receive
Chair
Dispense

Single entrance laboratory

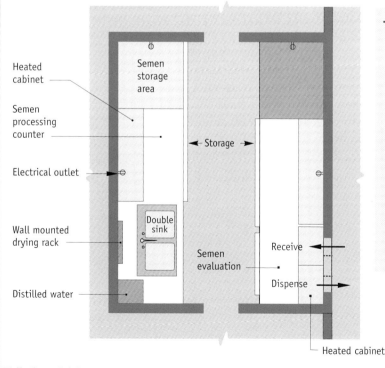

Heated cabinet
Semen storage area
Semen processing counter
Storage
Electrical outlet
Wall mounted drying rack
Double sink
Semen evaluation
Receive
Distilled water
Dispense
Heated cabinet

Walk-through laboratory.

The laboratory should have:

- A washable floor.
- Wipe-clean walls.
- Floor mounted cupboards.
- Wall-mounted cupboards.
- A washable work surface.
- A double sink.
- A drying rack.
- A source of hot and cold water.
- An electrical power supply with at least four well-placed receptacles.
- A refrigerator

Figure 6-13 **Plan views of two types of breeding laboratories.**

Consider these factors when designing a stud facility:

- Construction costs.
- Operating costs.
- Number of employees.
- Opportunities for future expansion.

Because of the wet nature of the laboratory, the electrical outlets must have ground-fault circuit-interrupter (GFCI) protection.

Every effort should be taken to equip and maintain the laboratory in the highest standard of hygiene and efficiency.

A semen processing and storage laboratory does not have to be highly sophisticated or expensive. A laboratory with 100 square feet should be adequate. Producers with multiple stallions or those routinely shipping cooled semen will require a greater investment in equipment than those planning to use AI occasionally.

AI can be done without a densimeter for estimating sperm concentration; however, a conservative approach needs to be taken and sperm cell utilization will not be maximized. It is essential that every on-farm AI laboratory have a microscope available to evaluate semen quality.

Specifications for Foaling Stalls

Foaling stalls are larger than standard stalls to help prevent casting by the mare and to allow additional space for delivery. Depending on the layout of stalls in the barn, 20 x 20 feet or 12 x 24 feet is adequate.

The lower 42 to 60 inches of the stall sides should be solid and flush with the floor. Provide windows or observation doors for mare inspection with minimal disruption. To minimize disruptions, many farms use electronic video monitoring of the mare while she is in the foaling stall.

Foaling stalls should be clean, dust free, free of buckets and feeders, and protected from weather extremes. The most commonly recommended bedding choice is straw. Bedding material with smaller particles may clog the newborn foal's airways or mouth when it inhales.

Foals tolerate colder temperatures, except the most frigid, as long as they are provided a dry, clean bedded area for comfort. Foals are more susceptible to chill from cold air blowing over them than from being in a cold stall. In colder climates, supplemental heat should keep foals warm. Radiant heaters work well to provide a centralized space or zone of warmth for foals, but these types of heaters do not work well to heat an entire room.

Farms with large investments in foaling mares have incubators for foals needing neonatal care. Foal incubators are designed to maintain a foal at 90 to 100°F and are large enough to accommodate a foal, a human attendant, and medical supplies.

CHAPTER 7

Environmental Control

Horses do not need an elaborate environment to live in. They have lived successfully outdoors in natural environmental conditions for thousands of years. A large pasture with a simple shelter can usually provide the healthiest environment for horses. However, there are times horses need to be housed inside. Structures without a properly designed and operated ventilation system can subject horses and handlers to an uncomfortable thermal environment and humidity levels that can increase the risk of respiratory diseases for the horse.

A horse is comfortable in nearly any temperature if the humidity is held to a comfortable level and there is enough air movement. The barn conditions most detrimental to horse health are when the air is cold and moisture is high. Airborne spores from dust and molds on hay, bedding and arena surfaces are more easily carried on moisture-laden air.

Adding a complete ventilation system after a building is completed is difficult; therefore, adequate ventilation for any building needs to be planned before construction starts. The objectives of ventilation are to provide fresh air and remove stale moist air. For a horse in a stall, stale air needs to be removed from the barn at the same time fresh air is brought in. Also, the fresh air must get to the horse's nose. A well-ventilated aisle and poorly ventilated stalls do not make for a properly ventilated stable. Proper ventilation depends on a system of components working together. Ventilation is more than just adding or installing a fan. In fact, fans may not be necessary to adequately ventilate most horse stables.

To provide for a good environment, an understanding of the basic ventilation process is needed.

Ventilation Basics

A well-designed and operated ventilation system maintains proper and uniform temperature, reduces humidity, removes odors, reduces dust and disease organism levels, and provides fresh air.

The basic ventilation process is shown in Figure 7-1. A properly ventilated stable will be cooler in the summer, less humid in the winter and be free of stale, odorous conditions by:
- Bringing fresh air into the building through planned inlets.
- Thoroughly mixing outside and inside air, picking up heat, moisture, and air contaminants, and lowering temperature, humidity, and contamination levels.
- Exhausting moist, contaminated air from the building.

Summer ventilation helps dissipate heat while winter ventilation aids in moisture control. Proper ventilation can decrease the level of respiratory problems and inhibit the accumulation of dust, molds and other air contaminants.

> **If properly designed and ventilated, indoor housing helps to:**
> - Provide comfort and convenience to handlers.
> - Maintain cleanliness, grooming, show coats, etc.
> - Prolong the training/riding season.
> - Manage breeding and foaling.

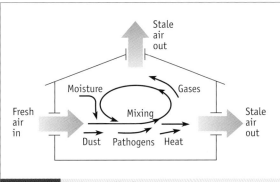

Figure 7-1 Basic ventilation process.

Failure to provide for any step of this process results in inadequate ventilation. Air requirements vary with horse size and outside environmental conditions. Ideally, the ventilation process provides enough airflow to maintain air quality in very cold weather, and enough airflow to reduce heat stress in hot weather. Design the system to provide at least three seasonal ventilation rates:

- **Cold weather ventilation** (also known as minimum ventilation) provides just enough air exchange to maintain reasonable moisture levels and remove air contaminants. The cold weather ventilation rate is determined by the need to remove moisture and maintain air quality. Provide continuous ventilation at a low airflow rate. Depending on location and housing systems, supplemental heating may be needed to maintain the desired inside temperatures and humidity.
- **Mild weather ventilation** modifies temperature. During mild weather this additional airflow controls the inside air temperature.
- **Hot weather ventilation** maintains the inside air temperature within a few degrees above outside temperature and increases air velocities over the horse. Moving the air directly across the horse causes a cooling or wind chill effect to enhance the horse's comfort. Circulation fans may be used when the indoor temperature exceeds a set level.

Environmental Comfort Zones

Horses, like many animals, have a different environmental comfort level than people. The ideal temperature for most horses is 55°F, with a range of 45°F to 75°F. Newborn foals require warmer temperatures, usually in the 75°F to 85°F range. Horses with a natural winter coat will tolerate winter conditions.

Ideal humidity for most horses is 60% with a range from 50% to 75%. A 1,000-pound horse exhales about 2.1 gallons of moisture per day (17.5 lb/day). If a barn is left unventilated, the relative humidity levels will rise causing damp conditions, which can lead to mold formation and odors. Horses can suffer from respiratory ailments and stiffness if humidity levels remain above the horses' normal comfort levels. When the humidity levels are too low, dust can become a problem.

Horses can tolerate cold temperatures well; however, many factors influence the comfort level of any animal. Within a certain temperature range, a horse's body does not have to make adjustments to the environment. This comfort zone is referred to as the thermoneutral zone. The lower limit of this zone is called the lower critical temperature. Below this point the horse's body adjusts to the cold temperature by increasing its food consumption and heat production, and by making the hair stand on end to create an insulated pocket of air next to the skin. The upper critical temperature is the point at which animals try to lose more heat through reduced feed consumption, sweating, and behavior changes.

Many things besides actual air temperature influence the lower critical temperature. For instance, wind or air movement caused by a ventilation system will increase the heat loss of a horse. This means that, although the air temperature may be above the lower critical temperature, the horse feels like the temperature is colder. This is referred to as the effective environmental temperature. Hair coat can influence the lower critical temperature a great deal because a heavy hair coat can insulate the horse. Table 7-1 gives estimates of the relationship between hair coat and lower critical temperature for horses in moderate

Table 7-1	Estimated lower critical temperature for horses in moderate body condition.
Hair coat	Lower critical temperature (°F)
Short (or wet)	60
Moderate	50
Heavy	30*

* A horse that has been well acclimated to a cold, dry, draft-free
  environment can withstand a temperature as low as 15°F.

body condition. Other things, such as exposure to cold walls, drafts, or drinking very cold water, can influence the lower critical temperature.

Horses kept at temperatures below their lower critical temperature will be required to consume more energy to maintain their body temperature. For example: a mature horse at 30°F might be consuming approximately 15 pounds of hay per day. If this same horse has no shelter from a wind of 10 to 15 mph, it would require an additional 4 to 8 pounds of hay per day for a total of 19 to 23 pounds. If it has no shelter from the wind and is subjected to rain at this temperature, it would require 10 to 14 additional pounds of hay per day to maintain heat production or a total of 25 to 29 pounds per day.

Consumption of forages will tend to be more effective in producing body heat than will consuming grain due to the differences in digestive processes. Some horses may not be able to consume enough feed to generate the needed heat to meet this requirement and will lose body conditioning instead. Pre-conditioning horses for winter by allowing them to build up a layer of fat may help to reduce the effects of cold temperatures. The additional fat also will reduce their heat loss. Allowing their hair coat to increase also will help with the cold tolerance. Horses kept outside should be allowed to grow a long hair coat, and the hair within the ears and around the fetlocks should not be clipped during winter.

Heat stress can affect horses a great deal. Most heat is lost from horses by evaporation of sweat and by convection across their skin. For pasture animals, shade should be provided along with an adequate supply of clean water. In stalls, air movement is very important along with water. Exposure to hot surfaces

such as the lower side of an uninsulated roof can increase the effective temperature, making the horse feel heat stressed even when the air temperature would lead one to think it should be comfortable. High humidity reduces the evaporation potential and will cause horses to be more susceptible to heat stress. Some researchers have suggested an index formed by adding the ambient temperature (in degrees F) and the relative humidity (in percent) as an indicator of heat stress. If this number is 150 or greater, the rider should use caution in exercising the horse so heat build-up doesn't become critical. Most riding activities involving long or intense exercise should be postponed when figures approach 180.

Another aspect of animal comfort is air quality. Research has shown that respiratory problems may be encountered with animals, especially foals, when the ammonia level exceeds 10 parts per million (10 ppm). This level is relatively low and nearly unnoticeable to some people. Ammonia is volatilized into the barn environment from urine. The best way to reduce ammonia levels is ventilation and frequent manure and urine removal. A barn that is closed up too tightly will have higher ammonia levels. Air in the box stalls may have more ammonia than alleys due to the proximity to the source (urine) and less air movement than alleys may have.

Airborne Contaminants

Several types of airborne contaminants can decrease the stable's air quality. Dust and molds are released from hay and bedding materials. Disease can be spread by pathogens attached to dust and moisture as air moves through the stable. Good ventilation will dilute airborne pathogens and therefore decrease the amount of time horses are exposed. Dust and mold are best reduced through good management practices.

A well-ventilated stable will not contribute to the moisture-laden conditions conducive to mold growth. Horses kept in clean, well-ventilated stables will have healthy respiratory systems that will be less challenged by introduced pathogens.

Microscopic evaluation of dust from hay fed to horses and dust from an arena floor has revealed the presence of 2-5 micron spores. These are small enough to enter deeply into the lower respiratory tract. In sensitive horses, such spores (i.e. *Apergillus fumagtatus* and thermophylic actinomycetes, such as *Micropolyspora faeni*) can cause an allergic response. This can result in chronic obstructive pulmonary disease, commonly referred to as heaves. This disease is quite similar to asthma in people. Veterinarians suspect that these types of allergens in dusty environments may also be a factor in reduced exercise tolerance and prolonged infectious diseases primarily induced by respiratory viruses.

Dust

In addition to increasing the dirtiness of a facility, dust creates respiratory problems for horses. Most stable dust comes from hay and bedding material. Select clean hay and bedding, and avoid overhead storage of these materials. Overhead storage allows dust and molds to rain down on the stalls. Consider vacuums rather than brooms when cleaning aisles of spilled hay and bedding. Vacuuming stirs up less dust. Bedding and hay distribution chores could be timed when horses are turned out to keep horses from breathing the higher dust and mold levels created when bales are broken apart and distributed. Recommendations suggest that ventilation rates of four to eight air changes per hour (air in structure completely exchanged with fresh air four to eight times each hour) will reduce airborne spore concentrations to below threshold levels for respiratory tract challenge.

Pathogens

Poorly ventilated, dark stables provide conditions for growth of many molds and pathogens. Moisture accumulation in stables is particularly harmful as many disease organisms prefer conditions of high humidity. Horse owners need to use ventilation to remove moisture, and they need to isolate sick horses to minimize the introduction of pathogens. Good stable management practices such as cleanliness, regular manure removal, cleaning food and water containers, and controlling rodents all diminish pathogen loads.

Ventilation Systems

Many people are afraid that too much barn ventilation will result in a drafty or cold barn. This is one of the biggest reasons modern horse barns are under-ventilated rather than over-ventilated. There is a difference between a properly ventilated barn and a drafty barn. Ventilation refers to the exchange of air, thereby removing moisture, excess heat, and air pollutants in favor of fresh air. Drafts are currents of relatively cold, untempered moving air that enter the building and strike the horse directly, thereby chilling the horse. A properly ventilated barn will not have drafts, but will have adequate air exchange and distribution to maintain a healthy environment for the horses.

Removing excess moisture from a building is very important during cold and mild weather. In addition to a horse's respiration, sweat, urine, spilled water, bath water, and wet evaporating surfaces also contribute to moisture in a stable. Heat and moisture production increases as the activity level of a horse increases. In many stables, doors and windows are closed during the winter in the hope of increasing barn air temperatures by trapping horse body heat. This results in the accumulation of stale, moisture-laden air that provides ideal conditions for growth of respiratory disease organisms, and condensation or frost on building surfaces. Condensation on building materials and insulation can lead to costly deterioration of these items. Ideal humidity for most horses is 60% with a range of 50% to 75%.

The types of ventilation systems used for horse barns are classified as natural and mechanical. To create an air driving force, mechanical systems use fans, whereas natural systems depend on natural air movements such as thermal buoyancy (i.e., hot air rises) and wind movement.

Mechanical ventilation systems have a uniform and controllable ventilation rate and generally distribute the air throughout the barn better than natural systems. Mechanical systems work well when heating systems are used because they can prevent over-ventilating and therefore reduce the wasteful discharge of heated air. The disadvantages of mechanical systems are that they are more complex to operate, require more maintenance of the mechanical parts, and consume energy. By contrast, natural systems depend on wind, which varies throughout the day and from day-to-day.

The choice of ventilation system will depend upon building design, climate, topography of the site, and the number of animals. Most horse stables and arenas are adequately ventilated using natural ventilation if they are not sealed up too tightly. Horse blankets are useful in colder climates to keep horses warm without increasing air temperature.

The advantages of natural ventilation systems:
- Low energy consumption.
- Simple to operate.
- Low maintenance costs.

Disadvantage of natural ventilation systems:
- More difficult to control air distribution, especially during cold weather.
- More difficult to automate.

Natural Ventilation

The primary driving force of natural ventilation is wind and thermal buoyancy. Because the animal density of horse buildings is typically very low in respect to the total air volume of a building, the effect of thermal buoyancy as a driving force of ventilation is much less a factor than in commercial livestock buildings where animal stocking densities are much higher.

The most effective natural ventilation design for stables incorporates continuous inlets along each sidewall of the stable and outlet openings along the length of the roof ridge. The inlets and outlets must have unobstructed airflow pathways and minimal interior obstructions. Open attic or roof areas help to facilitate the natural ventilation process. Buildings with steep interior roof pitches in the range of 4:12 to 6:12 slope direct the rising hot air to move along the roofline and exit at the ridge. Buildings with lower interior roof pitches (less than 4:12 slope) will tend to contain the warm, moist air within the building. Buildings with completely flat ceilings are typically the most difficult to naturally ventilate. Table 7-2 and Figure 7-2 show recommended inlet and outlet opening sizes and locations.

Locate naturally ventilated buildings so that nearby and attached buildings and land features do not block breezes. Provide at least 75 feet of open space between buildings or tall and wide obstructions. Orient the building to take advantage of the wind's driving force potential by positioning the eave-ridge vents perpendicular to prevailing summer breezes, Figure 7-3.

Airflow through a naturally ventilated building is expressed as *air exchanges* through the building. An air exchange is a complete replacement of the stable's volume of air. The air exchange rate is usually expressed in "air changes per hour" or simply "ach." The recommended minimum or cold weather ventilation air exchange rate range is 4 to 8 ach, Table 7-3. This air exchange rate will help remove moisture and reduce spore concentrations generated by hay and bedding to below desired threshold levels. For comparison, modern, tightly constructed residential houses have minimum air exchange rates of 0.5 ach in the winter. Likewise, horse stables built to a residential construction standard will have this low air exchange. Because air distribution is difficult to control at low ventilation rates, some buildings will use a mechanical ventilation system for cold weather conditions. During warm and hot weather conditions, the goal is to remove warm air that accumulates in the building as quickly as possible and replace it with cooler, fresher air.

Natural ventilation inlets

Air enters into buildings through openings called inlets. Inlets control how fresh air is introduced to the stable and distributed into stalls. Inlets bring air from the outside directly into the animal area or through an attic or

Table 7-2 **Minimum openings for naturally ventilated horse stables.**

Openings are continuous along the building length. Front wall heights of monoslope buildings may be excessive in wide buildings. A 6-inch minimum ridge opening prevents freeze up.

Building width (BW) (feet)	Winter		Summer minimum sidewall opening (SO) (inches)	Sidewall height with no ceiling (feet)	Sidewall height with ceiling (feet)
	Outlet width (WO) (inches)	Inlet width (HI) (inches)			
up to 24	3	1	72	10	12
26-30	3	2	72	10	12
32-34	4	2	72	10	12
36-40	4	2	72	10	12
42-44	5	3	72	10	12
46-48	5	3	72	10	12
50	5	3	84	12	14
52-54	6	3	84	12	14
56-60	6	3	84	12	14
62-64	7	4	84	12	14
66-68	7	4	84	12	14
70	7	4	96	14	16
72-74	8	4	96	14	16
76-80	8	4	96	14	16
82-84	9	5	96	14	16
86-90	9	5	96	14	16
92-94	10	5	96	14	16
96-100	10	5	96	14	16

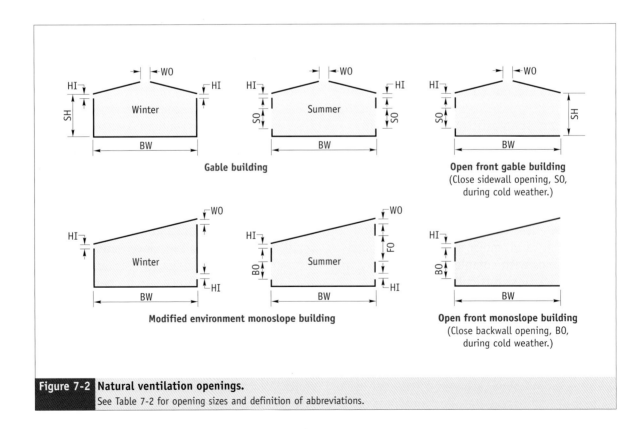

Gable building

Open front gable building
(Close sidewall opening, SO, during cold weather.)

Modified environment monoslope building

Open front monoslope building
(Close backwall opening, BO, during cold weather.)

Figure 7-2 **Natural ventilation openings.**
See Table 7-2 for opening sizes and definition of abbreviations.

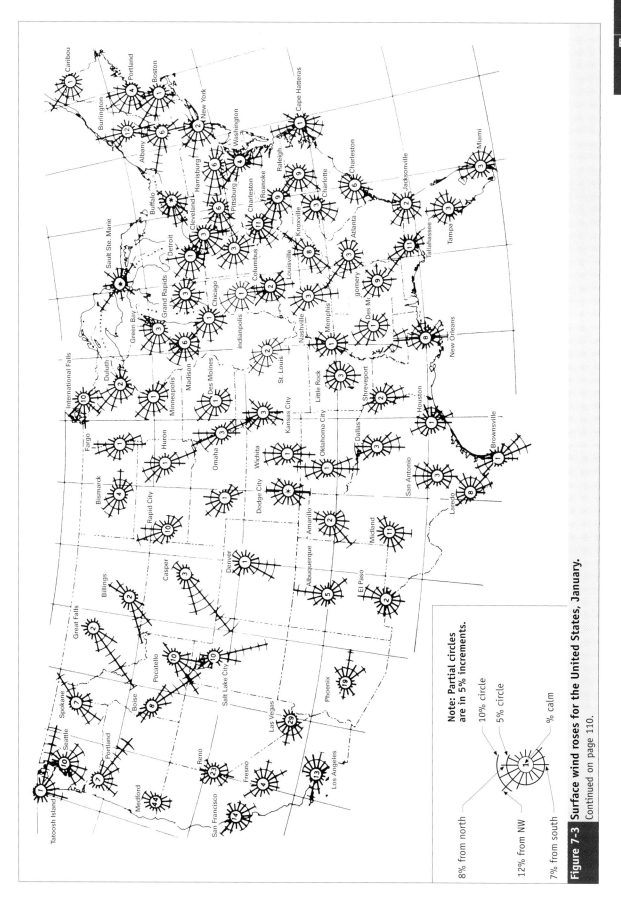

Figure 7-3 Surface wind roses for the United States, January.
Continued on page 110.

Note: Partial circles are in 5% increments.

10% circle
5% circle
% calm

8% from north
12% from NW
7% from south

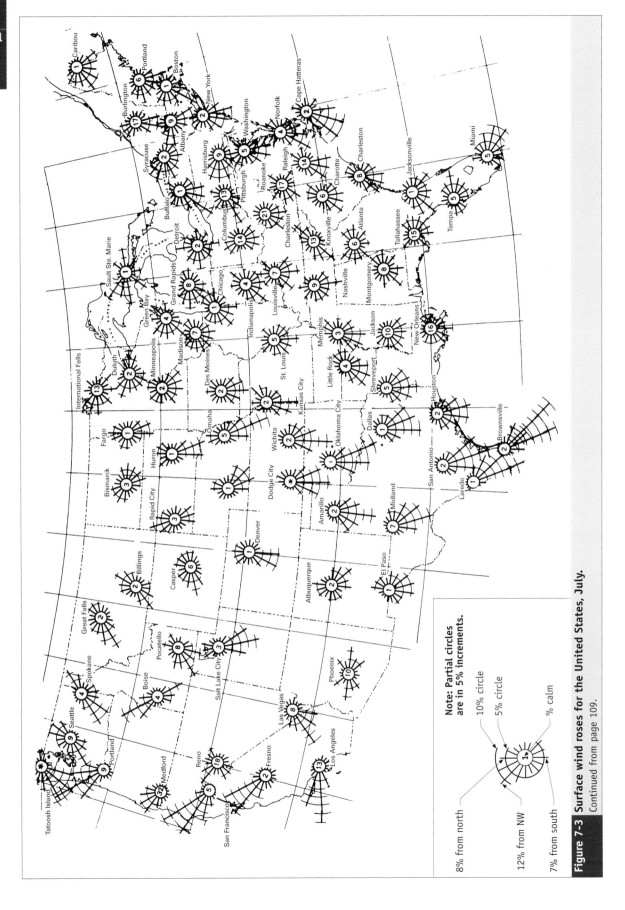

**Note: Partial circles
are in 5% increments.**

— 10% circle

— 5% circle

— % calm

8% from north

12% from NW

7% from south

Figure 7-3 **Surface wind roses for the United States, July.**
Continued from page 109.

Table 7-3	Recommended air exchange rates for horses.
Weather condition	**Air exchange rate (ach)**
Cold weather	2-4
Mild weather	8-15
Warm weather	20-30
Hot weather	40

grillwork stall door can be used to allow airflow from top to bottom of the stall. It is more desirable to introduce fresh outdoor air rather than potentially stale interior stable air into the foal's environment. Again, the objective is to provide fresh air where the horse will breathe it.

hayloft area. The goal of any ventilation system is to bring fresh outdoor air into a building and distribute the air at the nose level of the horse. To monitor the effectiveness of the inlets, check the air quality at the nose level of the horse at its standing and lying positions.

Air inlets are best positioned along the entire length of stable walls. Inlets are usually long, narrow slots located under the eaves and are sized for about 1 inch of opening width per 10 feet of building width. Minimum inlet width is 4 inches of clear and unobstructed openings (See Table 7-2). Size continuous eave openings so that each opening provides at least half as much open area as the ridge opening.

A properly designed soffit inlet typically will be designed with a fascia board or with an adjustable baffle, Figure 7-4. A fascia board or baffle will direct the incoming air upwards or horizontally into the building and prevent the air from dropping down directly into the building. Directing the air in this manner will allow the cold air entering the building to mix with the warmer indoor air. This mixing or entraining of air helps to temper the cold air and decrease the risk of drafty conditions.

The eave inlets should be under a roof with a minimum overhang of 12 inches to prevent rain, blowing snow, and wind entry into the eave inlets. Properly designed roof overhangs also minimize solar heating of the barn by the summer sun while allowing winter sun to provide direct light and solar gain to the barn interior, Figure 7-5.

In stalls with foals, inlets located about 4 feet from the floor can be built into the sidewall to provide fresh air at foal level. A baffle positioned inside the opening redirects the air and minimizes drafts on the foals. A

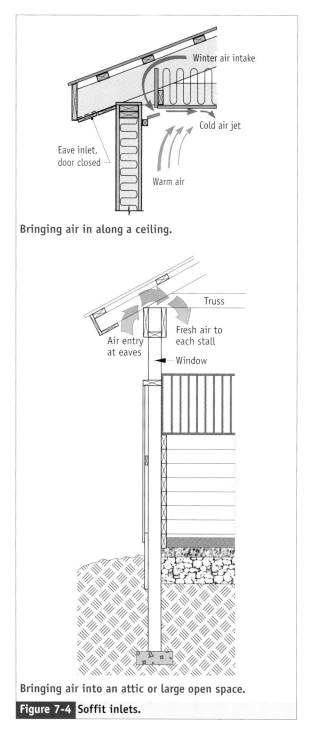

Bringing air in along a ceiling.

Bringing air into an attic or large open space.

Figure 7-4 Soffit inlets.

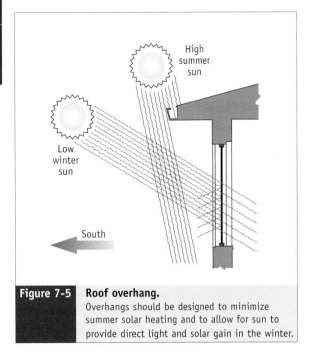

Figure 7-5 **Roof overhang.**
Overhangs should be designed to minimize summer solar heating and to allow for sun to provide direct light and solar gain in the winter.

covered with 2 x 2 mesh hardware cloth for a 42-foot wide building needs to be increased by a factor of 1.25 to 1.50. This means the inlet width (HI) will need to increase from 3 inches to 4 or 5 inches.

Inlets should remain open year-round. Adjustable inlets are recommended where a baffle or removable panels are moved seasonally to vary the opening size depending on the amount of airflow desired; the opening is never entirely closed off, just reduced in size. Even during the most severe weather, the opening should be no less than ½ inch per 10 feet of building width. Regular cleaning of any eave inlet, if screened, will be necessary for the eaves to perform as expected.

Do not obstruct inlets by fine screening or residential-type soffit panels. Inlets can be left unobstructed or covered with wire mesh, such as ¾-inch hardware cloth, to discourage bird and rodent entry, Figure 7-6. Table 7-4 shows effective eave inlet opening areas. If screening is used to cover eave inlets, the eave inlet width (HI) shown in Table 7-2 must be increased to compensate for the decreased effective clear area. For example, the width of the eave inlet

Figure 7-6 **Inlet screened on the building interior.**

Table 7-4 **Effective open eave inlet area.**

Based on Table 14 in *Horse Stable Ventilation*. E. Wheeler. The Pennsylvania State University. 2003.

Eave opening cover description	Open area	Area required to provide one (1) sq ft of clear open area	Effective area
Simple opening	100%	1.0 sq ft	**Recommended.** Full area allows airflow.
1" square wire mesh or poly bird netting with ¾ x 1⅛"	87 to 94%	1.0 to 1.1 sq ft	**Recommended.** Slight but acceptable restriction to air moving through mesh.
2 x 2 mesh hardware cloth with ½" openings	80 to 84%	1.25 to 1.50 sq ft	Potential for chaff, insects, and freezing condensate to clog openings.
Residential insect screening 18 x 16 mesh per sq in with 0.05" openings	66%	2.5 to 3.0 sq ft	**NOT recommended.** Too restrictive to airflow, and small holes will clog with dust.
Under eave louver or slot vented soffit with ⅛ to 5/16" slots	43%	2.5 to 3.0 sq ft	Restrictive to airflow and often includes an insect screen, which will clog with dust.
Soffit vented with ⅛" punched holes	4 to 6%	19 to 25 sq ft	**NOT recommended.** Designed for house attic insect exclusion. Provides almost no airflow and will clog with dust within months.

If properly sized, doors and windows also can be adequate inlets, especially during mild weather conditions. If doors and windows are used as fresh air inlets, position them so the horse has an opportunity to move away from them to avoid drafts.

Natural ventilation exhaust

A ridge opening should run continuously along the length of the stable and is sized to provide an open area equal to at least 1-inch width for each 10 feet of building width, Figure 7-7. Unobstructed airflow at the outlet is important. If the amount of precipitation coming through the ridge is objectionable, it is better to protect areas below the ridge than to build a simple cap. Raised ridge caps with upstands are expensive, can corrode, and require maintenance. A ridge vent upstand, Figure 7-8, helps keep out snow and rain and increases the airflow when wind is perpendicular to the ridge.

Stables often have cupolas for appearance, but they were originally designed and often still are used for exhausting warm, moist stable air, Figure 7-9. Cupolas must be designed to provide an equivalent amount of open space for air exchange because they provide restricted air openings compared to an open ridge.

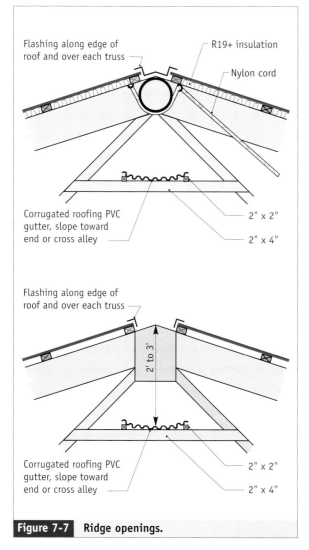

Flashing along edge of roof and over each truss

R19+ insulation

Nylon cord

Corrugated roofing PVC gutter, slope toward end or cross alley

2" x 2"

2" x 4"

Flashing along edge of roof and over each truss

2' to 3'

Corrugated roofing PVC gutter, slope toward end or cross alley

2" x 2"

2" x 4"

Figure 7-7   Ridge openings.

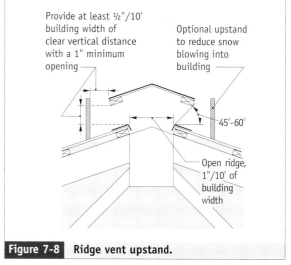

Provide at least ½"/10' building width of clear vertical distance with a 1" minimum opening

Optional upstand to reduce snow blowing into building

45°-60°

Open ridge, 1"/10' of building width

Figure 7-8   Ridge vent upstand.

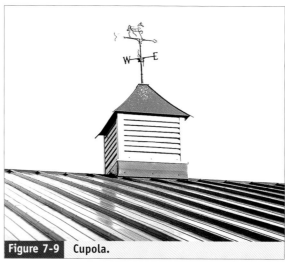

Figure 7-9   Cupola.

Monitor or offset gable roof systems shown in Chapter 3 can be used in place of a continuous ridge opening.

Air distribution

Inlets and outlets are important in good air distribution, but one of the biggest keys to making a natural ventilation system operate properly is to limit interior space obstructions. The use of grillwork rather than solid wall partitions between stalls is highly recommended. For an eave and ridge ventilation system to work, complete ceilings cannot be used in a stable.

Open grillwork and gaps, such as shown in Figures 3-10 and 3-15, can allow air to flow over a solid wall and into a stall. Grillwork should be located on the top of stall sides and fronts. Grillwork can have the added benefit of allowing horses to see each other, which can help prevent horses from becoming bored or developing bad habits. If a horse becomes aggressive towards its neighbor, a plywood panel or its equivalent can be placed over the grillwork.

Installing 1-inch gaps between boards can allow air to flow between stalls, which can help minimize or eliminate dead air locations in the lower stall corners. Installing a mesh stall door can also help airflow distribution.

Ceilings can provide a barrier for a naturally ventilated building that relies on warm air to exit through the ridge vent. If a ceiling must be used in stables, use a ceiling height with at least 12 feet of clearance for buildings up to 36 feet wide, Figure 7-10. Depending on normal wind conditions, buildings wider than 36 feet may need higher ceilings. The added benefit of having ceiling heights of at least 12 feet is that these buildings are easier to illuminate using natural and artificial light, and they give a more open and airy feel.

Overhead storage of hay, bedding, or other materials should be avoided, especially over stalls. If hay, bedding or other materials must be stored, locate this storage over a center walkway or aisle. Provide at least 3 feet of clearance between the top of the material being stored and the roof, Figure 7-11. This clearance will allow air to properly flow to the

Three design features can be incorporated into a stable's design to help facilitate air distribution. They are:
- Using open grill work and gaps in stall walls.
- Eliminating the ceiling or having sloped ceilings.
- Eliminating overhead storage.

ridge. Remember that any rain that enters through the ridge can damage any hay, bedding, or other materials stored below. It is best to eliminate all overhead material storage for enhanced ventilation and decreased fire potential.

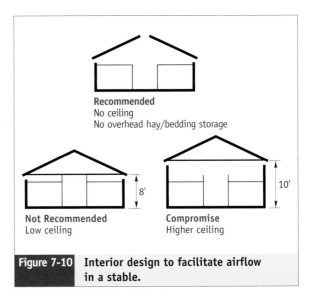

Figure 7-10 Interior design to facilitate airflow in a stable.

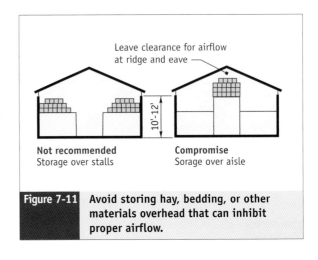

Figure 7-11 Avoid storing hay, bedding, or other materials overhead that can inhibit proper airflow.

Mechanical Ventilation

One of the most important details in a new or remodeled barn is to ensure plenty of ventilation. When remodeling an old barn, take care to ventilate the barn, considering air exchange strategies as well as distribution. Consider also the winter needs for ventilation and heating, as well as the summer needs for cooling.

As in natural ventilation, the pressure difference between inside and outside the stable is the driving force that moves air in and out of the stable. In many livestock buildings, negative pressure systems are used. With negative pressure systems, fans exhaust air, and fresh air comes in through inlets. This works well for buildings that are relatively tight in construction and makes air distribution work well. Buildings that have many doors and windows, as do most horse barns, may be difficult to seal; therefore, creating a pressure difference in the building is difficult. In a negative pressure system, each crack is an unplanned inlet and can harm the distribution of the fresh air.

Positive pressure systems have fans that blow air into the building, thereby creating pressure inside the building. Distribution ducts are important to move the air into stalls and portions of the building away from the fan. Cracks and other openings allow air to exit the building. A properly designed mechanical ventilation system will have a well-defined ventilation strategy that properly matches the system components with the desired ventilation rate.

Most of the time, the advantages of a natural ventilation system outweigh the advantages of the mechanical ventilation systems, but these systems can be used as supplementary ventilation in specific rooms or problem areas of the stable. Circulation fans are used in hot spots or dead air zones. Automatic mechanical ventilation with thermostatic control of fans should be considered if the stable is in a windless or protected area. In cold climates, stables should be mechanically ventilated during cold weather conditions and be well insulated to help keep them warm and to conserve energy while providing proper

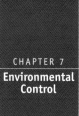
Advantages of mechanical ventilation systems:
- Easier to control air distribution.
- Can be used to automate ventilation.
- Preferred in windless areas or areas that protect the barn from the wind.
- Provide greater control of air movement in portions of the stable or riding arena where constant ventilation conditions are necessary.

Disadvantage of mechanical ventilation systems:
- Higher energy consumption.
- More complex to operate.
- Higher maintenance costs.

ventilation. Some horse owners rate the advantages of being able to effectively control air distribution much higher than the disadvantages of the higher energy and maintenance costs; therefore, they choose to mechanically ventilate year round.

Mechanical ventilation strategies

Depending on the situation, the strategy to properly ventilate a horse barn or arena varies. For higher animal stocking densities, ventilating based on **animal needs** is usually appropriate. In this design strategy the goal is to ventilate to remove moisture and gases during cold weather and to lower the temperature during hot weather. This strategy is independent of room size and is based on the number of horses. Table 7-5 shows ventilation rates based on cubic feet per minute of air. Ventilation airflow rates to meet cold weather requirements are usually based on the expected or minimal number of animals in a room or stall. Ventilation rates to meet hot

Table 7-5	Recommended ventilation rates for horses.

Based on 1,000-pound horse weight.

Weather condition	Ventilation rate (cfm)
Cold	25
Mild	110
Hot	400

weather requirements are usually based on a room at full capacity of animals.

When ventilating based on animal needs, a cold weather rate of 25 cfm (cubic feet of airflow per minute) per 1,000 pounds of horse weight should be adequate for moisture control. During hot weather, increase this rate to at least 400 cfm per 1,000 pounds of horse weight for temperature control. During mild weather conditions a ventilation rate of 110 cfm per 1,000 pounds of horse weight is adequate. When a combination mechanical and natural ventilation system is used, only provide mechanical ventilation for the cold weather ventilation rate. After the indoor temperature for the cold weather ventilation rate is exceeded, the system is shut down and natural ventilation is use.

Another mechanical ventilation design strategy is called the **air exchange method**. This design strategy is often used when few horses are being housed, which is common situation for many horse buildings including arenas. The design strategy is similar to the design strategy for natural ventilation systems. The goal is to replace all the air in the room or building a pre-determined number of times during each hour, Table 7-3. Because it is dependent on building size and independent of the number of animals in a building, the airflow rates calculated using the air exchange method would typically be higher than the rates calculated using the animal needs strategy. The ventilation rate using this method will typically be higher than the animal need method.

To meet seasonal requirements, total ventilation rates for the air exchange method are calculated by multiplying the total room volume (in cubic feet) by the air exchange rate (in air exchanges per hour), then dividing by 60 to obtain the required airflow rate (in cubic feet per minute). This method usually results in a lower total airflow rate and a compromise on animal comfort, especially during hot weather. This procedure should be used only with a full understanding and awareness of its limitations. It is a recommended method only for very sparsely stocked rooms such as a breeding building. This design is most practical in remodeled rooms with high ceilings and/or wide alleys, or a room that is partially full.

Example 7-1. Determining ventilation rate using the animal needs method. Determine the total amount of cold and hot weather ventilation needed for the following situations. Assume the horses have an average weight of 1,100 pounds.
a) *Single 12- x 12-foot box stall.*
b) *Stable with seventeen 12- x 12-foot box stalls.*
c) *A 36- x 118-foot building with seventeen 12- x 12-foot box stalls with a totally enclosed 10- x 12-foot feed room, and a totally enclosed 12- x 22-foot tack room.*

Solution:
a) *Using Table 7-5, the cold-weather ventilation rate for a single stall would be:*

$$Q_{cold} = \left(25 \ \frac{cfm/horse}{1,000 \ lbs} \right) \left(1,100 \ \frac{lbs}{horse} \right) = 27.5 \ cfm$$

The hot-weather rate would be:

$$Q_{hot} = \left(400 \ \frac{cfm/horse}{1,000 \ lbs} \right) \left(1,100 \ \frac{lbs}{horse} \right) = 440 \ cfm$$

b) *The ventilation rates needed for 17 stalls would be:*

$$Q_{cold} = \left(27.5 \ \frac{cfm}{stall} \right) (17 \ stalls) = 468 \ cfm$$

The hot-weather rate would be:

$$Q_{hot} = \left(440 \ \frac{cfm}{stall} \right) (17 \ stalls) = 7,480 \ cfm$$

c) *Because this design method is independent of space, the total ventilation rate needed for the entire building would also be 468 cfm for cold weather and 7,480 cfm for hot weather because there are 17 stalls, as there was in (b). The ventilation rate is independent of building configuration.*

Example 7-2. Determining ventilation rate using the air exchange method.
Determine the amount of cold weather ventilation needed for:
a) *Single 12- x 12-foot box stall.*
b) *Stable with seventeen 12- x 12-foot box stalls*
c) *A 36- x 118-foot building with seventeen 12- x 12-foot box stalls with a totally enclosed 10- x 12-foot feed room, and a totally enclosed 12- x 22-feet tack room.*

Assume a sidewall height of 10 feet, no ceiling, and a 4:12 roof slope. Assume the horses have an average weight of 1,100 pounds. The feed and tack rooms have ceilings, and hay is stored above the center aisle.

Solution:
Because the air exchange ventilation method is dependent on space, the ceiling information is needed to calculate airflow rates, but the animal size information is not needed. Using Table 7-3, the cold-weather ventilation rate for a single stall would be:

$$Q_{cold} =$$
$$\left(4 \ \frac{\text{air exhanges}}{\text{hour}} \right) \left(\frac{(12 \text{ ft})(12 \text{ ft})(10 \text{ ft})}{1 \text{ air exchange}} \right)$$
$$\left(\frac{1 \text{ hour}}{60 \text{ minutes}} \right) = 96 \text{ cfm}$$

The ventilation needed for 17 stalls would be:

$$Q_{cold} = \left(96 \ \frac{\text{cfm}}{\text{stall}} \right)(17 \text{ stalls}) = 1{,}632 \text{ cfm}$$

The first step to calculate the total ventilation rate for the building is to determine the volume of air that needs to be removed in air exchange. The basic volume calculation for this building would be:

Total volume =
roof space + lower building space −
tack room − feed room

Individually, the spaces are:

Roof space =
$$\frac{1}{2} \left(\frac{4}{12} \right) \left(\frac{36 \text{ ft}}{2} \right)(36 \text{ ft})(118 \text{ ft}) = 12{,}730 \text{ cu ft}$$

Lower building space =
$$(36 \text{ ft})(118 \text{ ft})(10 \text{ ft}) = 42{,}480 \text{ cu ft}$$

Tack room space =
$$(12 \text{ ft})(22 \text{ ft})(10 \text{ ft}) = 2{,}640 \text{ cu ft}$$

Feed room space =
$$(10 \text{ ft})(12 \text{ ft})(10 \text{ ft}) = 1{,}200 \text{ cu ft}$$

The total ventilation volume is determined by:

Total volume =
12,730 cu ft + 42,480 cu ft −
2,640 cu ft − 1,200 cu ft = 51,370 cu ft

The ventilation rate for the entire building would be:

$$Q_{cold} =$$
$$\left(4 \ \frac{\text{air exhanges}}{\text{hour}} \right) \left(\frac{51{,}370 \text{ cu ft}}{\text{air exchange}} \right)$$
$$\left(\frac{1 \text{ hour}}{60 \text{ minutes}} \right) = 3{,}425 \text{ cfm}$$

Because this building is be designed to replace all of the air in the building four times each hour, the ventilation rate is about seven times greater than the method to ventilate for only the horses' needs. It may be advisable to calculate and compare both cold weather rate methods; the larger rate will provide the more satisfying air quality, but in very cold weather it may be excessive and/or cause drafts.

Fans

Fans are sized according to how much air volume they must move. When designing a mechanical ventilation system to control the environmental needs for a wide range of weather conditions, it is best to have more than one fan to effectively cover the wide range of airflows needed. When designing a mechanical ventilation system to control the environmental needs for only one weather condition, such as cold weather, only one standard or variable speed fan is needed to cover the required airflow.

Most horse buildings that use mechanical systems use negative pressure. In a *negative pressure ventilation system*, fans may be located virtually anywhere in the building shell whereas air inlets are carefully located to deliver fresh air to each horse's stall. Fans control how much air is moved, and inlet location controls the fresh air distribution. For effective mechanical ventilation, the building must be kept tight so that the planned inlets are the only air inlets. Open stable doors and windows ruin this effect. Fans operated without a pressure difference across them have little effect except locally, where airflow is felt downstream. It is important to maintain a clear space on both the intake and exhaust sides of the fans equivalent to two to three times the diameter of the fan. For example, a 24-inch fan would require a clear space equal to 48 to 72 inches (4 to 6 feet) on the intake and exhaust sides of the fans.

Mechanical ventilation inlets

Inlets and soffits for mechanical ventilation systems are designed similarly to those for natural ventilation systems. Providing good air distribution in a box stall can be challenging, but a mechanical ventilation system can be effectively used to bring fresh air into a stall. Stables using only a negative pressure mechanical ventilation system during cold weather may not need to have a continuous open eave inlet. For this case, a section of eave opening can be used to direct fresh outdoor air into the box stall. If hay is stored above the stall, then a mechanical duct system will need to be installed so fresh air can be effectively provided to the stall.

Duct systems

Some box stalls in older facilities cannot be adequately ventilated with a negative pressure ventilation system. These stalls may need a *positive pressure ventilation system* in which a duct system is used to adequately distribute fresh air within stalls or building. The advantage of this system is that ducts can be used in old, retrofitted barns or in very wide stables with multiple rows of stalls.

In a typical positive pressure ventilation system, one fan is mounted in the wall to draw fresh air from the outside and blow it into the duct creating a positive pressure within the duct, Figure 7-12. This system is usually adequate for cold and mild weather conditions but will usually not have enough airflow capacity for hot weather conditions.

When designing a positive pressure duct system, size the fans to provide 100 cfm of airflow per 1,000-pound horse. Size the duct cross section to provide 160 square inches of opening per 1,000 cfm of fan capacity, which is also equivalent to providing one square foot of open cross section per 600 cfm of fan capacity. See Tables 7-6 and 7-7 to properly size ducts. Exhaust openings into stalls should be sized for about 5 cfm per square inch. A 3-inch diameter hole and a 1- x 5-inch slot will each exhaust about 25 cfm of air. For an adult horse, evenly space four, 3-inch diameter holes or 1- x 5-inch slots to provide adequate air distribution within a stall.

There are a few ways in which to construct the duct. In a stall that has floor joists above, a duct can be constructed in each stall by covering the bottom of a pair of floor joists near the center of the stall, Figure 7-13a. Another method is to install a continuous duct above the stalls or as part of the loft area along the outside wall that extends the entire length of the stall area, Figure 7-13b. Another design has the duct located near the alley, Figure 7-13c.

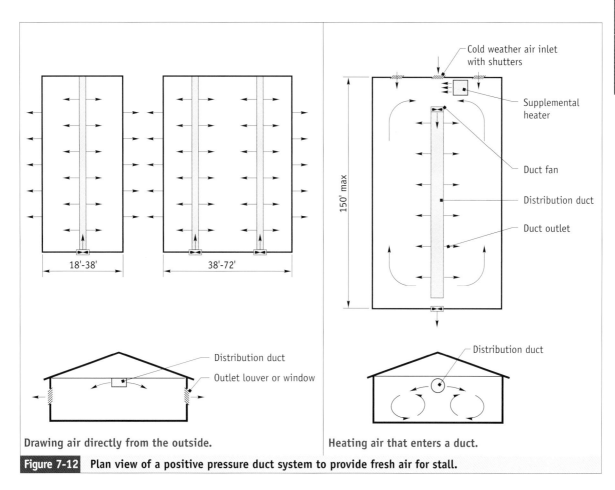

Drawing air directly from the outside.

Heating air that enters a duct.

Figure 7-12 Plan view of a positive pressure duct system to provide fresh air for stall.

Table 7-6 Rectangular duct areas.

Width (inches)	Height (inches)	Area (sq in)	Area (sq ft)	Max. duct airflow (cfm)[a]	Number of adult horses[b]
4	12	48	0.33	200	2
6	10	60	0.42	250	2
6	12	72	0.50	300	3
6	14	84	0.58	350	3
6	16	96	0.67	400	4
6	20	120	0.83	500	5
6	24	140	1.0	600	6
8	22	180	1.2	730	7
8	24	190	1.3	800	8
8	28	220	1.6	930	9
8	30	240	1.7	1,000	10
10	30	300	2.1	1,250	12
12	30	360	2.5	1,500	15
14	36	500	3.5	2,100	21
16	38	610	4.2	2,530	25
18	40	720	5.0	3,000	30

[a] Based on 600 cfm per square foot of duct.
[b] Based on 100 cfm per horse.

Table 7-7 Circular duct areas.

Diameter (inches)	Area (sq in)	Area (sq ft)	Max. duct airflow (cfm)[a]	Number of adult horses[b]
6	30	0.20	120	1
8	50	0.35	210	2
10	80	0.55	325	3
12	110	0.80	470	4
14	150	1.05	640	6
16	200	1.40	840	8
18	250	1.75	1,060	10
20	315	2.20	1,310	13
22	380	2.65	1,585	15
24	450	2.15	1,885	18
26	530	3.70	2,210	22
28	615	4.30	2,565	25
30	710	4.90	2,945	29

[a] Based on 600 cfm per square foot of duct.
[b] Based on 100 cfm per horse.

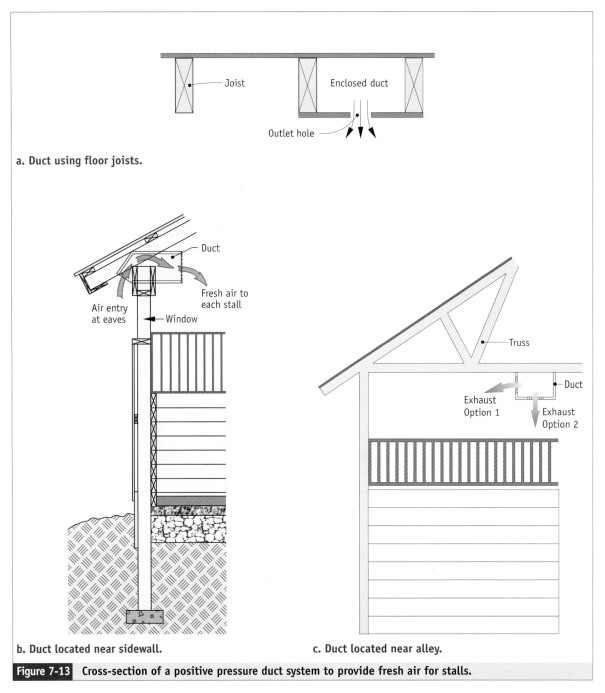

a. Duct using floor joists.

Joist

Enclosed duct

Outlet hole

Duct

Fresh air to each stall

Air entry at eaves

Window

Truss

Duct

Exhaust Option 1

Exhaust Option 2

b. Duct located near sidewall.

c. Duct located near alley.

Figure 7-13 Cross-section of a positive pressure duct system to provide fresh air for stalls.

Controlling dead air locations

Warm air may become trapped or stratified within a tall enclosure such as an indoor arena or a wide, gable-roofed stable. Paddle fans direct air downward and can re-circulate this air to more evenly distribute warmth. Paddle fans should be carefully placed when used in concert with eave-ridge vent systems to minimize any conflict in air movement. Place paddle fans away from the ridge vent, or use them only on stagnant days when the natural ventilation system is not operating efficiently. Paddle fans should be located high enough to be out of any possible horse, or horse and rider, reach. Paddle fans are more typically used to supplement mechanical ventilation systems in large buildings where even air distribution can be hard to obtain.

Dead air zones may exist at different spots within a stable due to obstructed airflow. A chronic problem should be solved permanently, but isolated incidents may be solved with a portable fan. Place the fan at least 14 feet high so the cord is out of horse reach and so the fan cannot be moved or damaged by the horse. Fresh air, rather than stale air, directed on the horse is more desirable.

Cold Weather Temperature Control

A horse can do well in nearly any temperature if the humidity can be held to a comfortable level and there is enough air movement through the building to keep the air clean and free of condensation. The conditions that are most detrimental to a horse's health are when the stable is cold and moisture is high. These are the optimal conditions to harm the respiratory system and allow the inhalation of pathogens.

Horses that are outside during cold weather will develop a natural winter coat that can allow them to tolerate temperatures down to 0°F. Horses that are clipped of their winter coats such as show and heavily worked horses can be housed in a stable with an indoor temperature as low as 40°F if the building is dry inside and the horses are given blankets, hoods, and leg wraps. The inside temperatures for buildings with waterers or waterlines should not go below 35°F.

Overall, very few horse buildings are insulated, but a well-insulated building will help minimize heat loss, condensation, and temperature swings within the building. Reviewing and increasing insulation levels in a building should be one of the first areas considered when looking to maintain an acceptable thermal environment.

Two methods can be used to help increase interior building temperature. The first and preferred method is to use supplemental heat. The other method is to reduce the ventilation rate. When the ventilation rate is reduced, moisture levels within the building will rise. As described in the introduction of the *Ventilation Systems* section, buildings must be ventilated well enough to exhaust the excess moisture otherwise building materials including insulation can sustain moisture damage. Also, higher humidity levels increase the potential for airborne diseases and odors. Do not ventilate below the rates shown in Tables 7-3 and 7-5.

Heating, Cooling and Tempering Air for Livestock Housing, MWPS-34, offers additional detail on stable heating options, heat exchangers, cooling systems, insulation, and examples of applications to various types of livestock operations including horse stables.

Insulation

Adequate insulation is a necessary element to consider in any environmental control system. Insulation is any material that slows heat transfer from one area to another. During cold weather, insulation maintains warmer inside surface temperatures, conserves heat, reduces supplemental heating requirements, and reduces condensation and radiant heat loss.

During warm months, insulation reduces heat gain by lowering roof and wall surface temperatures. The temperatures of walls and roofs of uninsulated buildings exposed to direct sunlight can be as much as 50°F above air temperature.

In a well insulated building, the inside roof or ceiling and wall surfaces are warmer than the dew point temperature of the indoor air. The warmer the surfaces, the less likely condensation will form, Figure 7-14. In a poorly insulated building, inside ceiling and wall surfaces become cold in winter. If the surface temperature is below the dew point, air next to the surface becomes saturated and moisture condenses, Figure 7-15. Frost occurs if the surface temperature is below freezing.

Insulation levels and materials

The resistance of a material to heat flow is indicated by its R-value. Good insulators have high R-values. The insulating value of a wall or ceiling is the total of the insulation, siding and lining, surface conditions, and air spaces.

Stables are not usually insulated as well as residential or commercial buildings. Recommended minimum insulation levels are listed in

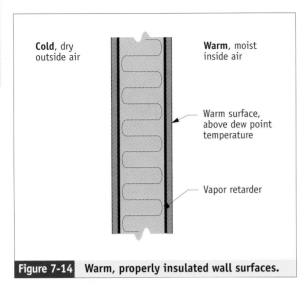

Cold, dry
outside air

Warm, moist
inside air

Warm surface,
above dew point
temperature

Vapor retarder

Figure 7-14 **Warm, properly insulated wall surfaces.**

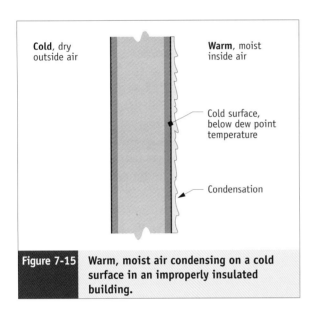

Cold, dry
outside air

Warm, moist
inside air

Cold surface,
below dew point
temperature

Condensation

Figure 7-15 **Warm, moist air condensing on a cold surface in an improperly insulated building.**

Table 7-8	Recommended minimum insulation levels (R-values) for stables.	

R-values are for building sections. Use with Figure 7-16.

Winter degree days	Walls	Roof or Ceiling
2500 or less	14	22
2501 to 6000	14	25
6001 or more	20	33

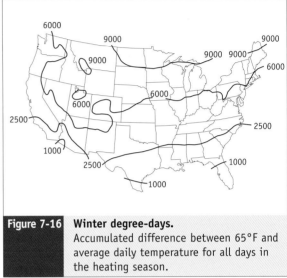

Figure 7-16 **Winter degree-days.**
Accumulated difference between 65°F and average daily temperature for all days in the heating season.

Several types of insulation can be used in buildings. Each has some advantages and disadvantages. The most common place to use insulation in a horse barn is in the roof area. Different types of insulation that can be used in horse barns include:

1. Blanket insulation with a kraft paper or aluminum foil vapor retarder. These vapor retarders are not usually strong enough to keep birds or rodents from making holes in the insulation.
2. Glass wool insulation with a plastic vapor retarder. Some of the heavier plastic vapor retarders are strong enough to keep birds from pecking holes in the insulation.
3. Rigid asphalt-impregnated wood fiber sheathing. Over a period of time, this material will absorb moisture and bow away from the under side of the roof and allow moisture to collect between sheeting and metal or plywood roofing.

Table 7-8. The R-value of common insulation materials is listed in Table 7-9. A soil backfill will complement but not replace insulation. The primary benefit of soil backfill is to reduce exposure to extreme temperatures. During the planning process, discuss the building insulation level with the builder.

Because of the relatively high moisture levels in stables (compared to residential levels), use only insulation materials that do not accumulate moisture and water. Unprotected fiberglass batts and loose fill materials usually are not acceptable insulation materials to use in most cases.

Table 7-9   Estimated R-values of selected material.

All insulation materials require a plastic vapor barrier
(6 mil recommended) between the insulation and animal space.
All insulation requires a washable protective overlay, i.e., wall
or ceiling interior liner. No insulation product is water-vapor,
bird proof, rodent proof, or completely fire proof.
See *Heating, Cooling and Tempering Air for Livestock Housing,*
MWPS 34, for more details in regards to insulation R-values.

Material	R-value (per inch of thickness)
Batt or Blanket Fiberglass, mineral wool	2.75-3.67
Insulating sheathing, 25/32-inches thick	2.06*
Polystyrene	
Expanded (Beadboard)	3.9
Extruded (Foamular, Styrofoam)	5.0
Polyisocyanurate, (Celotex)	6.0
Polyurethane (bronze)	6.2
Loose fill	
Cellulose	3.13-3.70
Glass or mineral wool	2.20-3.00
Vermiculite	2.13-2.27
Cellulose (paper, gray)	Not recommended
Ureaformaldehyde	Not recommended
Brick, common	
80 pcf	0.31-0.45
130 pcf	0.11-0.19
Concrete (cast-in-place)	0.08
Concrete block	
8-inch thick with hollow cores	1.0*
8-inch thick with insulation cores	1.9*
Floor perimeter (per foot of exterior wall length)	
Concrete, no perimeter insulation	1.23*
Concrete, plus 2" x 24" rigid insulation	2.22*
Hardwoods	
Ash	0.88-0.94
Birch	0.82-0.87
Maple	0.84-0.94
Oak	0.80-0.89
Metal siding or liner	0.00
Plywood (Douglas fir)	1.25
Plastic vapor barrier	0.00
Shingles	
Asphalt	0.44*
Wood	0.94*
Softwoods	
Southern pine	0.89-1.00
Douglas fir-larch	0.99-1.06
Hem-fir, spruce-pine, fir	1.11-1.35
Inside surface air film (for planning purposes)	0.68*
Outside surface air film (for planning purposes)	0.17*

* Estimated actual R-value.

Birds and rodents will make holes in this material.

4. Expanded polystyrene with or without aluminum foil surface. Without some type of rigid cover, birds and rodents will damage this material over a period of time.

Most of the insulation types listed above MUST be covered with plywood due to toxic gases that will be emitted if the insulating material is on fire. Check with the insurance company for their protection requirements in regards to insulating materials.

Installing insulation

Figures 7-17 through 7-20 show common construction methods for insulated roofs, ceilings, walls, and foundations. Do not compress or pack batt, blanket, or loose fill-type insulating products.

Perimeter insulation reduces heat loss through the foundation and eliminates cold, wet floors in heated buildings. Insulate the entire concrete exterior to a minimum of 24 inches below the ground line. Rodents can burrow as much as 36 inches below grade, damaging insulation and foundations. Use 2-inch rigid, closed-pore insulation, and protect it with high-density fiberglass reinforced plastic or foundation grade plywood above and below ground. See Figure 7-19.

Vapor retarders

Wet insulation loses its insulating effectiveness, which increases heat loss and building deterioration. Vapor retarders protect insulation effectiveness by restricting moisture migration through walls, ceilings, and roofs. Vapor retarders are classified by their permeability rating measured in perms.

Install 4- to 6-mil polyethylene (plastic) vapor retarders on the warm side of all insulated walls, ceilings, and roofs. Use polyethylene vapor retarders underneath concrete floors and foundations to control soil moisture penetration. Use waterproof rigid insulation if it comes into contact with soil. See Figures 7-17 through 7-20 for proper vapor retarder locations. Avoid puncturing or cutting

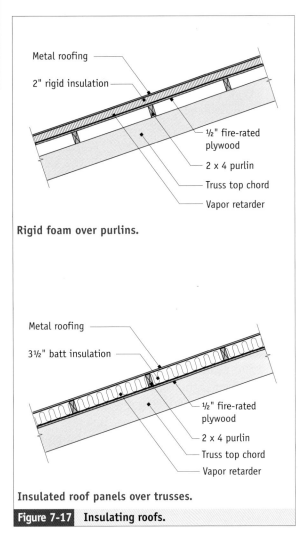

Metal roofing

2" rigid insulation

½" fire-rated plywood

2 x 4 purlin

Truss top chord

Vapor retarder

Rigid foam over purlins.

Metal roofing

3½" batt insulation

½" fire-rated plywood

2 x 4 purlin

Truss top chord

Vapor retarder

Insulated roof panels over trusses.

Figure 7-17 Insulating roofs.

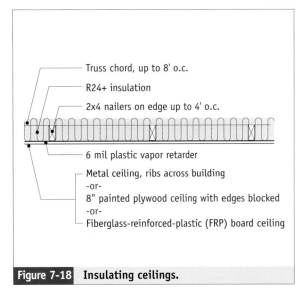

Truss chord, up to 8' o.c.

R24+ insulation

2x4 nailers on edge up to 4' o.c.

6 mil plastic vapor retarder

Metal ceiling, ribs across building
-or-
8" painted plywood ceiling with edges blocked
-or-
Fiberglass-reinforced-plastic (FRP) board ceiling

Figure 7-18 Insulating ceilings.

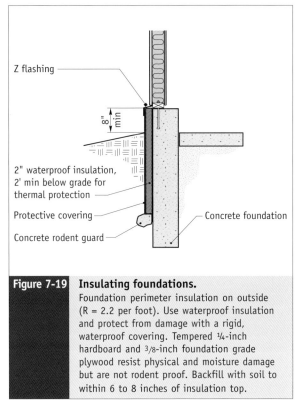

Z flashing

8" min

2" waterproof insulation, 2' min below grade for thermal protection

Protective covering

Concrete rodent guard

Concrete foundation

Figure 7-19 | **Insulating foundations.**
Foundation perimeter insulation on outside (R = 2.2 per foot). Use waterproof insulation and protect from damage with a rigid, waterproof covering. Tempered ¼-inch hardboard and ³/₈-inch foundation grade plywood resist physical and moisture damage but are not rodent proof. Backfill with soil to within 6 to 8 inches of insulation top.

holes into vapor retarders to minimize moisture migration through the holes. **Provide ventilation in the roof peak area on the cold side of insulated surfaces to help minimize condensation.**

Doors and windows

Loose fitting doors and windows, and cracks around window and doorframes, pipes, and wires can create cold spots, drafty areas, or condensation problems in mechanically ventilated buildings. Cracks and leaks also reduce the effectiveness of the ventilating system inlets. Use insulated and weather-stripped entry doors to minimize leaks and heat loss. Locate doors on the downwind side to minimize drafts during entry. For upwind entries, a vestibule or hallway between outer and inner doors prevents cold wind from blowing directly into the building. To conserve floor area, consider making the vestibule entrance part of a hallway, storage area, washroom, or office.

Minimize windows and skylights in animal housing. In warm buildings, windows and

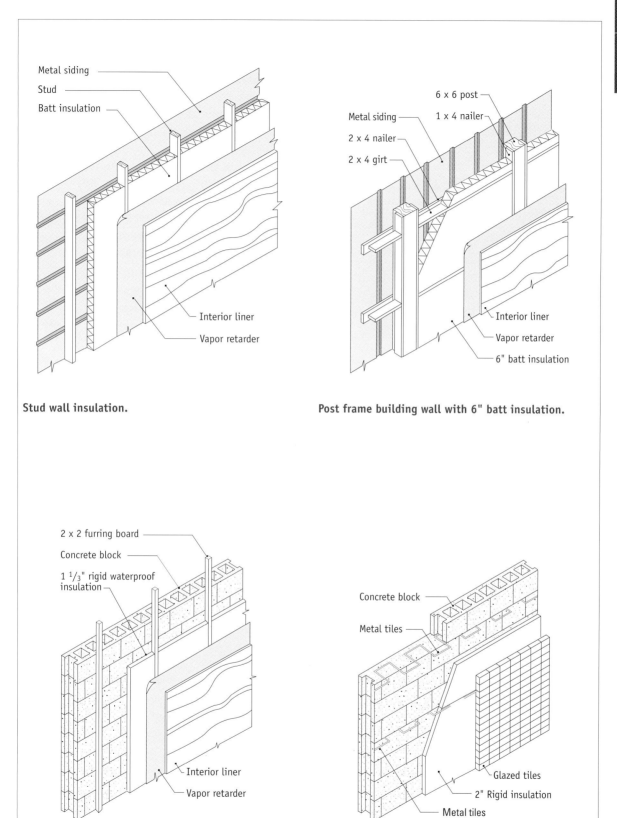

Stud wall insulation.

Post frame building wall with 6" batt insulation.

Concrete block wall insulation.

Glazed tile and block wall insulation.

Figure 7-20 **Insulating walls.**

skylights increase winter heat loss. The insulation value of single and double glazed windows (R = 1 to 2.5) is well below the R-value of an insulated wall (R = 13 to 15). In cold barns, skylights can cause roof water leaks and increase the summer heat load.

When remodeling a building, consider replacing all windows with insulated inlets or permanent wall sections. Insulated through-the-wall inlets can be used for summer ventilation. Caulk cracks and joints on outside surfaces.

Fire resistance

Many types of plastic foam insulation used in stables have extremely high flame spread rates and must be covered with a fire-resistant material. When plastic foam insulation is not covered, insurance may be refused for the structure.

To reduce risk, protect foam insulation with fire-resistant coatings. Do not use fire rated gypsum board (sheet rock) in high moisture environments such as animal housing.

> **Materials that provide satisfactory protection include:**
> - ½-inch thick cement plaster.
> - ¼-inch thick, sprayed-on magnesium oxychloride (60 pounds per cubic foot) or ½-inch of the lighter, foam material.
> - Fire rated ½-inch thick exterior plywood.
> - Fiberglass reinforced plastic (FRP).

Check with an insurance company for their protection requirements in regards to insulating materials. If using fiberglass reinforced plastic coverings, choose fire rated products.

Protection from birds and rodents

Protect insulation from bird and rodent damage with interior liners and exterior siding or roofing. Be sure to protect the ends of the insulation. An aluminum foil covering is not sufficient protection.

Cover exposed perimeter insulation with a protective liner. High density, fiberglass reinforced plastic is preferred. Foundation grade plywood ⅜-inch thick resists physical and moisture damage but is not rodent proof. Seal holes and cracks in walls and ceilings to limit rodent access. Maintain a rodent bait program.

Screen eave and gable openings with ¾-inch by ¾-inch hardware cloth to exclude birds. Remove any ice that accumulates on the screen during prolonged cold periods.

Protection from Physical Contact

In areas where horses or riders can come in contact with insulation and/or vapor retarder materials, choose either mechanically strong materials (insulation boards), or protect the insulation and vapor retarder with a stronger material such as plywood. If the vapor retarder is the only protection for insulation in ceilings, it must be strong enough to keep birds from pecking through it as well as rodents from chewing holes in it. Check with the local fire code as well as with insurance companies, as many of the insurance companies require insulation to be covered with a fire rated material.

Supplemental Heating

Many people find the comfortable temperature range for horses too low. A comfortable temperature for humans is around 75°F, which is at the upper end of the range for horse comfort. Many heated stables are heated to provide comfort to the people working in the buildings and not for the comfort of the horses. Heat is lost through building components and by exhausting ventilating air. In a well insulated stable, as much as 80% of heat produced in the building is used to warm cold air entering the room or building, evaporate moisture produced by the horses, and evaporated standing water.

Heating the entire stable to provide comfort to the people working in the building is usually inefficient and wasteful. Heaters are more often used in separate rooms where people congregate, such as the tack room and lounges. In cold climates, a separate support area with wash, tack, and grooming stations equipped with supplemental heat is a good alternative to keeping the entire stable heated

for human comfort. Providing a heated area in the stable where people can take the horse to work on it is also a good alternative. This leaves the stall area well ventilated and at a comfortable temperature for the horses while also providing handler comfort.

Typically, a well-insulated and well-ventilated stable will maintain an interior temperature within a few degrees of the outdoor ambient temperature. At a minimum, supplemental heat is needed to keep waterers and water lines from freezing; therefore, do not allow the interior building temperature to go below 35°F. Most heated stables are heated to about 50°F.

Some horse owners will have built-in heaters for the stall areas. Some show and foaling barns use portable electric heaters when needed.

The main types of heaters available are:
- Radiant.
- Space.
- Make-up.

Heat lamps, infrared heaters and gas catalytic heater are all type of radiant heaters. Both gas-fired and electric radiant heaters are available. Heat lamps are nothing more than a large light bulb with a reflector. They have the advantage of being very portable because they plug into anywhere that there is a 110 V outlet. Bulbs come in a variety of sizes but 175 and 250 W bulbs are the most common. Thick-necked bulbs, though more expensive, are more durable and are less of a fire hazard. Heat lamps need to be protected from animal contact and securely mounted so that they cannot fall onto bedding.

Single-unit gas brooders are similar to heat lamps in that they cover a small area to provide a localized heating effect. They are relatively inexpensive and some have modulated output based on a special thermostatic control. They require more maintenance than heat lamps but are less costly to operate. Some brooders will have an air filter to keep the unit clean burning, but it requires frequent

cleaning. Dirty brooders may give off more carbon monoxide. Because these heaters are unvented, it is wise to install a carbon monoxide detector in areas that are not well vented.

Tube radiant heaters consist of a long tube with a gas burner on one end. Air is pushed through the tube to make it hot, thereby providing radiant heat to the surrounding surfaces. There is generally a reflector on the top portion of the tube to reflect heat down and to protect nearby surfaces. Outdoor air is drawn into the tube, heated, and then exhausted at the far end of the building.

These heaters work very well for large spaces such as arenas or wash rack areas. As with any radiant heat, the horse or person being heated must be in the line of sight with the heater; therefore, using radiant heat in the alley would have limited effect on the comfort of animals housed in stalls with solid partitions. Tube heaters are safe but must be installed several feet away from surrounding surfaces. They are permanently mounted in one place and thermostatically controlled. Temperature and heat output vary from one end of the heater to the other with the vent end being cooler. Check and follow manufacturer's specifications before purchasing and installing any heater.

Keep flammable materials, such as hay and bedding, far away from radiant lamps. As a general rule, maintain a separation distance of 3 to 4 feet between the heaters, humans, horses, and combustibles. Some stables use radiant heat lamps for specific heat needs such as keeping foals warm. In this way heated stable air is not exhausted through the ventilation system yet an individual horse or work area feels warmer.

Unit space heaters heat room air directly. These heaters can be unvented or vented. Unvented unit space heaters recirculate and heat room air directly and discharge heat and the products of combustion (water, carbon dioxide, unburned hydrocarbons, and other pollutants) into the air. Unvented space heaters can be used in rooms equipped with a ventilation system that supplies a continuous air exchange rate recommended for cold weather. Provide at least 4 cfm of ventilation per 1,000 BTU/hr of heater capacity. Place a carbon monoxide detector within about 25 feet of any unvented heater.

Vented heaters use a heat exchanger to discharge heat into the room and discharge the products of combustion to the outside through a vent. Equip the heater with a damper and a fan-powered vent to ensure that the products of combustion actually leave the room with negative pressure ventilation. Clean and maintain these heaters according to manufacturer's instructions. **NOTE:** Most manufacturers will void their warranty if powered vent dampers are installed. Therefore, this is not considered a practical or viable option despite common use.

Locate unit space heaters so that the heated air is blown along the air inlet and creates a circular airflow pattern in the space. Use deflectors on heaters to split the hot air in two different directions.

Make-up air heaters are unvented and heat incoming ventilation air. They require less service and maintenance than space heaters.

The airflow rate is usually constant and fuel flow to the burner varies to maintain room inlet air temperature. The heated air is usually blown directly into the room and depends on air circulation for distribution. Do not install ducts on the heater exhaust without consulting the manufacturer.

When sizing a heater, consider the amount of heat produced by the horses. The rate of heat production is usually expressed in units of British Thermal Units produced per hour (Btu/hr). The amount of heat produced by a horse depends on size. Under average conditions a 1,000-pound horse will generate about 1,790 Btu/hr of body heat, while a 1,500-pound horse will generate about 2,450 Btu/hr. Recommended supplemental heat for a stable is 5,000 Btu/hour/stall.

See *Heating, Cooling and Tempering Air for Livestock Housing*, MWPS-34, for design information for sizing supplemental heating systems. See *Chapter 11. Utilities* for information on heater safety including venting and fuel storage requirements.

Manure Management

Proper design and management of the manure handling and containment system are essential to pollution control when operating any animal facility. Proper handling of manure is essential, especially as more horse facilities are located in suburban areas. Stables must be good neighbors. Failure to provide adequate manure collection, handling, and storage facilities in conjunction with adequate land area for proper application and utilization of manure nutrients could adversely affect air, water, and land resources. Also, degraded stream water quality and fish kills can result from manure and feed waste entering waterways from surface runoff. Improperly designed or constructed manure storage facilities, or over-application of nitrogen or phosphorus can lead to groundwater pollution. Many horse owners are conscious of manure's pollution potential and have taken steps to control it.

Independent of operation size or location, a proper manure management system and plan are essential.

A manure management system includes collecting, handling and transferring, storing, possibly treating, and marketing or land applying the manure. The collection of horse manure is pretty simple because it is almost always collected on the floor of a stall or inside an outdoor shed. Knowing the characteristics of horse manure is key to all the other aspects of the manure handling system.

Because horse manure is almost always in a solid form and most of the time with bedding, knowing common solid manure handling practices to handle and transfer the manure from the stall or shed floor to another location is essential. If manure is stored or treated by composting, then knowing the volume of manure is important. If the manure is marketed or applied directly to nearby land, knowing the nutrient content of the manure is key.

A complete manure management system has the following goals:
- Avoid pollution of soil, groundwater, or surface water.
- Reduce odors and dust.
- Control insects, rodents, and other pests.
- Comply with appropriate state and local regulations pertaining to manure handling.
- Balance capital investment, cash-flow requirements, labor, and nutrient use.

The remainder of this chapter will discuss:
- Basic manure characteristics.
- Bedding.
- Manure-handling systems.
- Locating, sizing, and designing a manure storage.
- Sizing, designing, and operating a composting treatment system and marketing tips to sell compost.
- Land application of manure.
- Overall system management to reduce odors, dust, and flies.

Manure Characteristics

Horse manure includes excreted material from the animal (feces and urine), soiled bedding, and any other substance that is deposited in this material, such as wasted feed and hay. There are several alternatives for handling manure, including immediate field application, stockpiling it for future handling, removing it from the site, and composting it. Some stables have developed markets to distribute or sell the manure.

Consistency is the primary factor that determines the method by which manure is collected, transferred, stored, and sold or land applied. Manure consistency is typically stated in terms of the wet basis solids content. Horse manure is almost always handled as a solid, which means that the moisture content of the material removed from a horse stall or manure storage area is 82% or less. Typically, the moisture content of excreted horse manure is around 85%. Bedding used in stalls or sheds will lower the moisture content of the manure to much less than 85%. Stall manure will typically be lowered to the 40 to 50% moisture content range.

Excretions

Knowing the volume, weight, and nutrient characteristics of excreted manure aids in proper sizing of the manure storage and developing a plan to handle the manure for land application or sale.

Table 8-1 shows common as-excreted manure weights and volumes for horses. The volume of manure typically produced by a single horse based on 1,000 pounds of horse live weight is between 0.70 and 0.95 cubic feet per day or about 255 to 350 cubic feet per year. This volume translates into a manure weight between 45 and 60 pounds per day or about 8 to 11 tons per year per 1,000 pounds of horse live weight. Remember that the addition of bedding and wasted feed and hay will have an effect on total manure volume.

Bedding

Horse stalls typically are bedded. Good bedding provides comfort to the horse so that it will encourage the horse to lie down and rest. Good bedding will also absorb any liquids that are deposited in the area so the area remains dry. Also, good bedding will help to minimize odors and minimize foot problems. Table 8-2 shows common bedding densities. Table 8-3 shows absorption properties of various bedding materials.

Dirty or soiled bedding should be removed daily from a stall. Bedding can account for another 8 to 15 pounds per day of manure. Total volume of manure removed from a horse stall can vary widely depending on management practices, but it is not uncommon for the total volume of manure-plus-bedding removed from the stall to equal almost twice the volume of as-excreted manure.

Bed stalls or sheds liberally with at least 6 inches of material, and preferably with 8 to 12 inches of material. Any bedding material used must be as dust free as possible, otherwise respiratory problems can develop in a horse. The type of bedding used will depend on quality, absorption qualities, ease of handling,

Table 8-1 Estimated weights and volumes of typical as excreted horse manure (urine and feces combined).

Based on ASAE Standards, 51st ed. 2004. D384.2: Manure Production and Characteristics. St. Joseph, Mich.: ASAE. Use these values only for planning purposes. Values will vary for individual situations due to genetics, dietary options, and variations in feed nutrient concentration, animal performance, and individual farm management.

Activity level	Animal weight (lbs)	Total manure (lbs/day)	Total manure (cu ft/day)	Feces (lbs/day)	Urine lbs/day	Total solids (lbs/day)	Moisture (% w.b).	Density lbs/cu ft
Sedentary	1,000	54.4	0.88	38	16	7.61	86	62
Intense exercise	1,000	55.5	0.90	40	16	7.78	86	62

Values apply to horses 18 months of age or older that are not pregnant or lactating. Production values for horses from 850 to 1,350 pounds can be roughly estimated by linearly interpolating the table values. Sedentary activity level would apply to horses not receiving any imposed exercise. Intense activity level would include race training, polo, and upper level combined training.

and sometimes even the effect it has on manure nutrient value, but usually the greatest influence on choosing a bedding material will be availability and cost.

Table 8-2 Estimated density of bedding materials.

Loose bedding material	Density (lbs per cu ft)
Straw	2.5
Wood Shavings	9
Sawdust	12
Sand	105
Non-legume hay	4
Peat moss	1.0-1.3

Baled bedding material	Density (lbs per cu ft)
Straw	5
Wood Shavings	20
Non-legume hay	7
Peat moss	1.8-2.5

Chopped bedding material	Density (lbs per cu ft)
Straw	7
Newspapers	14
Non-legume hay	6

Values are approximate.

Table 8-3 Estimated absorption properties of bedding materials.

Approximate water absorption and density of dry bedding (typically 10% moisture).

Material	Water absorption (lbs water absorbed per lb bedding)
Wood	
Tanning bark	4.0
Fine bark	2.5
Pine	
• Chips	3.0
• Sawdust	2.5
• Shavings	2.0
• Needles	1.0
Hardwood chips, shavings or sawdust	1.5
Shredded newspaper	1.6
Corn	
• Shredded stover	2.5
• Ground cobs	2.1
Straw	
• Flax	2.6
• Oats	2.5
• Wheat	2.2
Hay, chopped mature	3.0
Peat moss	9.0-10.0
Shells, hulls	
• Cocoa	2.7
• Peanut, cottonseed	2.5

Straw, sawdust, and wood shavings are the most common bedding materials. Straw is very absorbent material and in a study horses preferred straw over wood shavings. Clean straw is typically the bedding of choice for breeding farms because it is easy to clean off newborns and will not stick in the newborn's airway. The major drawback of straw is that it needs to be removed frequently from a stall. Because of frequent cleanings, a large quantity of straw is needed. Also, straw should be avoided for horses that like to eat it.

Sawdust and wood shavings are another very absorbent bedding material. Sawdust and wood shavings tend to keep odors down and require less frequent cleaning when compared to other bedding materials. Horses seldom eat sawdust or wood shavings. Some horse owners avoid using sawdust or wood shavings because of concerns that the material may contain black walnut. Black walnut (Juglans nigra) contains chemical agents that are toxic to horses. Eating only a few shavings can result in severe gastrointestinal irritation, and simply standing in the walnut shavings can lead to laminitis (founder).

Shredded corn stover (chopped stalks) and ground cobs can also make good bedding material. Shredded stover absorption properties nearly match the properties of straw. Like straw, sometimes horses will eat shredded stover.

Two other types of bedding that can be used that are not often considered are peat moss and shredded newspapers. Peat moss can absorb 9 to 10 times its weight in water, making it one of the most absorbent bedding materials available. The moss needs to be kept moist so that it sticks together when squeezed, but not too moist that it sticks to one's hand. Sprinkle the moss periodically with water. Soiled peat moss bedding needs to be removed daily and replaced with fresh material. Some horse owners have had success with a 50:50 mix of peat moss and screened topsoil. Solid manure still must be removed on a daily basis, but if properly managed by tilling every day or two and adding more material as needed, the mix can last up to 6 months. Some owners who use this mix will use a rototiller to till it.

Shredded newspaper or newsprint, if available, can make a good absorbent bedding material. It is not as absorbent as straw but typically is low in dust and is free of pollen.

Waste Materials

Manure management at larger facilities is not confined to horse manure and wasted feed and hay, but also includes trash such as twine string, bags, and feed sacks, and animal health consumables, such as needles, syringes, artificial insemination (AI) supplies, and plastic and latex gloves. Plastic, latex, and metal materials will not decompose during composting or after land application. For disposal purposes, all trash needs to be kept separate from manure. Manure applied to land containing these items can be unsightly and raise public concern that the owners are having a negative impact on the environment. Separate recyclable materials for collection. Keep fertilizers and pesticides and their containers out of the manure and manure storage.

Needles are an especially big concern in any operation and must be kept out of the manure. Any needles applied to fields present a hazard in several ways. One, needles in a field can result in tire puncture. Second, if this manure is applied to a neighbor's field (i.e., field not owned by the owner) without the knowledge of the landowner, negative relations can result because this neighbor most likely will not welcome the idea of having sharp objects applied to the fields. Finally, whether land applied or composted, needles and other sharps pose a health risk to people who come into contact with them. The preferred method to handle needles and other medical sharps is to collect them and have them properly incinerated. Contact a veterinarian, supply store, or public health authority to determine proper needle disposal recommendations.

Human waste from bathrooms requires a septic system or connection to municipal sewer and should not go into the manure storage. Grey water— without human waste such as shower and sink water—should also go to the septic system or sewer. Septic capacity is needed for grey water from the stable's horse wash stalls, tack, tack area, laundry, showers, and feed room.

Drainage and surface runoff from pavement, unvegetated paddocks, and exercise areas needs to be properly diverted. Diverting surface water drainage is especially important for areas where manure is allowed to accumulate between rainfall and thawing events. Runoff should not enter natural waterways where it could contaminate water or contribute to increased erosion. Remove excess manure from paddocks and exercise areas.

Handling

The cleaning of stalls, pens, sheds, and lots is a necessary task on all horse farms. The manure is usually applied to fields immediately, stored for future field application, or composted. Because horse manure rarely has a moisture content greater that 82%, it can be handled using solid manure handling methods. Solid manure can be easily moved and stacked using front-end loaders, tractor-mounted blades, or mechanical scrapers.

Most stables remove manure daily from the stalls and temporarily stockpile it in an accessible deposition area near the barn. Once the stall cleaning chores are finished or the temporary storage is filled, the stockpile is moved to the long-term storage location, composted, or removed from the stable site. To avoid additional handling, the manure can be temporarily stockpiled in a vehicle, such as a manure spreader or dumpster used for transport. Locate the long-term storage away and downwind from the stable. Use natural or manmade screening such as a hedgerow or fence to improve the aesthetics.

When handling large quantities of bulky material, use straight-line movement through wide doors. Avoid stable designs that necessitate turns and tight passages for travel from the stall to the manure deposition area. Hand labor and tools such as those shown in Figure 8-1 are the standard in horse stall cleaning. To increase worker efficiency, provide plenty of stall light, minimize lifting, and make the temporary manure stockpile area easily accessible from all areas of the stable.

Mechanization can replace some hand labor of stall cleaning. For example, a cart can be pulled behind a motorized vehicle through the working aisle of the stable. But the numerous repositionings of the cart and engine exhaust from this method can detract from its usefulness. The cart can efficiently transport manure to areas farther away from the stable.

Another mechanized alternative is the barn cleaner, a tool that automatically moves the manure from the stall area to the temporary stockpile area. A barn cleaner is a scraper that operates in a narrow gutter (about 16 inches wide) and has closely spaced flights on a chain drive, Figure 8-2. It is designed to handle manure with high solids content, such as horse stall manure. The automatic cleaner can be located under the floor at the back of the stall or along the side of an aisle servicing the stalls. Its advantages include minimal worker effort to move stall manure into the gutter: no need to lift, move carts, or travel to the temporary stockpile area. Barn cleaners do add an additional investment cost and will require maintenance, but this manure handling system will save in labor cost. Stall gutters must be covered and bedded over when horses are in the stall. Horses get used to stepping around aisle gutters even if they are left uncovered. Safety may become an issue if normally covered aisle gutters are left open.

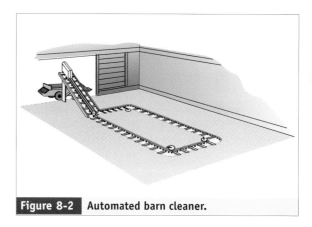

Figure 8-2 Automated barn cleaner.

Storage

Whether manure is stored temporarily or long-term, some kind of storage facility will be needed. The operation of a large horse facility on a small acreage can intensify nuisance problems not noticed at small stables or where the acreage per horse is substantial. Careful management and attention to detail can overcome potential problems. Controlling odors and flies is important. For horses in paddocks, do not store manure in paddocks because it can increase parasite exposure for the horses.

A well built storage pad, or a constructed or formed structure will aid in manure handling and minimize pollution potential. A pad can be as informal as a level, well-packed surface with a stub wall backstop for a manure stack (See Figures 8-3 to 8-5) and is commonly used for short-term storage. If topography permits and long-term storage is needed, a constructed or formed structure is a less objectionable method to keep manure confined to a small area and out of view. These structures are often three-sided with impermeable flooring and are sometimes covered or roofed, Figure 8-4.

On-site storage should not pollute the water. Drain storage runoff away from surrounding facilities and lots and to approved disposal facilities. Drain runoff polluted with animal manure to an approved disposal system such as septic tank and/or leachfield, especially if the site is in a geologically or socially

Figure 8-1 Wheel barrel used during manual cleaning.

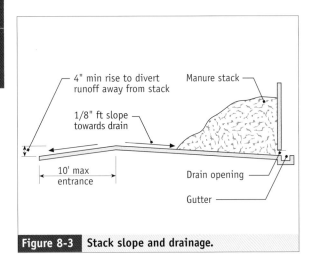

Figure 8-3 Stack slope and drainage.

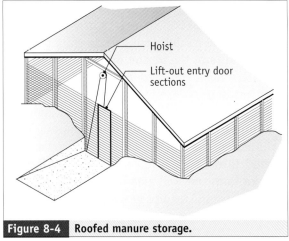

Figure 8-4 Roofed manure storage.

sensitive area where runoff is a concern. Prevent any pile leachate from contaminating groundwater or nearby waterways. Use a concrete pad with sidewalls to contain leachate from large, uncovered piles.

Siting and Managing the Manure Storage

Odors and flies are typically the biggest problems associated with storing manure. Properly siting the manure storage can help in the management of both of these potential problems.

Offensive odors can be generated from manure. If manure is allowed to decompose without enough oxygen, its microbe population will be anaerobic (without oxygen) and may produce offensive odors. Aerobic (with oxygen) decomposition, such as composting, does not produce such odors.

Even if odors are managed properly, people can still *visualize* odors; that is simply seeing a manure storage may cause people to *think* they smell odors emanating from the storage. Manure storages should be sited or screened from view with vegetation or fencing so they are out of sight of people driving down the road and preferably out of sight of people who visit. Vegetation may offer aerial dust and odor trapping benefits.

Before selecting a site for the manure storage, review the impact that odors carried by prevailing winds could have on other facilities and neighbors. Summer breezes are the main concern if winter and summer wind

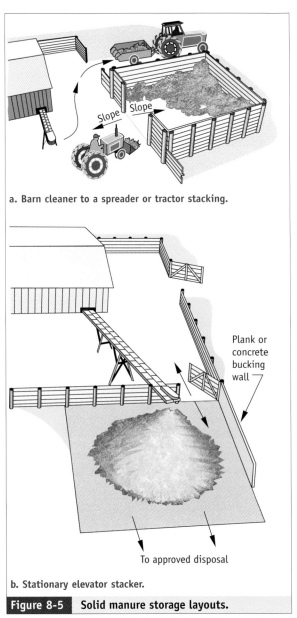

a. Barn cleaner to a spreader or tractor stacking.

b. Stationary elevator stacker.

Figure 8-5 Solid manure storage layouts.

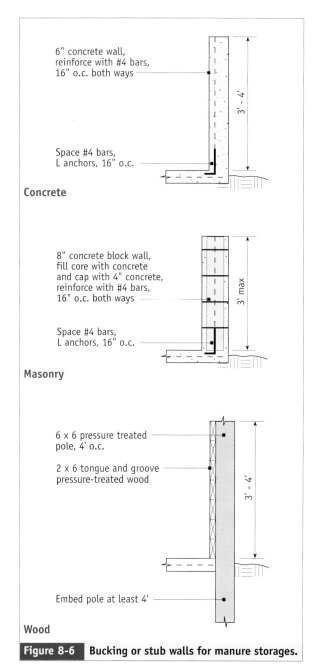

Figure 8-6 Bucking or stub walls for manure storages.

- 6" concrete wall, reinforce with #4 bars, 16" o.c. both ways
- Space #4 bars, L anchors, 16" o.c.

Concrete

- 8" concrete block wall, fill core with concrete and cap with 4" concrete, reinforce with #4 bars, 16" o.c. both ways
- Space #4 bars, L anchors, 16" o.c.

Masonry

- 6 x 6 pressure treated pole, 4' o.c.
- 2 x 6 tongue and groove pressure-treated wood
- Embed pole at least 4'

Wood

horse owners have a land area on which they always apply manure. Over time if manure is applied at high enough levels, a buildup of nutrients can result in surface and ground water contamination. Nitrogen and phosphorus are the nutrients most often over applied.

To minimize the possibility of contaminating surface and ground water, a manure nutrient management plan should be developed. A manure nutrient management plan is a written document that shows the calculation of the application rate based on manure nutrient content needed to match the soil nutrient characteristics and estimated nutrients required for crop usage. A nutrient management plan should be reviewed and revised, as needed, each year. Certified professionals are available in some states to develop farm nutrient management plans on a consulting basis.

A complete manure nutrient management plan includes:
- Estimate of annual manure production.
- Estimate of annual nutrient production.
- Estimate of annual crop nutrient utilization potential.
- Cropping rotation.
- Land available for application during the year.
- Adequate collection, handling, and storage facilities.
- Analysis of animals' rations to avoid overfeeding nutrients.
- An emergency action plan to quickly deal with accidental manure spills or other environmental emergencies.

potential while at the same time protecting the environment.

Nutrient Management Plan

Beyond the concern for pollution control and compliance with local, state, and federal standards, livestock producers benefit from the manure's fertilizer value. Using manure nutrients in crop production wisely can be a practical method of controlling pollution, but some

Knowing the nutrient content of the manure and soil is important to minimize the chance of over applying nutrients to the soil. Over applying nutrients to the soil can result in contamination of ground and surface waters. Manure nutrient content can vary widely. Some factors that will influence manure nutrient content are management, diet, bedding, amount of feed and hay wastage, and the age of the horse. Sampling and

Table 8-7 — Estimated horse as-excreted manure nutrient characteristics (urine and feces combined).

Based on ASAE Standards, 51st ed. 2004. D384.2: *Manure Production and Characteristics*. St. Joseph, Mich.: ASAE.
Based on Table 8-1 volume and weights. Use these values only for planning purposes. Manure should be sampled and tested prior to field application. See *Manure Characteristics*, MWPS-18, Section 1 for more information on sampling and test procedures. If high quality forages are fed, use Table 8-3 where applicable for estimating.

Activity level	Weight (lbs)	Nitrogen (N) (lbs/day)	Phosphorus (K_2O_5) (lbs/day)	Potassium (K_2) (lbs/day)	Calcium (Ca) (lbs/day)	Magnesium (Mg) (lbs/day)
Sedentary	1,000	0.178	0.061	0.064	0.046	0.018
Intense exercise	1,000	0.304	0.151	0.229	0.058	0.026

testing the manure is the best method of knowing the nutrient content of the manure. *Manure Characteristics*, MWPS-18, Section 1, is a publication that provides more detail about the proper sampling techniques to obtain the most accurate test results. The *Manure Characteristics* publication discusses how to interpret test results to maximize use of manure.

When manure test results are not available, use the most recent and most reliable published data, Table 8-7. Contact the local state extension service for assistance on determining the best methods of soil sampling and testing. Records of manure and soil test results should be maintained. Note any trends in changes of the soil nutrient, and adjust application rates accordingly.

Another good practice in verifying that manure nutrients are being properly utilized is to maintain a written log of application. These records are also important in case of odor complaints by neighbors. Logs should include application rates, dates and location of application, and weather conditions such as temperature, sky conditions, and wind direction and speed.

Notify neighbors two to three weeks prior to applying manure or make them aware of typical manure application practices if manure is applied frequently. Notifying neighbors in advance can help minimize misunderstandings. Avoid applying on days when the neighbors are holding specialty events such as a family gathering.

Finally, if manure is applied to land not owned by the horse owner, develop a written agreement with the person who owns the land. A formalized agreement can help avoid misunderstandings over when the responsibility and ownership of the manure and manure application begins and ends. This agreement can be especially important in the event there is litigation due to the application of the manure. Contact a lawyer to help develop a formalized agreement.

Land Application

Applying manure may not be possible each week, year-round. Fields may not be accessible due to heavy snow accumulation or soil that is too wet to support equipment traffic. Avoid applying manure to frozen ground because there is a higher potential for runoff water that can occur during periods of snow melt or spring rains to carry away manure that is left on the fields. Avoid applying manure immediately after it rains, especially moderate to heavy rainfall events. Manure in this situation can be carried with runoff water that continues to flow after the rainfall. If possible, do not apply manure within 100 feet of waterways or surface waters. Manure application to cultivated fields may be limited to times prior to when crops are planted and after crops are harvested.

When applying manure to land, spread it thinly over the soil to help it dry out. This method of application will discourage fly breeding and parasite hatching. A thin layer of manure also spreads the nutrients for more optimal plant use. A tractor and spreader is usually the best method to spread a thin layer of manure.

Apply manure at the rate determined in the nutrient management plan. Applying manure uniformly is critical for good application to meet the requirements of the nutrient management plan. A typical solid manure spreader will spread manure in a swath. Typically, more manure is deposited in the center of the swath than the edges. Overlapping application at the edges will result in more uniform overall application.

Checking the application rate is one method to help ensure that manure is being properly applied. The tarp method is one of the easiest ways to check or calibrate the application rate for a solid manure spreader, Figure 8-7. A solid manure application rate is usually measured in tons per acre. In the tarp method, a 56-inch by 56-inch tarp is placed on the ground where manure will be applied. The 56-inch by 56-inch tarp is 1/2000th of an acre and a ton is equal to 2,000 pounds. After the manure is applied, the manure deposited on the tarp is weighed. The scale reading will equal the tons per acre that are being applied to the land. To check consistency, this procedure should be performed at least three times. The average of all the measurements will best estimate the application rate.

If possible with any manure application, disking or incorporating manure into the soil within 24 hours will reduce odors and flies. This practice is only an option in non-cropped fields and is not an option in pasture, hay ground, or other areas that have vegetation.

Contract or Commercial Haulers

Another option is to contract with a hauler who will remove the manure from the stable facility. The manure can be used in a commercial composting operation. Dumpsters are typically used for temporary manure storage at the stable. Dumpsters should be sized so that the contents are emptied at least weekly during the summer fly breeding season. Make sure the dumpster is located so that barn manure can be conveniently dumped into it and that trucks can access and empty it during all weather conditions. A concrete pit or pad is useful to contain any dumpster leachate.

Pasture or Field-kept Horses

Field-kept horses, either full- or part-time, have different manure management needs. These horses often spend time in open sided sheds, from which manure and bedding need to be periodically cleaned out. Bedded pack manure material has a different composition than stall manure and is usually partially decomposed. Like stored manure, field-deposited manure can serve as a fertilizer.

Substantial amounts of manure can accumulate where horses congregate around gates, waterers, favorite shade areas, and feeders. Clean weekly for better pasture management and parasite control and to diminish fly breeding. Spread any uncollected manure piles into thin layers by dragging the field, but realize that this may spread the parasite contamination over a larger area.

Composting Treatment

Many suburban horse facilities often have limited land area on which to apply manure; therefore, composting is often a good option. Composting is a biological process in which microorganisms covert manure and bedding into a soil-like material called compost. Composting reduces the volume of manure by

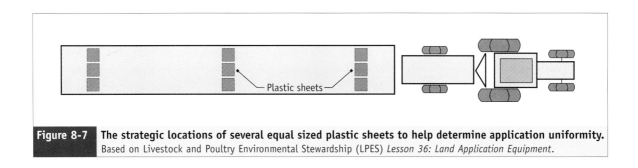

Figure 8-7 **The strategic locations of several equal sized plastic sheets to help determine application uniformity.**
Based on Livestock and Poultry Environmental Stewardship (LPES) *Lesson 36: Land Application Equipment.*

40 to 70%. Other advantages of composting over storing manure are a reduction in odors, flies, pathogens, and weed seeds.

Composting horse manure will provide a material that is more readily marketable than raw stall manure. Finished horse manure compost is more organically stable and less of an environmental threat. Compost can enhance soil tilth and fertility by improving soil moisture retention in light soils and increasing pore volume in heavy soils. Compost-improved soils have a relatively stable structure and are more erosion resistant. Compost's fine texture, high organic matter content, and fertilizer value make it desirable as a garden soil amendment. Stables have successfully given away, or even sold bulk and bagged horse compost. Golf courses and nurseries often buy truckloads of compost.

The disadvantage of composting is that it will be another operation to be managed daily at the stable. This responsibility may not be of interest to all stables. Time will be required to market and sell the compost, if the compost is sold. Having a ready outlet for compost will make the facility and time investment more worthwhile. Several farms could manage a centralized cooperative facility efficiently, with limited hauling and more effective process labor, marketing, and equipment. Extra space is also needed to store and process the compost.

Composting Management Basics

Normally, well-managed horse manure will take from four to six months to fully compost. With frequent turning, horse manure can fully compost in as little as two months.

The most important factors for the composting process are:
- Particle size.
- Moisture content.
- Oxygen.
- Temperature.
- Initial carbon-nitrogen ratio.

A composting operation requires daily monitoring, and, usually on a weekly basis, the pile needs to be mixed or turned and reformed. Finished compost is dark brown to black, practically insoluble in water, smells slightly earthy or musty, and has a loose, friable texture. The composting process will shut down during periods of cold weather then start up again as the weather warms.

Table 8-8 compares the output of a successful composting operation and horse manure. The more carefully these biological factors are controlled, the more sophisticated the compost facility becomes. A finished compost product can take six months to produce, depending on the sophistication of the system and the quality of compost desired.

Particle size

Composting performs best with small particle sizes because the smaller the particle size the greater the total surface area, and the more access for the degrading organisms. Care must be taken to not get the particle size too small because particles that are too small can limit pore space, which will restrict the amount of oxygen entering the pile for proper composting.

Table 8-8   Characteristic comparison between successful composting and horse manure.

Based on *On-Farm Composting Handbook*, NRAES -54, Tables 3.1 and A.1, and ASAE Standards D384.2, Manure Production and Characteristics.

Characteristic	Composting operation		Horse manure	
	Reasonable range	Preferred range	Typical	Average
Carbon-to-nitrogen ratio (C:N)	20:1 to 40:1	25:1 to 30:1	20:1 to 50:1	30:1
Moisture content	40 to 65%	50 to 60%	40 to 80%	72%
pH	5.5 to 9.0	6.5 to 8.5	—	—
Bulk density (pcf)	less than 1,100	—	1,200 to 1,600	1,380

Particle size can be reduced by grinding, especially with crop residues like corn stalks. Most times bedding is the material that will result in the largest particles, bedding should be ground or shredded prior to its placement into the stall or shed. Particle sizes from 1/8 to 2 inches usually obtain good results in composting.

Moisture content

Water in the compost allows for chemical reactions, transport of nutrients, and movement of microorganisms. Compost microbes live most comfortably at moisture levels from 40 to 65% moisture content. Typically, the optimum moisture content for composting is 50 to 60%. Manure piles greater than 60% moisture content can be successfully composted with the proper amount of aeration, but more commonly, composting is suppressed because at high moisture content, voids fill up with liquids, hindering aeration. Low moisture levels retard or stop microbial activity, although some composting occurs with moisture as low as 25%.

Managing the moisture of the material is one of the easiest ways to successfully control the composting process. Providing a cover for the material is one of the most effective and simplest management tools that can be used to improve the composting process. A cover keeps rain from soaking the pile and making it too wet. A cover also prevents the material from drying out too much in the sun. A cover can be as permanent as having a roofed structure over top of the pile or as simple as placing a tarp on top of the pile.

Other methods to control high moisture content are to increase the aeration rate or turn the pile more frequently. High moisture content could also mean that the size of the pile is too large. If the material is too dry, adding and mixing water into the material will help increase the moisture content. Typically water is added using a spray hose or pouring water into the pile with a bucket.

Oxygen

Compost develops more rapidly when it is in an aerobic condition. Aerobic composting requires a large quantity of oxygen to properly compost manure. The need for oxygen, which is obtained from the air, is greatest at the beginning of the composting process as the manure degrades. The need for oxygen decreases further into the composting process. A minimum of 5% oxygen concentration is needed in the pore space for proper composting. Without the proper amount of oxygen, the process will enter an anaerobic state. Anaerobic composting is slower, less efficient, and utilizes a different set of microorganisms. A big benefit to faster composting is that less space is needed for processing and storage.

To provide the proper amount of oxygen, the pile will need to be aerated. Manure compost piles are usually aerated by turning or remixing the material. Turning the pile basically fluffs the pile, which results in the creation of air pockets within the pile. When turning the pile, make sure outer material is thoroughly mixed with the more processed inner core material. Compost piles also can be aerated using more elaborate and expensive mechanical aeration systems. Because of the expense, most operations do not use mechanical aeration systems.

Oxygen-analyzing equipment can be purchased to monitor oxygen content of the pile, but periodic monitoring and turning of the pile is the least expensive method to ensure oxygen is present within the pile.

Temperature

Monitoring pile temperatures is important. Composting takes place in three heating phases:

1. A short warm-up phase.
2. A hot composting phase.
3. A cool curing phase.

The initial warm-up phase is the shortest of the three phases. This phase occurs from the time the pile is formed until the pile reaches a temperature of 105°F. During this phase, microorganisms become active, and the breakdown of the material into compost begins. This phase should last a few days to a month.

The next phase is the hot composting phase and starts about the time the pile reaches a temperature of 105°F. This phase can last up to 4 months and sometimes longer. Compost microbes live most comfortably at temperatures from 110 to 150°F. Bacteria create the heat during the hot composting phase. Sustained high temperatures above 135°F will destroy most pathogens, including pathogens with human origins, and insect eggs and larvae. The critical temperature to destroy most weed seeds is 145°F. Generally, the interior of compost piles reaches these elevated temperatures but not the outer surfaces. The temperature difference from outer surfaces to inner core is another reason that turning and mixing the pile is important. Temperatures can go above 160°F. At this temperature the microorganisms will die off or become dormant. Temperature should be monitored and maintained between 110 to 150°F. The pile should be turned before temperatures reach 160°F.

The last phase is the cooling or curing phase, which is often the neglected phase of the entire process. This phase also can last up to 4 months and sometimes longer. Curing takes place at lower temperatures usually below 105°F. Compost is further processed during this phase by fungus, worms, and other animals. Stall manure that has gone through hot composting makes good fertilizer, but the nitrogen and organic matter in cured compost are more stable than in uncured compost. Most gardeners want cured compost because adding this is like giving the garden an extra dose of fertilized soil. Raw stall manure may take up to eight months to compost and cure.

Temperatures of the composting pile core should be monitored during all phases. Special composting thermometers with a stem that is 20 to 36 inches long can be purchased from most garden supply stores.

If the temperature for a new pile does not rise significantly above its initial temperature, the material may be too dry or too wet; it may be a poor mix (see *Initial carbon-to-nitrogen* section), or the weather may be too cold. Adding already composted material can help introduce microorganisms into the pile. If the pile does not reheat after turning, the composting process is complete.

Initial carbon-to-nitrogen ratio (C:N)

Composting also depends on microbe food and nutrient supplies. Typically the proper balance between carbon and nitrogen helps facilitate the composting process. Carbon is an energy source, and with nitrogen, builds protoplasm. This balance is typically referred to as the proportion of carbon-to-nitrogen or the C:N ratio. This balance between carbon and nitrogen is sometimes referred to as the recipe needed for proper composting. More carbon than nitrogen is required, but activity decreases with too much carbon. An initial C:N ratio of 30:1 is about optimum for rapid composting. With initial C:N ratios lower than 20:1, nitrogen is lost during composting and escapes as ammonia. The nutrient content of horse manure is usually adequate. Microbes needed to decompose the bedding and manure occur naturally in stall manure.

Horse stable manure, with its high percentage of carbon-based bedding material, typically has an initial 20:1 to 30:1 carbon-to-nitrogen ratio, which is often ideally suited to composting. The initial C:N ratio for manure from horse tracks will tend to be higher, usually ranging from 30:1 to 55:1 with 40:1 being the average.

If the initial C:N ratio is too high then a nitrogen source such as grass clippings or hay should be added. Table 8-9 shows materials to add to lower initial C:N ratio. If the initial C:N ratio is too low then a carbon source such as straw or wood shavings should be added. Table 8-10 shows materials to add to raise initial C:N ratio.

Composter Designs

A well-designed composter should incorporate features that allow for easy management. Systems should be designed to minimize the addition of "unplanned" water from entering the system. Piles should be covered if possible. Piles should also be located at a higher elevation than the area surrounding them so water does not accumulate in the area. The area should be landscaped so that drainage water is directed around the area.

Any piles should be located on a durable base. A durable base allows for easier turning and removal of material, and act as a barrier between the ground and the pile so leachate does not affect ground water. A concrete pad works the best. Asphalt can also work but is not as durable as concrete. Some people use a compacted crushed rock base, an inexpensive alternative to concrete and asphalt. A crushed rock base will require more maintenance because rock will be removed or displaced during the turning and removal of material. Also, leachate can penetrate the barrier over time if the base and pile are not properly managed.

Smaller horse farms usually choose composters that require very little initial investment. Larger horse farms tend to choose composters that require less management and labor because the higher initial investment can be spread over more horses. The designs that follow are common to horse farms. Each design has advantages that can be used no matter the size of operation. More details about composter designs can be found in *On-Farm Composting Handbook*, NRAES-54.

Passive composting piles

This is the simplest method of composting. Manure is placed in a location and left undisturbed. Optimum pile size is 5 to 7 feet wide at the base and 3 to 4 feet in height. In this system, composting can take a year or longer for complete composting because the pile is not turned or mechanically aerated; therefore, the slower anaerobic composting takes place. The outside layer of the pile typically will not be completely composted because it has not been through the heating process needed for composting like the interior core.

Dynamic composting piles

A dynamic pile or windrow is one of the more common methods of composting. In this system manure is stacked in a single location, or in the case of a windrow, a long strip. Manure is stacked 4 to 8 feet high, 10 to 20 feet wide, and 10 to 200 feet long. The dynamic part of this system refers to the need to turn the pile.

Table 8-9 Amount of bulk material (in pounds) to add to 100 pounds of manure to lower the C:N ratio to 30:1.

Material	Bulk density (pcf)	Avg. material C:N ratio	Initial manure C:N ratio			
			35:1	40:1	45:1	50:1
Hay, general	—	22:1	40	70	95	115
Hay, legume	—	16:1	15	30	40	50
Grass clippings, loose	300 to 400	17:1	20	35	45	55
Grass clippings, compacted	500 to 800	17:1	20	35	45	55

Based on *On-Farm Composting Handbook*, NRAES-54.

Table 8-10 Amount of bulk material (in pounds) to add to 100 pounds of manure to raise the C:N ratio to 30:1.

Material	Bulk density (pcf)	Avg. material C:N ratio	Initial manure C:N ratio			
			10:1	15:1	20:1	25:1
Straw, general	227	80:1	295	150	75	30
Straw, oat	—	60:1	370	190	95	40
Straw, wheat	—	125:1	240	125	65	25
Sawdust	350 to 450	440:1	195	100	50	20
Wood shavings, hardwood	varies	560:1	190	100	50	20
Wood shavings, softwood	varies	640:1	190	100	50	20
Newsprint	195 to 240	625:1	190	100	50	20
Leaves, loose dry	100 to 300	55:1	415	215	110	45
Leaves, compacted & wet	400 to 500	55:1	415	215	110	45

Based on *On-Farm Composting Handbook*, NRAES-54.

The size of the pile or windrow is dependent on the volume of manure produced; turning frequency, and total composting time.

These piles should be placed on a concrete pad to allow for easier turning. The pad should be at least twice the pile design width to allow the pile to be turned from one side or edge of the pad to the other side or edge. If multiple windrows are used, space windrows at least 20 feet apart so a bucket and loader can operate, Figure 8-8.

Figure 8-8 Multiple composting windrows.

Aerated static piles

Aerated static piles can be a good option for people who have fewer than ten horses and do not have access to a convenient means to turn the pile such as a tractor and loader. Also, odors from this system tend to be lower when compared to the dynamic system. As the word static implies, this pile is not turned. To provide the oxygen needed for proper composting, an aeration system is required. This system can be located above or below ground. The advantage of an above ground system is that the necessary aeration tubes can easily be removed, and the system can be located on a concrete pad. The disadvantage to an above ground system is that care must be taken so that the aeration system is not damaged during pile formation and removal. The advantage of a below ground aeration system is that forming and removing the pile is easier. The disadvantage of this system is that the cost to construct and maintain this system is higher.

Aerated static piles typical are smaller than dynamic piles because of the power limitations of the fan or fans to provide the needed airflow. Piles are usually triangular in configuration, with a width of 8 to 12 feet and a height of 4 to 6 feet. Centrifugal fans are typically used because they provide high airflow at high static pressures, and they are quieter than axial fans.

Continuous bin composting system

A continuous composting system is a system that has been used for farms with less than 12 horse stalls. This system reduces the amount of labor and management. In this set up, manure is added to the front of the pile and mixed with old compost. The mixture is wetted with a garden hose as needed. Only the first six feet of the pile needs to be mixed. The older compost in the back of the pile will cure if no new manure is added to it. After 6 or 8 months, cured compost can be removed from the back until the hot core is reached. Once the core is reached, fresh material is added and the pile will grow in the opposite direction. Other than mixing when new material is added, no turning of the pile is necessary.

Figure 8-9 shows the construction and operation of a continuous composting bin for one to three horses in stalls. Table 8-11 lists the number and size of bins for various operations. More detail on how this system works can be found in the Oklahoma Cooperative Extension Service publication titled *Composting System for Small Horse Farms*, F-1729.

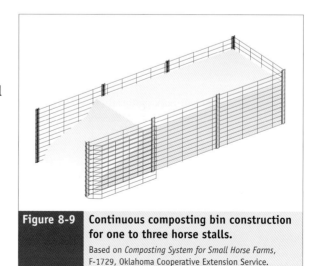

Figure 8-9 Continuous composting bin construction for one to three horse stalls.

Based on *Composting System for Small Horse Farms*, F-1729, Oklahoma Cooperative Extension Service.

Table 8-11 Size and number of bins needed based on number of horses in stalls.

Based on *Composting System for Small Horse Farms*, F-1729, Oklahoma Cooperative Extension Service.
Each bin is 6 feet wide.

Number of stalls	Number of bins*	Length of bins (feet)	Number of posts	Number and length of fencing rolls
1 to 3	1	18	8	one 50' rolls
3 to 5	1	30	12	one 75' rolls
6	2	18	16	two 50' rolls
7 or 8	2	30	24	two 75' rolls
9	3	18	24	three 50' rolls
10 or 11	3	30	36	three 75' rolls

* Bins are designed to fill in approximately eight months. Where two or three bins are listed, all the bins should be used at the same time so all bins fill evenly. Adding an extra bin provides storage room for times when cured compost cannot be removed.

CHAPTER 9

Bulk Feed and Bedding Storage

Feed stuff for horses is available in various types and sizes. Processed or whole cereal grains and complete formulated rations are available in bagged or bulk form, while minerals are available in bagged or block form. Dry forages are available in pelleted, loose, or, more commonly, in baled form. Pasture for grazing represents another form in which nutrition can be delivered to the horse. Each horse caretaker must consider all available feed sources to decide which are best for the particular situation. Cost is not the only consideration. Convenience, available labor, weather, and placement and amount of feed delivered daily are all factors to consider when designing a feeding system.

Keep feed storage areas free of batteries, petroleum products, chemicals, and other non-feed items. Store bagged feed in a rodent- and bird-proof area. Store bags on pallets that leave an air space under the bags to prevent moisture migration from the floor to the bags. In order to maintain rodent proofing and allow for cleaning up spilled feed, a concrete floor is desirable. Once bags are opened, it is best to empty a whole bag into a plastic or metal container with a tight fitting lid rather than

Store bagged feed in a dedicated room or compartment that is designed to reduce the four common problems of bag storage areas:
- Rotation of stocks.
- Excessive moisture.
- Rodent control.
- Clean up of torn bags and spilled feed.

feed directly from an open sack each day. An open bag exposes the feed to moisture from the air and makes it difficult to measure feed accurately. Open bags are also more prone to spillage and more accessible to rodents and horses that get into the feed room. Label containers to preserve identification of feeds. In smaller operations, a large metal or wooden cabinet that can store several bags and a container with a lid that will hold more than one bag of feed can be useful. Plan space for the disposal of empty bags. A small set of scales (10 pounds) and a scoop are necessary for accurate daily feeding of concentrates. The feed room can be combined with the tack room if feed is stored in containers to promote a clean room and protect the feed.

Bulk Feed

A bulk bin storage system can be used when larger quantities of flowable feed (pelleted or ground) are used, Figure 9-1. Bins can be galvanized metal or plastic/fiberglass. Depending on the company, minimum delivery amount is normally one ton. To preserve feed quality, size bulk bins to contain a month's supply. Emptying a bin monthly ensures that no feed is bridged in the bin, which might cause feed to gather moisture and become moldy.

The most popular bulk storage is an elevated hopper-bottom bin with an outlet 3 feet above the concrete base. Bin fill height of most commercial feed trucks is 20 feet, but check the bin fill height and delivery quantity/cost relationships with local feed suppliers. The slope (degrees from horizontal) of the bin floor depends on the flow characteristics of the feed. Whole grains and pellets will flow at a 45° angle, Figure 9-1a. Ground grains require a 60° angle, Figure 9-1b. The bin outlet can be in the center or at the side. Side outlets are the most popular for manual slide operation to flow the feed into a bucket. Feed withdrawal can also be accomplished with an auger. In larger operations, the bulk bin is located outside the horse barn for truck access to fill the bin. An auger is used to bring the feed inside the horse barn to fill carts or buckets. Centerless augers can be curved to make changes in direction and height of the delivery auger. A manual off-on switch controls the feed flow. Table 9-1 gives the capacities of hopper-bottom round bulk bins.

A new feed delivery method uses a large bag with a capacity of 1,000 to 2,000 pounds, Figure 9-1c. These bags are normally loaded at the feed mill in a pickup truck belonging to the horse caretaker to reduce hauling costs. Upon arrival at the farm, a front-end tractor loader is required to lift and hang the bag in a metal frame. The lower end of the bag has a manual slide which regulates the feed delivery. The bag is returned to the mill for refilling when it is empty.

Forages

The major feed in most horse barns is dry forage, usually in small bale form. The larger bales (round and rectangular) are useful in operations when groups of horses may be fed in outside pens. Cubed forages are available in some areas and are popular because of less wastage, easier handling, and a more uniformity. Nutritional considerations and costs usually result in some portion of the horse ration being dry forages. Most horse operators prefer to store large quantities of dry forages away from their horse barns for fire safety and rodent control. A two-week supply of baled forages is normally stored in or near the horse stall barn.

Baled forages require about 10 pounds per cubic foot or 200 cubic feet per ton and should be kept under roof to maintain quality. Long-term storage of baled forages on concrete

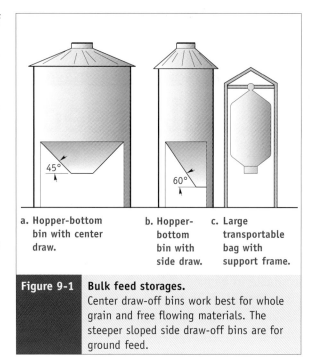

a. Hopper-bottom bin with center draw.

b. Hopper-bottom bin with side draw.

c. Large transportable bag with support frame.

Figure 9-1 **Bulk feed storages.**
Center draw-off bins work best for whole grain and free flowing materials. The steeper sloped side draw-off bins are for ground feed.

floors may cause moisture migration into the forages unless an air space is provided. Dry forages can be stored for two years without appreciable nutrient loss if stored properly. Bale quality can change throughout a stack, so it is important to inspect each bale for mold and poor quality as it is fed. Dispose of bale twine or wire to minimize danger to the horses.

Indoor hay storage helps preserve quality and reduces dry matter loss. Ideally, provide separate storage for hay, Figure 9-2. Because hay can be a fire hazard, avoid long-term storage of hay inside buildings where horses are kept. Some insurance companies will insure buildings where horses are kept if the building is used for short-term hay storage or the building stores a small amount of hay on a continuous basis, while others will not insure buildings if any hay is stored in the buildings.

Hay and Bedding

Store hay and straw under cover and, preferably, raised off the ground for air circulation underneath. Tightly stacked damp hay

Table 9-1 | **Capacities of hopper-bottom round bulk bins.**

Based on Aeration System Design for Cone-Bottom Round Bins, Oklahoma State University Extension Facts F-1103. Approximate values. Overall height is the distance from ground to rooftop and includes 2 feet of clearance between ground and hopper bottom. Roof angle of 35°. Bin volume includes roof volume.

Bin diameter (feet)	Hopper angle	Overall height (feet)	Total volume (cu ft)	Total volume (bushels)	Volume per foot of bin height* (cu ft)	Volume per foot of bin height* (bushels)
Sidedraw						
6	60°	15	227	182	28	23
	20	368	295			
	25	510	410			
9	60°	22	760	611	64	51
	26	1,015	815			
	30	1,270	1,109			
Centerdraw						
6	60°	10	145	117	28	23
	15	286	230			
	20	428	344			
9	60°	18	681	547	64	51
	22	935	751			
	26	1,190	955			
12	60°	24	1,613	1,296	113	91
	30	2,292	1,841			
	36	2,970	2,386			
12	45°	20	1,493	1,199	113	91
	30	2,624	2,108			
	40	3,755	3,016			
15	45°	24	2,739	2,200	177	142
	36	4,860	6,903			
	48	6,980	5,607			
18	45°	24	3,512	2,821	255	204
	36	5,268	4,231			
	48	9,619	7,726			
21	45°	24	4,191	3,366	346	278
	36	8,348	6,705			
	48	12,504	10,043			

* To calculate volume of different height bins, add or subtract from table value.

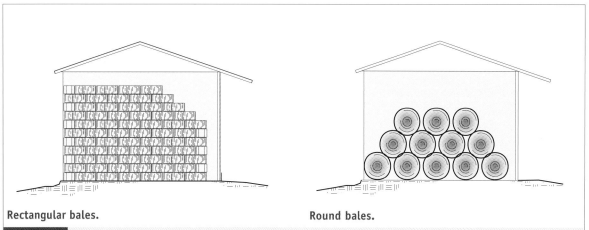

Rectangular bales.   Round bales.

Figure 9-2 | **Dry hay storage.**
Do not stack bales against sidewalls unless the building is designed for these loads. Indoor hay storage helps preserve quality and reduces dry matter loss.

can burn spontaneously. Keep hay and bedding dry and free of birds and rodents.

Hay and bedding are most economical to buy during a particular season. You may want to store a year's needs, but probably not in the stable. A separate hay and straw storage at least 70 feet from other buildings, especially the horse barns, is safer and cheaper. Pole or post barn construction is typical.

Hay storage considerations:
- Stable storage is labor saving, but the risk is great. Many operators store bales in a fireproof room.
- Small rooms and narrow doors are inconvenient for handling hay.
- Supply kept with the horses should be a minimum, usually not more than a week's worth.
- Unoccupied stalls can be used for hay and straw storage.
- Haylofts in the same facility or in an older barn may suffice. Lofts or a separate floor insulate the ceiling below. Damp hay may spontaneously combust, so provide good ventilation. Overhead storage is expensive to construct. Overhead storage can also hinder airflow.

- Firewalls for a fireproof room or as a partition between storage and animals can be made of cement block, fire retardant lumber, or metal.
- Storing hay and straw on ground level saves labor and reduces climbing and falls.
- Bedding straw can be stored with the hay.
- Store sawdust, shavings, peanut hulls, etc. in a plywood bin or piled under a cover. Size the storage for several months' supply. Bins can be added to an outside wall of a feed room or storage area.

Storage Size:
- Bedding: 8 to 15 lb/day/1000 lb of animal weight in occupied stalls. Amount depends on type of floor, bedding material, stable management, and weather.
- Hay: 1½ to 3 lb of hay/day per 100 lb of body weight.
- Store hydrated lime for disinfecting stalls.

Tables 3-8 through 3-10, and Tables 9-2 and 9-3 can be used to estimate storage space needed for grains, feed, and bedding.

Table 9-2 | Storage space requirements for feed and bedding.

GRAINS

Crop	Unground density lbs/bu	lbs/cu ft	Freshly ground density lbs/bu	lbs/cu ft
Corn 15½%				
• Shelled	56	44.8	48	38
• Ear	70	28.0	45	36
Corn 30%*				
• Shelled	67.5	54.0	—	—
• Ear, ground			89.6	35.8
Barley 15%	48	38.4	37	28
Flax 11%	56	44.8	—	—
Grain Sorghum 15%	56	44.8		
Oats 16%	32	25.6	23	18
Rye 16%	56	44.8	48	38
Soybeans 14%	60	48.0	—	—
Wheat 14%	60	48.0	50	43

HAY AND STRAW

Material	Density (cu ft per ton)	Density (lbs per cu ft)
Loose		
• Alfalfa	450 to 500	4 to 4.4
• Non legume	450 to 600	3.3 to 4.4
• Straw	670 to 1000	2 to 3
Baled		
• Alfalfa	200 to 330	6 to 10
• Non legume	250 to 330	6 to 8
• Straw	400 to 500	4 to 5
Chopped		
• Alfalfa, 1.5-inch cut	285 to 360	5.5 to 7
• Non legume, 3-inch cut	300 to 400	5 to 6.7
• Straw	250 to 350	5.7 to 8

OTHER MATERIALS

Material	Density (cu ft per ton)	Density (lbs per cu ft)
Lime, hydrated	50	40
Sand		
• Dry	18	110
• Fine	16	125
• Moist	15	130
Wood		
• Chips	110	18
• Sawdust, fine	110	18
• Sawdust, moist	70	28
• Shavings	200	10

* Amounts to yield a bushel or cubic foot of 15.5% grain.

Table 9-3 | Hay shed capacity with 20-foot sidewall, tons per foot length of building.

Shed width (feet)	Small rectangular bales [a]	Large rectangular bales [b]	Large round bales [c]	Chopped
24	1.6	3.0	1.6	1.9
30	2.0	3.8	2.0	2.3
36	2.4	4.5	2.4	2.8
40	2.7	5.0	2.6	3.1
48	3.3	6.0	3.2	3.7

[a] 7 to 9 pounds dry matter per cubic foot; 85% stacking efficiency.
[b] 13 to 15 pounds dry matter per cubic foot; 90% stacking efficiency.
[c] 9 to 13 pounds dry matter per cubic foot; 60% stacking efficiency.

CHAPTER 10

Fences

Good fences are a must, especially in commercial horse operations where the perception of potential injury to a horse can mean lost business. Fences provide containment to keep horses on the property and to keep unwanted nuisances such as dogs and visitors away from the horses. Fencing aids in good horse management and is a major component of training and breeding facilities. Fencing helps to segregate groups of horses according to sex, age, value, or use. Fences allow for good pasture management by allowing for controlled grazing. The type of fencing used can vary depending on the horse activity or location. Training rings, tracks, and isolation paddocks usually require a different type of fencing than pasture fencing.

Well-constructed and maintained fences can enhance the aesthetic appeal and the property value of a site. By contrast, poorly planned, haphazard, unsafe, or unmaintained fences can detract from the value of a site and reflect poor management. Good fences can be formal or informal in appearance, yet all should be well built and carefully planned.

Good fences usually entail a major capital investment; therefore, any fencing project should be carefully evaluated and designed before construction, because moving and replacing fences can be expensive and time consuming. There are many types of effective horse fencing, but there is no best fence. Each type has inherent tradeoffs in its features. Don't be surprised to find that different types of fences will be needed in different areas of a site.

Ideally, a fence would be highly visible to a fleeing, frightened, or playing horse so it can avoid contact with the fence. It would be high enough to discourage jumping and solid enough to discourage testing its strength. No gaps would be present to trap a head or hoof. The ideal fence would have no sharp edges or projections that could injure a horse leaning or falling into it. The ideal fence would be aesthetically appealing, not be expensive to purchase or install, would not require much maintenance, and would last twenty years or more. Unfortunately, no type of fencing meets all these demands. Each type of fence has its place based on management objectives. The overriding factor in most fence selections is cost. Table 10-1 shows some comparative costs for various types of fences used for horses.

Planning

The true test of a fence is not when horses are peacefully grazing but when they are excited, playing, or panicked. During these times, horses run into fences because they do not see the fence during their excitement, play, or attempt to escape as they panic. It is during these emergency conditions that fences need to hold up under the pressure of a horse.

Some basic planning can help eliminate fencing mistakes. Always keep in mind during all stages of planning and constructing a fence that sharp edges and projections must be eliminated. It is best to eliminate fence corners and dead end areas when fencing a pasture for more than one horse. Instead, install smoother angle corners, Figure 10-1. By smoothing corners into curves, it is less likely that a bully horse will trap a less dominant horse. The disadvantage of not having corners

Table 10-1 Comparative costs of common fences.

Types	Comparative cost index (Material only)	Approximate life (Humid climate) (years)	Upkeep
Four-rail (posts spaced at 8 feet)			
1" x 6" treated boards	200	10-20	Medium
2" x 6" treated boards	350	10-20	Medium
PVC rails	500-600	20	Low
High-tensile polymer coated			
5-inch rail width	330	33	Medium
Mesh wire (diamond or 2" x 4" rectangular)			
12½ gauge	150	38	Low
High-tensile electric—12½ gauge			
Four strand	20	25	Medium
One strand	7	25	High
Reflective tape or rope (electric)			
½ inch, one strand (temporary)	11	25	Medium
1½ inch heavy duty, two strand (permanent)	33	25	Medium

Based on *Fences for Horses*, Bulletin 1192, J.W. Worley and G. Heusner, The University of Georgia College of Agricultural and Environmental Sciences, Cooperative Extension Service, 2000.

is that it does not give a place for the owner to catch the horse.

Fencing should be highly visible to the horse. Visible fences will prevent playful horses from accidentally running into them. A frightened horse may still hit a visible fence while blinded with fear. For this reason, forgiving fences that contain the horse without injury are better than unyielding solid fencing such as brick walls. Wire is the least visible fencing material. Installing boards at the top of the fence or adding strips of visible material to the wire can help make these fences more visible to the horse.

Horses, especially a single-kept horse, naturally desire other equine companions and can test fence strength in an attempt to join neighbors. Strong, solid-looking fences usually provide enough protection. When constructing a fence, the fencing material, whether it is rails or wire mesh, is fastened to the inside (single-kept horse side) of the posts. If horses lean on the fence, the fasteners are not pushed out by the horse's weight. Make sure the fence is not climbable and that social and antisocial activity over the fence will not lead to a stuck head or foot.

An alternative favored by farms with particularly valuable stock is to double fence so that each paddock has its own fence with

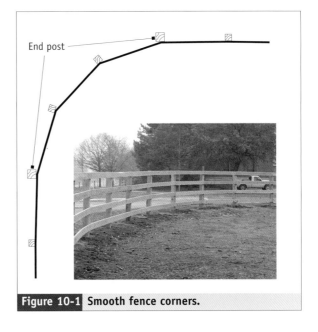

Figure 10-1 Smooth fence corners.

an alley in between. Double fencing is also frequently used where human contact with horses is to be discouraged. The first fence keeps the horse in, and the second fence keeps the people away from direct horse contact. Double fencing is common for stallions. Stallion fences need to be higher, stronger, and better maintained than fences for geldings or mares, because stallions often find mares to be motivation to test fence strength.

The more attractive types of fences tend to be more expensive. In general, safer fencing is also higher in cost. Some types of fences have higher initial cost but significantly less maintenance cost and/or a long lifetime. Some cost advantage is gained by placing the more aesthetically pleasing fencing along the public side of the property while less attractive, yet equally functional, fences are used in more remote locations.

Finally, planning includes more than selection of fence type. It is best to develop an overall plan where the fencing's influence on aesthetics, chore efficiency, management practices, safety, and finances is considered.

Selecting and Sizing a Pasture or Paddock

Some sections of a site may be too steep or rocky for pasture use, or the soil may be unsuitable for adequate grass growth. Soils that do not drain readily will cause wet areas, which horse hooves churn into a grassless eyesore. Contact the USDA Natural Resource Conservation Service (NRCS) for soil type information on a particular section of land and recommendations for types of pasture vegetation to use on the site. Unsuitable soil areas should be fenced off. Because horses usually strip bark off trees left within their reach, valuable tree specimens should be fenced so that horses are unable to chew off the bark, which can cause trees to die.

The size of the enclosed area depends on the number of horses to be confined, how they are allowed to interact with each other, type of stable operation, and expected type of activity of the horse such as exercising or eating. Unless supplying supplemental feed, plan an average of 2 to 10 acres per horse for year-round feeding by grazing for areas that typically have a good vegetative cover.

Often times, horses are turned out individually rather than in groups. This arrangement means more, and perhaps, smaller paddocks which increases the amount of fencing. Stalled horses may be kept in a stall most of the time and only turned out for exercise a few hours daily. One paddock will then serve to exercise several horses, in succession, each day.

The area of a nearly square or rectangular paddock can be determined by using Equation 10-1:

Equation 10-1. Estimated area calculation for a nearly square or rectangular pasture or paddock (acres).

$$\text{Area (acres)} = \frac{(\text{Avg. Length, feet})(\text{Avg. Width, feet})}{43,560 \text{ sq ft/acre}}$$

Use Equation 10-2 and Table 10-2 to help determine the total length of fence.

Equation 10-2. Estimated fence length calculation for a nearly square or rectangular pasture or paddock (feet).

$$\text{Length (feet)} = 2\big[(\text{Avg. Length, feet}) + (\text{Avg. Width, feet})\big]$$

Table 10-2	Design aid for determining rectangular pasture and paddock fence dimensions.					
Area	Perimeter dimensions			Total fence length		
(acres)	(feet)	(rods)	(miles)	(feet)	(rods)	(miles)
1.25	165 x 330	10 x 20	1/32 x 1/16	990	60	3/16
2.5	330 x 330	20 x 20	1/16 x 1/16	1,320	80	1/4
5	330 x 660	20 x 40	1/16 x 1/8	1,980	120	3/8
10	660 x 660	40 x 40	1/8 x 1/8	2,640	160	1/2
20	660 x 1,320	40 x 80	1/8 x 1/4	3,960	240	3/4
40	1,320 x 1,320	80 x 80	1/4 x 1/4	5,280	320	1
80	1,320 x 2,640	80 x 160	1/4 x 1/2	7,920	480	1 1/2
160	2,640 x 2,640	160 x 160	1/2 x 1/2	10,560	640	2

Basic Design Guidelines

Select and install fencing that allows easy access to pastures and does not inhibit convenience of stable chores. Gates should be easy to operate with only one hand so the other hand is free. Fencing should also allow easy movement of groups of horses from pasture to central holding facilities. All-weather lanes should connect turnout areas to the stable. Lanes can be kept in grass or graveled depending on the type and amount of traffic that uses them. Make sure they are wide enough to allow mowing equipment or vehicles to pass. Vehicles such as cars, light trucks, and tractors can be up to 8 feet wide. Vehicular traffic demands lanes 12 feet wide to negotiate comfortably. Narrower lane widths are acceptable for smaller tractors or mowing equipment.

Fence height should be 5 feet above ground level. Larger horses, stallions, or those adept at jumping may require taller fences. Keep the lower edge or rail of the fence 8 to 12 inches off the ground. An 8-inch clearance will leave enough room to avoid trapping a hoof and will discourage a horse from reaching under the fence for grass. A bottom rail no higher than 12 inches will prevent foals from rolling under the fence. Clearances less than 12 inches can make mowing under the fence difficult. If wire mesh is used, a 3- to 4-inch ground clearance is recommended to allow for mowing and to help prevent rusting that could result from ground contact. Higher clearances for wire mesh fences will result in the horse pushing out the fence at the bottom so it can graze, which will bend the fence and decrease its attractiveness. If no mowing is needed, mesh fences can be flush with the ground.

With any type of fence, a single strand of electric wire can be run 4 to 6 inches above or just inside the top rail. The electrified wire will discourage horses who are confirmed fence leaners, scratchers, or reachers.

Managing Fenced Areas

Controlled grazing of pasture grasses demands that some areas are periodically without horses in them. If temporary or cross fencing is used to designate controlled sections, it should be just as safe to the horses as the permanent perimeter fence. A temporary fence does not have to be quite as impenetrable because a loose horse will eventually be contained by the perimeter fence. Through the use of perimeter fencing around the facility complex, many farms make sure that no loose horse can leave the property. Containment of loose horses becomes more important as traffic and neighbors increase around the horse facility.

Fence Types

Different types of fencing have different functions. Strong, safe, highly visible fencing should be used in areas where many horses congregate or crowd each other such as near gates or shelters. In areas where horses do not have constant contact with the fence, such as in very large pastures, a less substantial fence can suffice. Additionally, fences around training rings or tracks will likely be different than paddock fences.

Sturdy fences are essential. Horses will both casually and deliberately test the strength of a fence. Horses often reach through or over fences for attractions on the other side. Fences that do not allow this type of behavior are best. Positioning an electrified wire over the top rail will discourage horses from leaning and scratching themselves on fences. Openings in the fence should be either large enough to offer little chance of foot, leg, and head entrapment or small enough that hooves cannot get through. Small, safe openings have dimensions of less than 3 inches.

Fence types are usually categorized by construction material. Common fences incorporate one or more materials such as wood, steel, plastic, and rubber/nylon. Table 10-3 and Figure 10-2 show some general fence designs. Electricity, although not a material, is a component of several successful fence types. Many modern, safe fences are hybrids of traditional and new technology materials. Always purchase posts and other fencing materials from a dealer who is known for handling quality fencing products.

Wood

The two main types of wood fencing are board and post and rail. Board, or estate, fence is the classic beauty of horse fencing while post and rail is a more rustic alternative. Other fence types incorporate wood as posts and visibility boards at the top. Wood fence is the first choice for many horse facilities owing to its natural and classic beauty. With new preservative treatments, wood fences can last longer with less care than they used to. A drawback of wood is that it can splinter and injure a horse. Be aware that a horse who is a confirmed wood chewer may pose a threat to wood fence. Pressure treated wood can be dangerous to the health of a horse that chews it. Wood chewers can be deterred with an electric wire strand or lumber protected by metal (without sharp edges) or plastic. Properly installed, however, a wood fence generally poses little threat to the horse it confines.

Board or plank

Board or plank fences grace some of the most attractive horse farms in the country. They are highly visible and relatively safe. Many variations on this fence exist depending on board thickness, board number and spacing, type of posts, species of wood, and color. They can be painted white, creosoted black, or left to naturally weather, Figure 10-3. Painting or staining every few years maintains the

condition of board fences; otherwise, a properly installed board fence is fairly maintenance free. A board fence is an expensive fence to build and one of the most time consuming to install properly, but it is also one of the safest fences. Any boards that do break must be replaced immediately.

Pressure treated fencing is usually cheaper than a white painted wood fence. The first coat of paint on a fence lasts about three years with the second coat lasting five to seven years, depending on weather conditions.

Fence strength depends on the wood species, lumber dimensions, and how the assembly is fastened together. Hardwoods are stronger, for the same size, than softwoods. Fence posts can be square, round, or half-round in cross section. For hardwood posts, choose for strength or for longevity. Pressure treated softwood posts are equally acceptable. Board thickness is usually 1 inch rough cut for hardwoods such as oak, cypress, or fir or 2 inch

The most common fencing material categories are:

- Wood.
- Wire and metal.
- Synthetic non-metals.

Table 10-3 General fence design.

	Fence				Post		
Fence type	Number of strands or rails	Spacing (inches)	Height to bottom (inches)	Distance[a] between braces (feet)	Top diameter (inches)	Height[b] (feet)	Spacing (feet)
Board	4-5	2x6 at 8"	10-14	N/A	4	5-6	6-8
High tensile (9 to 15½ ga)	5-8	5-12	4-14[c]	60	6	4-5	16[d]
Cable	4-7	7-12	16-20	N/A	5	5	8
Woven or welded wire	N/A	N/A	0-4	660	4[e]	4-5	8
Electric	2-3	16	16-32[c]	N/A	3[e]	4	30-50
Suspension	4-6	10	16	1,320	4[e]	4	80-120[f]

[a] Up to one-quarter mile on flat terrain.
[b] Add embedment depth (3 feet minimum) to determine post length. Assumes clay loam; sandy or wet soils require greater depths or concrete encasement. For rocky soils where 3 feet cannot be achieved, use concrete backfill or decrease post spacing.
[c] Lower wire is for foals.
[d] Increase spacing to 60 feet if battens used.
[e] Steel posts are an option.
[f] Space stays 12-16 feet.

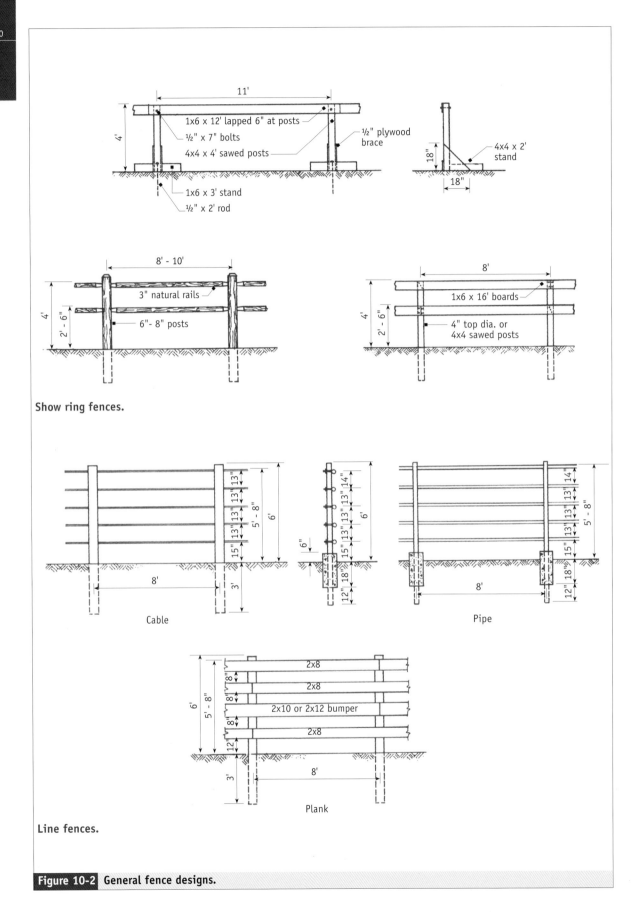

Show ring fences.

Cable

Pipe

Plank

Line fences.

Figure 10-2 General fence designs.

Figure 10-3 Wooden board fence.

nominal thickness for pressure treated soft-woods. Weathered oak boards are very hard and when broken tend to splinter into long jagged pieces. Pine boards break more cleanly and are therefore preferred for fencing young stock.

The most common and most balanced looking board width is the 6-inch width. With a 6-inch wide board, the most aesthetically pleasing spacing between boards is based on multiples of 6, 9, or 12 inches apart. Usually, all rails are the same distance apart. One attractive variation positions the top two rails closer together. Do not use diamond- or cross-patterned rails as these provide narrow angles to catch feet and heads.

Posts are set so that fence panels are 8 feet long. Corner and gate posts are 25% larger, and set more deeply than line posts. Boards are positioned on the inside (horse side) of the fence. A face board on top of the nailed ends provides increased strength and safety by prohibiting board ends from becoming loose projections. Boards are usually 16 feet long so they span two fence panels. Boards are staggered so that alternate boards end at each post. (See wire mesh fence section for post selection information)

A three-board fence with boards spaced 9 inches is adequate for mares and geldings. The smaller size of foals and ponies demands a fourth, lower board and 6-inch spacing. Fence height should be no less than 5 feet for placid animals. Stallions require at least a 6-foot high, five-board fence.

Post and rail

Post and rail fences have a rustic attractiveness that is highly visible and sturdy yet will yield a bit on impact. They are relatively easy to install and have low maintenance, but are fairly expensive (but less so than board fencing). Like board fences, they need at least three rails to contain horses. For foals, the bottom rail should be no higher than 12 inches off the ground. Fence height should be at least 5 feet, and up to 6 feet for jumpers and stallions.

Much of post and rail fence safety and strength depends on proper installation. The posts have to provide firm, undisturbed support over the lifetime of the fence; otherwise, rails will work loose as the post changes position. Posts that experience frost heaving or settlement will not be suitable for this type of fencing. The rails are inserted into precut holes in the posts as the fence is assembled. Rails are placed into the appropriate holes, and then the posts are tamped firmly into place. Rather than using nails to fasten the fence together, post and rail fence depends on juxtaposed pressure of two rails in one hole. The rails need to be installed tightly enough so that the ends will not come out upon horse impact or contact. Loose rails present a hazard similar to a spear.

Fence panels are typically 8 to 10 feet long. Pressure treated lumber and cedar are often used.

Wire and Metal Fencing

Wire and metal horse fencing options include smooth, high tensile wire strands, wire mesh, steel pipe, and cable. Electric fencing also falls into this broad category. Barbed wire should not be used with horses due to the severe injury caused by horse entanglement. The common woven wire stock fences, with 4-inch or longer squares, should not be used for horses due to the danger of entrapped legs and the associated lacerations.

Wire mesh

Wire mesh fencing designed for horse use, with a top board for visibility, is considered to be among the safest horse fencing. It can range from intermediate in cost to one of the more expensive depending mainly on the type of wire. It is a low maintenance fence, with care limited to post treatments, and is relatively easy to install with proper equipment. Opinions vary as to its attractiveness; the well built varieties have an understated beauty. It is excellent for keeping most interlopers, such as other animals and humans, away from the horses.

Horse-variety wire mesh is manufactured in diamond or rectangular design mesh. The diamond, or triangular, mesh is nearly impossible for a horse to get a hoof through, Figure 10-4. Rectangular mesh ("turkey wire") with upright openings 2 inches wide and 4 inches high is not quite as safe because these openings are big enough for a pony or foal-sized striking hoof to pass through. The wires then form a trap around the ankle when the horse tries to escape. Because wire fences of all types can be nearly invisible from a distance, add boards to increase fence visibility for the horse. Mesh fence will not cut a horse that falls against it, is sturdy yet has some give, and is virtually breach-proof if installed correctly. Some horses have caught shoes and halter buckles in the mesh of even the safest wire mesh fences.

Correct installation calls for the wire mesh to be strung tightly between posts using a fence stretcher. Mesh is then stapled securely onto solid rectangular or round posts spaced 8 to 10 feet apart. (Also see *Wooden Post Selection*). Ideally, wire is installed on the same side as the horses to present a smooth surface that prevents hooves and heads from becoming trapped between wood and wire. The wire requires very little maintenance and rarely sags once stretched onto the posts. Wire mesh fence goes up faster than board fence.

The better wire mesh fence installations include a top board to increase fence visibility and to keep the top, unsupported wire portion from sagging from the pressure of horses leaning over it. This top board overlaps the top of the mesh to provide a normal fence height of 5 feet, including the top board. In some cases, the top board can be economically replaced with an electric wire strand positioned 4 inches above the mesh to discourage

Figure 10-4 Diamond wire mesh.

fence leaning. The top board provides important visibility and presents little danger to the horses compared to an electric wire strand on top. The newer flexible plastic rail and electrical tape fence materials can be used instead of a top board to increase visibility. More boards, such as a bottom board, can be used to further increase fence visibility and safety. With or without a bottom board, leave 3- to 4-inches of clearance under the mesh to aid in mowing and weed removal. Visibility boards are similar to those used on board fences and would be 1 x 6 rough cut or 2 x 6 nominal boards.

Horses entangled in strands of smooth wire can be cut severely, for this reason, the horse-type wire mesh is recommended. Many mesh fence materials sold for general farm fences are lighter gauge wire with improperly sized mesh openings so they suffer from material weakness. The larger mesh size (6 x 6-inch or greater) increases the risk of a horse's leg becoming entangled. Wire fence must be heavier than 12-gauge wire to be strong enough for horse use. When selecting wire note that the lower the gauge number the heavier the wire.

Smooth wire fence

Five to eight strands of electrified smooth wire on wooden posts make the least expensive fence. Wire fence is potentially the most dangerous horse fence, but with top rails for visibility and an electrified top wire to dis-

courage contact, it can be used for ordinary and quiet horses. Smooth wire fences are not recommended for use between two populated paddocks where horses will be reaching across the fence and risk entanglement. Once posts are set, the fence installs quickly. The wires must be stretched tight (using a stretcher or permanent in-line tensioners) during installation, and maintenance mainly involves keeping things tight.

The wire must be installed taut and kept that way with spring loaded tension units. Maintenance involves patrolling the fenceline for downed branches and trees resting on the wire fence. Individual strands may need to be tightened periodically as the wire stretches with age or warm temperature. Loose wire is a hazard for horse entanglement.

Wooden fence posts are recommended for smooth wire fencing. These can be set up to 15 feet apart, but visibility boards will be long and difficult to attach. One alternative is to use white plastic pipe on the top strand for visibility. Steel and fiberglass posts make connection of visibility boards difficult, and these posts can impale a horse attempting to jump the fence.

One alternative within the wire strand category is the high tensile wire fence. This uses wire of 11- to 14-gauge with a tensile strength of up to 200,000 pounds per square inch. (In comparison, conventional galvanized, Type I, fencing wire has about a 55,000-psi tensile strength.) The fence can withstand livestock contact and low temperature contraction without losing its elasticity. The high elastic limit reduces common stretch or sag associated with conventional fence wire. Wire tension is set at 200 to 250 pounds at installation and is maintained by permanent in-line stretchers or tension springs. Electric versions are common.

Wires are held in tension along sturdy posts spaced up to 60 feet apart. End posts must be well braced. Battens or light posts are used in between posts to maintain wire spacing. High tensile wire fence is most suitable to flat or gently rolling terrain to take advantage of the long, straight line distances between support posts. It is no more difficult to build

than other fence. Each wire is tightened with a ratchet in-line stretcher. Once end posts are solidly set and braced, the wire installation proceeds rapidly. Features, limitations, and costs are similar to those of a conventional smooth wire fence.

Electric fence

Smooth wire, of conventional or high-tensile variety, can be connected to an electrical charger to provide a reminder to horses to stay away from the fence. The electric shock provides a degree of respect that a plain, smooth wire fence cannot always provide. Electric fences, like all wire fences, suffer from lack of visibility and the potential for severe cuts to horses entangled in them. Electric fence can be successfully constructed from more visible products such as multiple strands of wire incorporated into a woven plastic tape. Large strips of plastic or cloth can be tied to conventional wire for increased visibility but at the expense of professional, good looks. A single electrified strand is often used with other, more substantial horse fences to discourage horses from contacting the fence.

Electric fences used as cross-fences are an ideal management tool for pastures. Attach two electrified strands of wire to steel or fiberglass posts set 20 feet apart. Locate one wire 42 inches off the ground and the other 18 inches off the ground.

Many types of plug-in or battery-powered electric chargers are offered; low impedance, high voltage, short impulse models are considered the best. Another option is a solar powered battery charger. Heavy-duty batteries designed to withstand a deep discharge before recharging are recommended. Some models are capable of electrifying up to 50 miles of wire. Shock duration is about 1/4,000th of a second, with 45 to 65 shocks per minute, at about 1,000 to 3,500 volts peak. Electrical grounding is very important with modern chargers. Do not use an existing household ground rod. For grounding each charger, provide three driven ground rods 6 to 8 feet long positioned at least the rod length apart, a minimum of 20 to 50 feet of buried galvanized pipe or an existing steel culvert. Use additional grounds for each 3,000 feet of fence in areas with normal rainfall.

Older weed-burner chargers, which claim to burn weeds growing over the wire, are not recommended with horses. They put out a higher charge at intervals that can burn or electrocute horses and could start brush fires. The new low impedance chargers do not set grass fires even though wires touch vegetation. Do not electrify barbed wire because children and animals can become entangled and be repeatedly shocked, even to death.

It is good practice, and is the law in some states, to identify electric fence with signs.

High vegetation will inhibit electric fence function. Maintenance of electric fence requires removal of heavy vegetative growth so the voltage necessary to repel animals is available. Check fence voltages often at different points along the line. Use a meter to check for electrical current leaks due to grounding and weed growth. Inspect fencelines after heavy wind and rainstorms to clear away fallen trees and debris that can inhibit fence function.

Install electric wires and insulators on gates so that the charge goes off when the gate is opened.

Chain link fence

Chain link fence is common in residential and commercial applications but not so in agricultural settings, Figure 10-5. It is relatively expensive and does not maintain its original attractiveness if abused by horse contact. Unless well supported, edges tend to sag and sway. Unprotected chain link edges have looped metal projections that can catch halters and cut horses. It could be a suitable fence for suburban or urban horse facilities where one objective is to discourage humans from interacting with the horses. Chain link can be easily built to heights beyond those normally encountered with farm fences. It is fairly visible and sturdy while yielding on horse impact.

Stallion runs have been fenced with 7-foot high chain link. For any horse application, all piping supports should be at least 3 inches in diameter, and the top and bottom of the fence

Figure 10-5 Chain link fence used as a gate.

should be finished: the top with pipe and the bottom with a pressure treated 2x10 board positioned with its bottom edge 2 inches below the wire and attached to the outside of the fence. Keep the bottom fence edge at least 8 inches above ground. One common problem with chain link is from pawing horses loosening and pulling shoes.

Pipe fence

Galvanized steel pipe fence is more common in certain areas of the country. It is extremely sturdy and visible yet usually has a high labor cost to construct because welding is required. At least one manufacturer offers a design where the rails slide through post holes for easier assembly. Pipe fence requires little maintenance if properly treated during installation. It is successfully used for paddocks and riding arenas.

Typical pipe fence height is 5 feet. Posts are usually 4-inch outer diameter pipe set about 3 feet deep. Rails can be 2- to 3-inch outer diameter pipe spaced 18 inches from the ground and then 17 and 16 inches apart for a 60-inch fence height. Posts can be spaced up to 15 feet apart.

Cable fence

Cable fence makes a good, sturdy horse fence with more give to it than pipe fence. Cable fences are typically 60 inches high with four, 1/2- or 3/4-inch diameter cables spaced

16 inches apart, with the bottom cable located 16 inches above the ground. For a 54-inch fence, cables are positioned 14 inches off the ground and then 12 inches apart. Posts can be 8-foot long, 4-inch outer diameter steel posts or 5-inch square wood posts. Steel posts use welded rings to position cables, and wooden posts have drilled holes. Post spacing is up to 20 feet with good corner posts. Cable tension is maintained by high tensile wire-type tensioners or car springs spaced every 1/8 mile. A pipe top rail with three to four strands of cable is another design. Cable fencing has been associated with abrasion and puncture injury.

Combination pipe and cable fence

A pipe fence of up to 72 inches high has two pipe rails, one at the top and the other at 36 inches, and four strands of cable. Two strands of cable are equally spaced between the top and middle rails, and the other two cables are spaced in between the middle rail and the ground.

Non-metal Synthetic Fences

Non-metal synthetic materials such as polyvinylchloride (PVC), other plastics, rubber, and nylon are increasing in popularity. These materials provide many benefits such as high visibility and low maintenance.

PVC rigid board

High grade polyvinylchloride (PVC) is treated with ultraviolet light inhibitors to resist discoloration and brittleness, after being molded into fence posts and board stock. Many designs resemble whitewashed plank fence and are manufactured specifically for horse use, Figure 10-6. PVC fence has a long life span with companies offering 15 to 25 year warranties. It requires virtually no maintenance because it does not require periodic painting, staining, or tightening. Horses will not chew on it; decay and insects will not destroy it. PVC fencing is a semi-rigid material that can absorb some of the impact of a horse hitting it without breaking. If it does break, it may not splinter. PVC fences are not considered horse-proof construction. A PVC fence may need an electrified strand of wire to deter horses from

Figure 10-6 Rigid PVC fencing.

dismantling it. For all these features and safety, PVC is the most expensive to purchase of all fences. But, when construction, material, and maintenance costs are considered over the life expectancy of a fence, the PVC fence becomes cost competitive due to its minimal maintenance.

The fence is built in 8-foot sections. The boards are usually hollow-core PVC with dimensions similar to those of wooden boards. The posts are also PVC, and the boards fasten onto them using brackets molded or screwed onto the posts. Posts are often set into concrete which increases installation time and cost. The PVC material expands and contracts, and hence, changes length, with temperature fluctuation so this must considered during assembly. Boards are set in sleeves with a gap between them, rather than being nailed onto the post. Variations in PVC fence stock exist so that rails can be round rather than board shaped or in colors other than white.

PVC rigid board fences may not work well in cold climates because the material can become brittle and fragile at very cold temperatures.

High tensile polymer

This hybrid fence combines high tensile wire strands, which provide support and form the core of the fence rails, with a flexible covering of PVC plastic, Figure 10-7. These fences have become very popular because of their highly visibility, low maintenance, and

Figure 10-7 High tensile polymer fencing.

longevity. High tensile polymer fences are very strong and absorb impact and rebound when horses hit them. They require some attention to wire tightness for proper maintenance of the high tensile wire fence properties. Cost for materials and installation is more than for an equivalent high tensile wire fence yet significantly less than for PVC board fence, and in many cases is less than a 2x6 pressure treated board fence.

High tensile polymer fences are assembled similarly to high tensile wire fences. Tensioners are used to keep the rail assembly tight. The number of wires in each PVC strip varies by manufacturer. The material can be attached to wooden or PVC fence posts. The corner and end posts must be sturdy to maintain the approximately 250 pounds of tension in the wires.

Plastic fences

Plastic fence products are increasing in number as new applications and materials are identified. Many horse owners like the enhanced visibility and maintenance-free materials compared to more traditional electric or wood fencing. Some plastic fencing products initially had problems with material expansion and contraction with weather conditions causing rails to pop out of the posts. Some discoloration and brittleness occur with exposure to sunlight. Squeaks that occur during breezy conditions can spook unaccustomed horses. These are points that

should be discussed with fence manufacturers; design and material improvements are overcoming many of these problems.

Similar to PVC rigid board, plastic fences can become brittle and fragile at very cold temperatures.

Braided electric

Braided fence is highly visible and can be electrified. The fence material is a plastic or vinyl braided rope with copper or stainless steel strands incorporated into the weave. This allows electrification while preventing crimping and breakage of the wires. The braided rope is forgiving to a horse that runs into it, yet it will not break. The fence design creates a slippery surface that will allow a hoof or head, which may have gotten through the fence, to be removed easily without cutting the skin. Some manufacturers offer a 25-year guarantee.

Rubber and nylon fence

Reprocessed tires and conveyer belts form the raw material for rolls of nylon and rubber fence rails. It is one of the less expensive fencing options. Nylon and rubber fences can be used for paddock and riding arenas. They are visible and sturdy yet yielding upon horse impact making them safer fences. They can sag under pressure. Digestive impaction problems can result if curious horses chew the fence. Modern materials and careful installation have eliminated frayed threads, hazardous loose strands, and problems with material deterioration. But, when enclosing young horses or confirmed chewers, rubber or nylon is probably not the best choice because they may still try to eat the material.

The rubber fence construction follows a conventional four-rail wooden format with 4- inch, top round poles spaced 8 to 10 feet apart and rubber or nylon material that is 3/8 to 5/8 inches thick and 2½ to 3½ inches wide attached with nails or staples. The strips of rubber or nylon are stretched tightly between posts so corner and end posts need bracing. The minimal maintenance amounts to periodic tightening of any sagging rails. If the manufacturer has not sealed the rails to prevent frayed ends, use a propane torch to shrivel the nylon along the edges.

Fences to Avoid

Not all types of fencing materials are compatible with horses. Any fences or fencing products that could lead to injury to a horse or horse and rider need to be avoided at all costs.

Some fences to avoid are:
- **Barbed wire.** Barbed wire was designed to keep placid cattle within bounds on large tracts of land. The majority of horses never learn to stay away from barbed wire despite severe cuts from fence encounters. Savings in initial fence cost will be negated by veterinary bills. Barbed wire fencing is definitely not recommended for use with horses.
- **Stone walls.** Despite their elegant and traditional look, stone walls are unforgiving to any horse that tries to go through or over them. The cost of constructing new walls is prohibitive.
- **Snake fences.** Zigzag wooden enclosures may be picturesque, but they are easily pushed over due to their loose construction, or jumped over due to their low height. Pointed projecting rail ends are hazards; especially to horses cornered by pasture mates.
- **Wood fences with diamond or cross-patterned rails.** These fences provide narrow angles that can catch a horse's hoof or head.
- **Welded wire panels**. These panels should be avoided as long-term fencing because the wire can break at the welds from horses bumping, leaning, or kicking the panels. Injury to the horse can result due to the broken wires.

Fencing may seem costly, yet good fencing can be considered an enhancement of the property's value and will have a long lifetime of use. Cost savings can be realized by self-installation, buying fence materials in large lot sizes or shopping around for reasonably priced, locally available materials. Availability and prices for materials vary widely. Keep in mind that some types of fencing are difficult to install properly without specialized equipment, such as wire stretchers. Miles of fence installation will go faster with a tractor-driven post-hole driver. Books and fence material manufacturers are available to instruct in the details of construction.

Wood Posts

Many different types of materials, such as PVC and steel are used to make fence posts, but wood is still the most common type of post used for horse fences. Wood is fairly inexpensive and has good strength characteristics. Table 10-4 shows some comparative fence post characteristics. Suitable wooden fence posts are similar for board and wire mesh fence types. In addition, other fence types, such as high tensile wire, require appropriate post selection.

Posts can be round or square with round posts generally coming from tree stock

> The fence post is the foundation of the fence, so its importance cannot be over emphasized.

Table 10-4	Fence post characteristics.				
Post type	Bending strength	Expected life (years)	Initial cost	Fire resistance	Maintenance
Pressure treated wood	Good	30-35	Medium	Poor	Very low
Untreated wood	Good	7-15	Low	Poor	High
Steel-tee, concrete	Fair	25-30	Medium	Good	Low
Steel rod 5/8-inch diameter	Poor	15-20	Low	Good	Medium
Heavy duty fiberglass-tee	Fair (flexible)	25-30	High	Poor	Low
Light-duty fiberglass-tee	Poor (flexible)	15-20	Low	Poor	Medium

having a similar diameter. Square posts are milled to size, and the removal of wood from the original blank removes strength as well. Thus, a 4-inch round post is stronger than a 4-inch square post of the same lumber. Longer life is expected from round, pressure treated poles because the sapwood is easier to treat than the exposed heartwood of sawn square posts. Post life can be extended by treating the bottom end with rot retardant coating. Square posts, with their flat surfaces, make it easier to attach boards securely. Round posts can be slabbed on one or more sides, to make half- or quarter-round poles, to provide a flat surface for better board fastening.

The depth of set on posts for structural stability varies considerably with soil conditions. Past experience with area soils is useful in determining depth of set and the type of fill material (natural soil, another soil, or concrete) to be used around the post. A common line post depth is 36 inches. Corner and gate posts are required to handle more substantial loads. Because of the increased loading, corner and gate posts are about 25% larger in diameter and are set more deeply than line posts. Setting a corner post 48 inches deep or deeper in the ground is not uncommon. Because horse fences are typically 5 feet high, it is not uncommon to have post lengths of 8 feet for line posts and 9 feet for corner posts.

Pressure treated posts usually are the best investment. The preservative must be properly applied to be fully effective. Initially, treated posts appear more expensive than untreated ones. With the exception of a few wood types (Osage orange, western red cedar, western juniper heartwood, or black locust heartwood), untreated posts have only about one-quarter the useful life of treated ones. Depending on soil conditions and preservative treatment quality, a pressure treated post can last up to 35 years.

In particularly wet and heavy soils, preservative treated wood will help retard rot. In wet soils, fill the bottom 6 inches of the posthole with granular material such as sand or gravel to promote drainage and keep water away from the base of the post. (See *Appendix C. Wood Preservatives*).

The common element in virtually all good fences is well set posts. Setting posts properly is the most time-consuming and hardest part of fence building, but it is absolutely the most critical to the long-term success of the fence. Soil must be packed tightly around the post not only to secure the post properly, but also to keep both water and air away. Air and water can contribute to rotting of the post bottom. A properly tamped post can support fencing for 20 years or more.

Each post must be properly located. Holes are dug once the post locations are established. A minimum line post depth of 30 inches (preferably 36 inches deep) is needed to securely set an 8-foot post. Corner posts may need to be longer and set more deeply depending on the amount of pull on them by the wires. In colder areas where frost heave is a concern, bottoms of posts should be located below the regional frost depth. Contact the local extension service to determine the regional frost depth.

Setting posts represents the hardest work and the most time-consuming part of fence building and is absolutely the most critical to the long-term success of the fence.

Driven posts are more rigid and therefore recommended over handset posts or those set in pre-drilled holes. Driven posts are pounded into the ground through a combination of weight and impact by specialized equipment. The principle behind driven posts that makes them so secure is that the displaced soil is highly compacted around the post and thus resists post movement. Even for do-it-yourself projects, it is suggested that you contract the job of driving posts. Post driver equipment can be difficult to rent due to liability concerns. Under some dry, hard, or rocky soil conditions, a small-bore hole will be necessary for driven posts.

People who decide to dig and set their own posts must be careful to do it properly. The posthole itself should be at least twice but not more than three times the diameter of the post. A hole that is too narrow will have limited room to tamp effectively; a hole that is too wide means that too much tamped soil is needed to provide the most secure post.

When set in the hole, the post needs to be properly lined up on two different planes before tamping begins. A well placed post will have its center of gravity located directly over its base. The post must be vertical and on a line with the other posts. Ideally, when eyeballing the posts in a straight line fence, all posts should line up directly behind the first post in the line.

The most important part of setting posts is tightening the soil around the post in the ground. To tighten the soil around the post, the soil must be tamped. Tamping of the soil begins once the post is properly positioned and granular material, if any is needed, has been placed. Tamping can compress the soil by about 25%. The post will replace some of the removed soil volume, but depending on the size of the hole, extra soil may be needed for tamping the hole level full.

A tamping tool, or digging iron, of heavy metal or wood is used to compact the fill soil. Dump 4 to 6 inches of loose soil into the bottom of the hole around the base of the correctly positioned post and tamp it down until the soil is so solidly compacted that it cannot settle later. The tamped area will be much more solidly compacted than the surrounding soil. Push in another 4 to 6 inches of loose soil and repeat. Do not fill in the entire hole with loose soil before tamping because the soil at the base of the post will not be properly compacted. Improper tamping can lead to posts loosening, leaning, and eventually falling over.

Concrete also can be used in place of tamped soil to secure posts in the ground, especially posts that will be under high loads such as corner posts. The concrete provides more surface area to resist pulling out of the ground in addition to a larger base that helps lower the center of gravity, which aids in preventing the post from leaning under fence loads. Overall, concrete secures posts in the ground better than tamped soil does but is much more expensive.

Gates, Passages and Latches

Gates need to be durable and sturdy. Because horses are accustomed to passing through these locations, they will lean on and test gates. Gates should have at a minimum the same strength and safety as the fence. Fencing near gates needs to withstand the pressures of horses congregating around the gate, which means it needs to be sturdy, highly visible, and safe from trapping horse feet and heads.

Gates that are capable of swinging both into and out of the enclosure offer advantages when moving horses. In most horse operations, gates are located toward the middle of a fence line because horses are individually moved in and out of the enclosure. This eliminates the entrapment of horses in a corner near a gate. On operations where groups of horses are herded more often than individually led, gates positioned at corners will assist in moving them along the fence line and out of the enclosure.

Gates should be as tall as the fence to discourage horses from reaching over or attempting to jump the gate. Gates should be a minimum of 12 feet wide to allow easy passage of vehicles and tractors. Gates up to 16 feet wide may be needed in locations where larger machinery needs to pass through. Horse- and handler-only gates should be no less than 4 feet wide, with 5 feet preferred.

Gates are hung in order to swing freely and not sag over time. The post holding the swinging gate is responsible for maintaining this free-swinging action. This necessitates a deeply set post of a diameter larger than line posts. Gate hardware must withstand the challenges of leaning horses and years of use. A short post that the bottom edge of the gate rests on may be installed at the free gate end to diminish the pressure on the gate post and hinges when the gate is shut. A person should be able to unlock, swing open, shut, and lock a properly designed gate with only one hand so that the other hand is free.

Gates can be bought or built in as many styles as fence but do not have to be the same style as the fence. Most common materials are wood and steel tubes. Easy-to-assemble kits for wooden gates with all the hardware, including fasteners, braces, hinges and latches, can be bought from farm, lumber, or hardware stores.

Try to avoid gates with diagonal cross bracing as the narrow angles present traps to legs and feet and possibly heads. Cable supported gates offer a similar hazard to horses congregating around the gate. Some gates will have a wheel at the end to help support the gate, thus eliminating the need for diagonal cross bracing, Figure 10-8.

Tubular steel gates have 1½-inch outer diameter tubes that are rounded at the corners and have welded cross pipes for a smooth, sturdy, horse-safe gate. By contrast, the more flimsy channel-steel livestock gates are not recommended for horse use due to their less sturdy construction and numerous sharp edges. Either wooden or strong tubular steel, pre-formed gates are recommended for horses.

Gates that need to be opened often, opened while riding, or need to be opened or closed quickly should have easy-to-operate latches. Figure 10-9 shows an easy-to-open latch. Personnel passages are useful for chore time efficiency, Figure 10-10. Cattle guards or grates over holes are not recommended for use with horses because a horse's hoof could potentially become entrapped.

Gate latch.   Gate in closed position.

Figure 10-9 **Easy to open gate hardware.**
Lifting up on either one of the latches releases the gate. Gates are automatically locked by swinging the gate to the closed position where the latch will slide up once the gate's hardware strikes the latch and then fall back into place once the gate's hardware passes by the latch.

Figure 10-8 **Wheel used to support gate.**

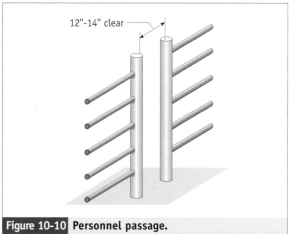

12"-14" clear

Figure 10-10 **Personnel passage.**

CHAPTER 11

Utilities

Utility needs for equine facilities can include electricity for lighting, heating, ventilating, and pumping water; water for washing and drinking; gas for heating; and domestic sewage treatment for restrooms. Plan for necessary utility service for new buildings and consider how the additional load from future expansion will change the total needs for the site. Work with the local utility provider, insurance company, licensed contractors, and local building officials to ensure that utilities are designed to provide the necessary services during normal operation as well as during times of drought, flood, high water usage, or power outages.

Electrical

Appropriate electrical wiring practices are often overlooked when remodeling or constructing equine facilities. Some electrical equipment is located in wet or damp areas such as wash racks or AI labs. The use of chemicals to aid in maintaining sanitary conditions and controlling disease make the wet environment even more corrosive.

Moisture, minerals in feed, and dust hasten deterioration of electrical components. Many equine buildings have been wired using practices and materials that cannot withstand these conditions. Some have electrical systems that have deteriorated to the point of creating dangerous situations.

Wiring methods and materials that minimize deterioration and maintain electrical safety and equipment function in agriculture-type facilities are described in the National Electrical Code® (NEC, National Fire Protection Association). Because equipment will fail, use equipment, wiring, and installation methods that will assure that the equipment fails safely.

The standard for electrical work in the United States is the NEC. The NEC is a standard for selection and safe installation of equipment and materials, and many insurance companies require electrical installations based on it. Article 547 in the NEC provides additional specific requirements for wiring in agricultural buildings, or any damp, corrosive environment. Proper design, selection, and installation of electrical systems for equine facilities are crucial to using electricity safely and efficiently. Improper wiring methods and inferior equipment cause hazardous conditions for humans and livestock, and often result in higher insurance premiums, increased maintenance costs, and greater risk of fire. The mere fact that an electrical system *works* doesn't mean it's safe or will *fail-safe*.

This section outlines general materials and methods for electrical equipment and wiring in equine facilities. It does not cover wiring from the power supplier to the buildings or sizing of building distribution panels. Electrical power requirements vary greatly depending on the size of the facility and the equipment used. Refer to the *Farm Buildings Wiring Handbook*, MWPS-28, for more detailed information on electrical service, wiring, circuits, equipment, grounding, and lightning protection.

Wiring

Most stables and arenas are structures that are not for human habitation nor are they places of employment where agricultural products are processed, treated, or packaged.

To ensure proper wiring, consult:
- The local power supplier to help plan and install the distribution system.
- A licensed electrician to help plan and install distribution panels and motor circuits, select conductors and fixtures, and verify compliance with state and local codes.
- Electrical equipment suppliers for dust- and moisture-tight fixtures and wiring required for damp and wet buildings. Plan ahead because some of this equipment may have to be ordered from electrical wholesale supply stores.
- Insurance companies to determine coverage requirements.
- Local building officials where applicable.

Following this definition, stables and arenas typically are considered agricultural buildings not used by the public.

Most buildings on horse farms have dust that is generated by using hay, straw, or dry feeds, but very rarely do these items generate dust levels similar to a grain elevator that could result in a potential explosive situation. Because these buildings will have some dust

Agricultural buildings are classified as:
- Dry, or buildings that are dry 100% of the time such as a heated tackroom or office; therefore, do not require special wiring materials (NEC 547-2).
- Damp, or buildings that require special materials and wiring methods, because high levels of moisture and corrosive dust and gas can quickly corrode standard electrical equipment. (NEC 547-1 (b)). Horse stalls and in particular wash stalls.
- Dusty, or buildings that have relatively high levels of explosive dust and therefore require special "dust-ignition-proof" materials and wiring methods (NEC 547-1 (a)). Grain elevators are structures that can create explosive dust levels.

and can at times have high humidity and/or have a wash area, these buildings should be designed as damp buildings.

Wherever possible, provide service through a single service entrance panel with enough circuit breakers to meet present needs and future expansion. If multiple service entrance/distribution panels are required to meet the needs of the installation, install a separate main disconnecting switch ahead of the multiple panels. Each distribution panel is then wired as a sub-panel from the main disconnect.

Article 547 of the National Electrical Code requires all electrical equipment used in livestock facilities to be corrosion resistant, waterproof, and dust-proof. Light fixtures must be watertight. Use only Type UF cable or appropriate conductors in non-metallic conduit. (See Tables 10-1 and 10-2.) Except for lights that are within reach of a horse in a box stall, surface mounting (i.e., not recessed into or concealed in walls or ceiling) of all electrical equipment is recommended. Electric wires should be in conduits so the horse cannot chew or rub against them, Figure 11-1. Some insurance companies require this type of mounting.

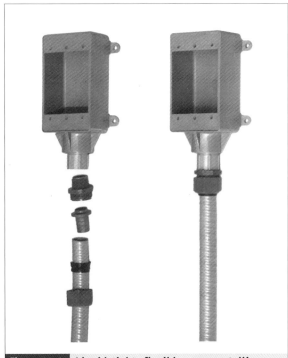

Figure 11-1 Liquid-tight, flexible, non-metallic, surface conduit.

Pay particular attention to the wiring length and the load it carries. Some equine buildings are quite long. If the service panel is located at one end of the building and fan motors are located on the other end, wiring must be sized to limit the voltage drop. Large voltage drops will cause motors to run hot and eventually shorten the life of the motor. Use Tables 11-1 and 11-2, and Figure 11-2 for sizing service conductors based on electrical load and

Table 11-1 Minimum copper conductor size for UF-B and NM-B cable branch circuits (American Wire Gauge (AWG)).

Conductor length is one way. Use for individual circuits and for general-purpose circuits that do not meet the criteria in *Figure 11-2*. Based on the conductor ampacity or 2% voltage drop, whichever is limiting. Do not use Type NM-B cable in damp or wet locations. Use Type UF cable in wet or damp locations because it is moisture resistant and allows use of watertight connectors and fittings at box connections (NEC Article 547-4).

120 V service

Load (amps)	Conductor length (feet)									
	30	40	50	60	75	100	125	150	175	200
5	12	12	12	12	12	12	12	10	10	10
7	12	12	12	12	12	12	10	10	8	8
10	12	12	12	12	10	10	8	8	8	6
15	12	12	10	10	10	8	6	6	6	4
20	12	10	10	8	8	6	6	4	4	4
25	10	10	8	8	6	6	4	4	4	3
30	10	8	8	8	6	4	4	4	3	2
35	8	8	8	6	6	4	4	3	2	2
40	8	8	6	6	4	4	3	2	2	1
45	6	6	6	6	4	4	3	2	1	1
50	6	6	6	4	4	3	2	1	1	1/0
60	4	4	4	4	4	2	1	1	1/0	2/0
70	4	4	4	4	3	2	1	1/0	2/0	2/0
80	3	3	3	3	2	1	1/0	2/0	2/0	3/0
90	2	2	2	2	2	1	1/0	2/0	3/0	3/0
100	1	1	1	1	1	1/0	2/0	3/0	3/0	4/0

240 V service

Load (amps)	Conductor length (feet)									
	50	60	75	100	125	150	175	200	225	250
5	12	12	12	12	12	12	12	12	12	12
7	12	12	12	12	12	12	12	12	10	10
10	12	12	12	12	12	10	10	10	10	8
15	12	12	12	10	10	10	8	8	8	6
20	12	12	10	10	8	8	8	6	6	6
25	10	10	10	8	8	6	6	6	6	4
30	10	10	10	8	6	6	6	4	4	4
35	8	8	8	8	6	6	4	4	4	4
40	8	8	8	6	6	4	4	4	4	3
45	6	6	6	6	6	4	4	4	3	3
50	6	6	6	6	4	4	4	3	3	2
60	4	4	4	4	4	4	3	2	2	1
70	4	4	4	4	4	3	2	2	1	1
80	3	3	3	3	3	2	2	1	1	1/0
90	2	2	2	2	2	2	1	1	1/0	1/0
100	1	1	1	1	1	1	1	1/0	1/0	2/0

Table 11-2 Minimum copper conductor size for THW, THWN, RHW, and XHHW branch circuits (American Wire Gauge (AWG)).

For moisture-and heat-resistant thermoplastic (THW and THWN) and rubber (RHW) wire, and flame retardant cross-linked synthetic polymer (XHHW) wire. Conductor length is one way. Use for individual circuits and for general-purpose circuits that do not meet the criteria in *Figure 11-2*. Based on conductor ampacity or 2% voltage drop, whichever is limiting.

120 V service

Load (amps)	Conductor length (feet)									
	30	40	50	60	75	100	125	150	175	200
5	12	12	12	12	12	12	12	10	10	10
7	12	12	12	12	12	12	10	10	8	8
10	12	12	12	12	10	10	8	8	8	6
15	12	12	10	10	10	8	6	6	6	4
20	12	10	10	8	8	6	6	4	4	4
25	10	10	8	8	6	6	4	4	4	3
30	10	8	8	8	6	4	4	4	3	2
35	8	8	8	6	6	4	4	3	2	2
40	8	8	6	6	4	4	3	2	2	1
45	8	8	6	6	4	4	3	2	1	1
50	8	6	6	4	4	3	2	1	1	1/0
60	6	6	4	4	4	2	1	1	1/0	2/0
70	4	4	4	4	3	2	1	1/0	2/0	2/0
80	4	4	4	3	2	1	1/0	2/0	2/0	3/0
90	3	3	3	3	2	1	1/0	2/0	3/0	3/0
100	3	3	3	2	1	1/0	2/0	3/0	3/0	4/0

240 V service

Load (amps)	Conductor length (feet)									
	50	60	75	100	125	150	175	200	225	250
5	12	12	12	12	12	12	12	12	12	12
7	12	12	12	12	12	12	12	12	10	10
10	12	12	12	12	12	10	10	10	10	8
15	12	12	12	10	10	10	8	8	8	6
20	12	12	10	10	8	8	8	6	6	6
25	10	10	10	8	8	6	6	6	6	4
30	10	10	10	8	6	6	6	4	4	4
35	8	8	8	8	6	6	4	4	4	4
40	8	8	8	6	6	4	4	4	4	3
45	8	8	8	6	6	4	4	4	3	3
50	8	8	6	6	4	4	4	3	3	2
60	6	6	6	4	4	4	3	2	2	1
70	4	4	4	4	4	3	2	2	1	1
80	4	4	4	4	3	2	2	1	1	1/0
90	3	3	3	3	3	2	1	1	1/0	1/0
100	3	3	3	3	2	1	1	1/0	1/0	2/0

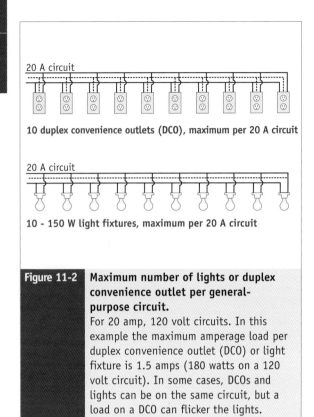

20 A circuit

10 duplex convenience outlets (DCO), maximum per 20 A circuit

20 A circuit

10 - 150 W light fixtures, maximum per 20 A circuit

Figure 11-2	**Maximum number of lights or duplex convenience outlet per general-purpose circuit.**

For 20 amp, 120 volt circuits. In this example the maximum amperage load per duplex convenience outlet (DCO) or light fixture is 1.5 amps (180 watts on a 120 volt circuit). In some cases, DCOs and lights can be on the same circuit, but a load on a DCO can flicker the lights.

distance. Voltage drop exceeding 5% causes dimming of lights, a shortened life of motors, controllers, and other equipment. Voltage drop is also a major source of *stray* voltage.

A common mistake in many horse barns is not to provide enough receptacle outlets. There should be at least one duplex outlet for every two stalls. A duplex outlet should be located in a barn so that a 100-foot cord can reach any location in the barn. Feed and tack rooms should have an outlet positioned a minimum of every 12 feet along the wall.

If an artificial insemination (AI) laboratory or an office area that will hold pharmaceuticals or purchased semen is planned, provide dedicated circuits to ensure proper climate control. AI labs often have the appearance of a small kitchen and should be wired to support the electrical load that may be added due to the use of counter top equipment used for processing collected semen or preparing for insemination of mares. Provide for either gas or electrical water heater needs. Consider providing air conditioning. Provide power for

computers and printers for record keeping that may be done in the AI lab. All circuits should be wired with ground-fault circuit interrupts (GFCI). Due to the expensive nature of some semen processing and storage equipment, provide surge suppression and lightning arrestors to prevent equipment damage. Any circuit near wash racks should also be GFCI protected.

Lighting

Light is necessary for chores, observation, and maintenance throughout all buildings. Light is important to the horse's physical and psychological well-being. Exposure to natural sunlight synthesizes Vitamin D_3, or more specifically cholecalciferol, in horses. Cholecalciferol is important in bone growth and strength, and in the regulation of calcium and phosphorus.

Natural light

Windows provide light and in some systems essential ventilation. Horses that have a window to look out from their box stall seem to be more content, but having a window in each box stall is not always practical and can be expensive. For adequate natural light, a minimum of 1 square foot of window area per 30 square feet of barn floor area is needed. Recommended window sizes for box stalls are one 2- x 3-foot window per 12- x 12-foot box stall in a building with a 10-foot wide alley between box stalls.

Windows used in box stalls should face the brightest light and prevailing summer breezes, and face away from cold winter winds. Use bottom hinged windows that open inward to reduce drafts. Sliding and jalousie windows can also be used. Protect window glass from horses by placing metal bars or wire mesh on the inside. Make the guards removable for cleaning windows.

Window height varies depending on how well windows are protected. Bottom hinged windows need to be located out of a horse's reach, which is usually a minimum of 8 feet above the floor. Sliding or jalousie type windows with bars are well protected so they can be located lower on the wall to allow horses to see out of them. Usually these windows are located a minimum of 4 feet and preferably 6 feet above the floor.

Translucent panels such as translucent fiberglass reinforced plastic panels can be used as a replacement for windows for natural light. These panels can be installed along walls, along eaves, or in the roof. Large areas of glass or translucent panels exposed to direct sunlight increase the solar heat gain in the summer and increase the chance for condensation and frost in cold weather. Translucent panels in the roof tend to develop leaks. If translucent panels are used as windows, make sure they can be opened for ventilation.

Artificial light

Position stall switches on the outside of stalls to prevent electrocution and the horse switching it on and off. Install switches protected against a horse's bite to avoid electrocution. Recessed or out of the way fixtures are preferred for safety in areas of horse traffic. Install lights with dust and moisture shields. Recessed lights flush with the ceiling are ideal for ceilings 10-feet or less in height. Reflectors increase brightness.

Use covered switch plate controls for aisle lights and any outdoor floodlights. Provide covered outlets outside; they are also safer indoors. A three-way switch can control lights from both ends of an alley and flood lights from the barn and the house.

Three types of lights are common in horse facilities. Each type has individual properties of light output, maintenance, color, efficiency, and cost that affect selection for a particular task. All lighting fixtures must be moisture tight. The three main types of lights are:

- **Incandescent.** These lights are used in areas where lights are turned on and off frequently. While more expensive to operate, their initial cost is relatively low and they operate well in most conditions including low temperatures. Provide dust- and water-tight fixtures with a heat resistant globe to cover the bulb.
- **Fluorescent.** Fluorescent fixtures cost more than incandescent but produce three to four times more light/watt (lumens/W).

Turning these lights on and off frequently reduces lamp life. Fluorescent lights are a good choice where the on time will be at least one hour per cycle. Typical residential fluorescent lights are mainly limited to indoor use because they are temperature sensitive. Standard indoor lights perform well down to 50°F; with special ballasts, down to -20°F. Relative humidity of 65% or higher makes fluorescent tubes difficult to start. Use fiberglass enclosures with gasketed Lexan (REG) covers on all fluorescent lights.

Select fixtures designed for corrosive industrial environments equipped with cold-start ballasts. Fixtures made of ABS plastic and equipped with acrylic diffusers generally do not hold up well in the environment of agricultural buildings. Fluorescent lights are available in 4- and 8-foot tubes or compact versions. Compact tubes are good for retrofitting an incandescent system with fluorescents.

- **High intensity discharge (HID).** Metal halide, high-pressure sodium, and mercury vapor lights are part of a group of energy efficient long-lasting, high intensity discharge lights. They are used to light large areas such as arenas, or in outdoor security lamps, for extended periods of time. They are mounted 10 to 18 feet high. HID lamps require time to start and warm up before becoming fully lit. Start time varies from lamp to lamp, but the average warm-up time is 2 to 6 minutes. HID lamps also have a restrike time, which means the lamp cannot restart for several minutes (5 to 15 minutes) after a momentary power interruption that extinguishes the lamp.

Metal halide lights put out a fairly white light with a CCT (correlated color temperature) value up to 5,000 K and CRI (color rendering index) values up to 80%. Their use in horse facilities is growing. High-pressure sodium lights put out a gold or yellowish light with a CCT value up 2,700 K and CRI values up to 60%. The lower CCT and CRI values can lead to some color distortion. High-pressure sodium lights are widely used for outdoor security lighting. Mercury vapor lights give off a bluish light and have been used commonly as yard lights. They are not recommended for use in horse facilities because the mercury in burned-out lights is an environmental hazard; they are less energy efficient than other HID options; their output decreases with time; and their CRI values are lower than the CRI values of other options.

The type of lighting that is most satisfactory for stables is the fluorescent tube with a cold weather ballast for quick start up in cold weather. A protective covering over the tube provides dust and moisture protection and makes the fluorescent bulbs safer for use in stall areas or feed rooms. If a tube breaks, the glass particles are retained inside the plastic cover that surrounds the bulb.

Light levels and locations

Most equine facilities have inadequate lighting with little thought given to appropriate lamp placement. When lights are put in stalls, they should be out of horse reach (10

feet or more) or recessed or have unbreakable covers. Stalls and alleyways should be well lit with at least 30- to 40-foot-candles of light output. Riding rings should be lit with a uniform light pattern that eliminates dark spots and shadows.

Good lighting is a combination of quality, quantity and color. Quality of light requires freedom of glare, control of shadows, and the absence of sharp differences between light objects and their background. Glare causes discomfort, which can be reduced by shading the light source or placing the light well above eye level. Many of the newer HID or quartz incandescent lights provide more light than the older types. If the electrical circuit is broken they require a start up time, which should be taken into account if the barn or riding arena is used as a public facility at night. A barn that contains 10 or more horses requires a 200-amp service, which allows an adequate number of lights and additional circuits.

Proper lighting levels allow efficient animal inspection. Table 11-3 provides recommended minimum levels for different phases of the operation. In the animal area, space

Table 11-3 Light levels for equine facilities.

Task	Level of illumination (foot-candles)[a]	Recommended light	Explanation
Arena	30 to 40	High intensity, cold-weather ballast fluorescent light with protective cover.	Required for safety of the operator in moving about readily and safely.
Stalls and alleys	30 to 40	Fluorescent in alleys if at least 10 to 12 feet high. Incandescent if recessed or with a protective cover in stalls, or fluorescent in stalls with 9-foot high ceilings.	Required to observe the condition of the horse or foal and to detect hazards to the horse and operator. Portable supplementary lighting units can be used to examine or treat horses or foals when required.
Veterinary or farrier area	40 to 50	Fluorescent with protective cover.	Required to observe the condition of the horse or foal and to detect hazards to the horse and operator.
Feed storage/ processing	20	Incandescent or fluorescent	Required for safety of the operator in moving about. Need to read labels and scales.
Tack room	30	Incandescent or fluorescent	Required for safety of the operator in moving about readily and safely.
Wash rack	30 to 40	Incandescent or fluorescent with protective cover	Required to observe the condition of the horse and to detect hazards to the horse and operator.
Office or AI lab	70[b]	Incandescent or fluorescent	General lighting for cleanliness, inspection, and sanitation.
Restrooms	30 to 40	Incandescent or fluorescent	—

[a] To determine lumen equivalency, one lumen (lm) is equal to one foot-candle (fc) for each square foot of surface.
[b] Additional under cabinet lighting should be provided for counter work. Work area lighting should be approximately 100 foot-candles.

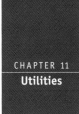

As a general rule:

- Provide a minimum of 100-watt incandescent bulb or 40-watt fluorescent fixtures per stall.
- Lights mounted on walls or the ceiling should be out of horses' reach with wiring running up to the ceiling.
- Use fluorescent fixtures in alleys, tack room, feed room, etc., because they are brighter and more efficient than incandescent. Provide about one, 2-tube 40-watt fluorescent per 100 to 150 sq ft of floor area.
- Use cold-start fluorescents if stable temperatures are expected to be below 50°F
- Use mercury halide lights in a stable or arena with high ceilings (at least 16 feet to diffuse evenly). These are even more efficient and several times brighter than fluorescent, so fewer fixtures are needed. Less wiring is needed, but the fixtures cost more. These lights take a long time to warm up, especially in cold weather.

incandescent lights at twice their mounting height and 1.5 times their mounting height in alleys. White walls and ceilings improve light levels and are especially useful in areas where animals are inspected frequently.

Place ceiling-mounted fixtures so they are not in the direct path of the jet leaving the air inlets. Improperly placed lights can deflect air preventing proper distribution through the room.

Electric Motors

Use totally enclosed, farm-duty rated motors on equipment subject to dust and moisture accumulation. Use totally enclosed, air-over motors for ventilating fans—the air stream cools the motor.

Provide overload protection for motors in addition to the circuit breakers or fuses. Also, install a fused switch with a time delay fuse at each fan sized at 125% of the motor's full load current. Locate the fused switch within 10 feet of the controlled motor or fan. Wire each ventilating fan on a separate circuit so that, if one circuit fails, fans on another circuit will

come on in response to thermostat settings and changes in room temperatures. See *The National Electrical Code Handbook* and *Farm Buildings Wiring Handbook,* MWPS-28, for specific wiring requirements.

Lightning Protection

Install lightning arrestors at electrical service entrances to control voltage surges on electrical wiring. Provide a lightning arrestor at each service panel. Always mount arrestors on the outside of panels. Because arrestors can explode and discharge a shower of sparks due to a nearby intense lightning strike, mount lightning arrestors outside the building if possible. If mounted directly on an inside panel, the surrounding area must be kept free of combustible materials to reduce the risk of fire.

Install surge or spike arrestors to provide additional protection for electronic equipment such as semen processing equipment, computers, and any other equipment that can be severely damaged by a power surge.

Lightning protection for buildings is usually a system of lightning rods with metal conductors attached to several grounds. Install lightning rods 20 feet on center and within 2 feet of the ends of a gable roof. Fasten the metal conductors to the roof and walls at 3- to 4-foot intervals. Use aluminum lightning rod cable on buildings clad with aluminum roofing or siding. Use copper cables within 18 inches of the soil and wherever the cable will be against painted or galvanized steel. Special fittings are available and should be used to interconnect aluminum and copper cables and control corrosion.

Drive the ground rod at least 8 feet into moist earth. Locate the ground rod at least 2 feet away from the building. A location at or beyond the eave or drip line is desirable. Install both the ground rod and cable at least 8 inches beneath the soil surface to minimize the risk of equipment damage. Keep lightning rod ground rods at least 6 feet away from the electrical system ground rods.

Metal clad buildings with a continuous connection between roofing and siding can be partially protected by grounding the siding unless there is flammable insulation directly beneath the roofing. Install at least two grounding cables (on opposite corners) on metal clad buildings up to 250 feet long—add another cable for each additional 100 feet of length or fraction thereof.

It should be noted however, that most insurance companies require lightning rods on metal clad buildings as well. Make sure the lightning protection installer has qualified for Underwriter's Laboratories *Master Label* designation. Use only UL listed equipment when installing a lightning protection system.

Electrical Safety

All electrical installation should be done according to the *NFPA National Electrical Code (NEC)*, published by and registered trademark of the National Fire Protection Association (NFPA). Article 547-Agricultural Buildings specifies proper wiring methods for livestock confinement buildings. Even though many agriculture-type buildings do not presently fall under code jurisdiction, it is a good idea to follow *NEC*. Insurance companies often require an installation that meets *NEC* standards for approval. Before starting construction, check to see if a wiring permit is required. The *Farm Buildings Wiring Handbook*, MWPS-28 is another good source of wiring information that is directly related to agricultural applications.

Grounding

A grounding electrode is required at the main service for each building Figures 11-3 and 11-4. Rods 8 feet long (minimum) are commonly used, but the NEC permits several other methods. (See NEC Article 250-81.) Resistance from a single grounding electrode to surrounding soil must be 25 ohms or less (NEC Article 250-84). If a second rod is installed to reduce the resistance, multiple rods should be spaced at least twice the length of the ground rods (e.g., two 8-foot rods should be at least 16 feet apart) and interconnected with a copper conductor and ground rod clamps approved for direct burial, Figure 11-5.

The grounded service conductor (neutral) must be connected to the grounding electrode with a properly sized grounding electrode

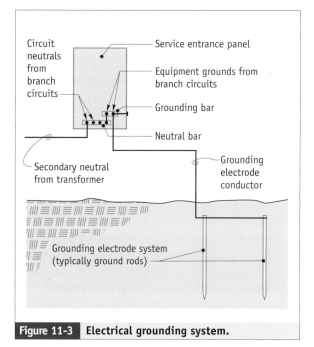

Figure 11-3 Electrical grounding system.

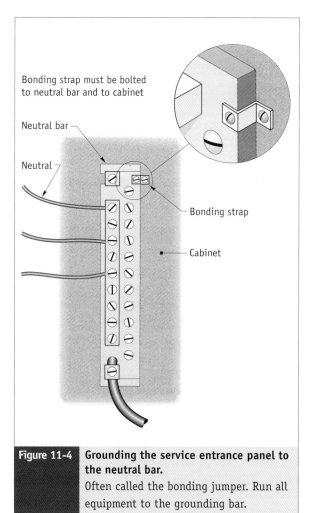

Figure 11-4 Grounding the service entrance panel to the neutral bar.

Often called the bonding jumper. Run all equipment to the grounding bar.

conductor to provide system grounding, Table 11-1. (**Note:** With a four-wire service, the grounding electrode conductor is attached to the grounding bus, not the neutral bus.) The grounding electrode conductor must be protected from physical damage and must be continuous. If splicing is required, only nonreversible splices, e.g., compression connectors, are permitted.

Grounded conductors carry current during the normal operation of 115-volt equipment. They must have white or gray identification (insulation color if size No. 6 or smaller, or

tape for larger gauge conductors). They also carry fault current from the building service equipment to the transformer because of the bonding to the grounding conductors in the distribution panel (in a single-phase, three-wire service).

Grounding conductors are intended to carry current only under fault conditions and are commonly referred to as the *grounding* wire. Grounding conductor size is based on the circuit overcurrent protection rating. The NEC requires that grounding conductors be bare or be identified with green or green with yellow stripe insulation (size No. 6 or smaller, NEC Article 310-12) or markings. All new wiring in agricultural complexes must include a copper equipment-grounding conductor (NEC Article 547-8(c)) as part of the circuit. Equipment such as motors or electrically heated waterers must be grounded by means of this equipment-grounding conductor, Figure 11-6.

Installing a ground rod at such equipment as a substitute for an equipment-grounding conductor is not permitted (NEC Article 250-51), but a ground rod may be installed as a supplement to the grounding conductor. The grounded and grounding conductors are permitted to be interconnected only at the service equipment (NEC Article 250-23). The *Farm Building Wiring Handbook,* MWPS-28, has many circuit diagrams showing the proper connection and separation of the grounded and grounding conductors.

Standby Power

Most horse operations do not need standby power. Large breeding facilities or racetracks that need to have electrical power to operate fans, heaters, or other important equipment

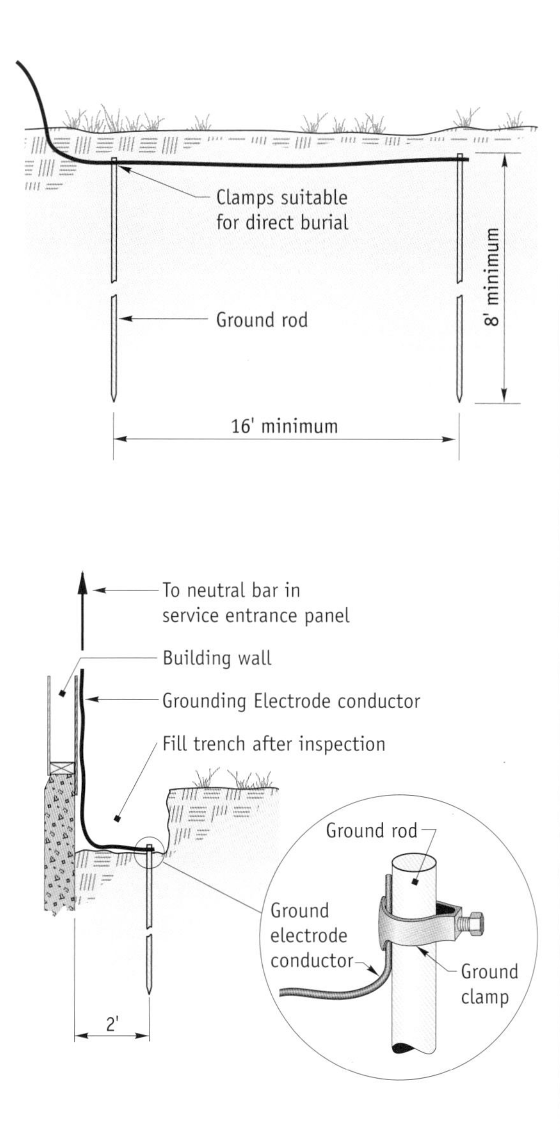

Figure 11-5 Ground rod installation.

A standby power system requires:
- A transfer switch to isolate the system from power supply lines.
- A generator or alternator to produce alternating current.
- A stationary engine or tractor PTO to run the generator.

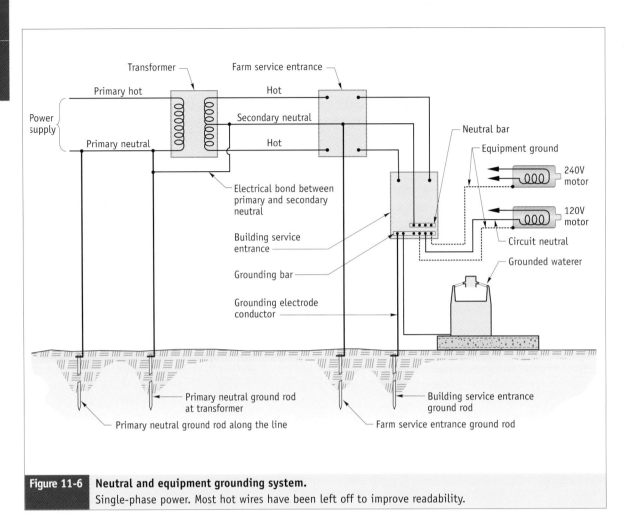

Figure 11-6 **Neutral and equipment grounding system.**
Single-phase power. Most hot wires have been left off to improve readability.

should consider installing standby power generators to operate necessary equipment during power outages.

Select either a full- or a partial-load system. A full-load system must handle the maximum running load and peak-starting load of the facility. A partial-load system carries only enough load to handle vital needs and is usually controlled manually. The maximum running load and peak-starting load should include at least feed processing, ventilation, and water delivery. For a partial-load system, sum the starting wattage of the largest essential motor, running wattage of all other essential motors, name plate wattage of essential equipment, and wattage of essential lights. When sizing standby electric generators, consider the power requirements of future expansion and equipment needs.

Tractor-driven generators are common and are generally the most economical. During heavy snowfall conditions, getting the tractor to the generator can be a problem. If short duration outages are critical, consider an engine-driven unit with automatic switching. Operate engine-driven units at least once a week and tractor-driven units every month to ensure they will function when needed. Operate the generator or alternator long enough and with sufficient load to cause it to warm to normal operating temperature; this will keep the battery charged on engine-driven units and ensures starting when needed.

Install a double throw transfer switch at the main service entrance just after the meter so the generator is always isolated from incoming power lines. This switch keeps generated power from feeding back over the supply lines, protects power line repair crews, and prevents generator damage when power is restored. Contact the power supplier for assistance in sizing and installing a transfer switch.

Refer to *Farm Buildings Wiring Handbook,* MWPS-28 for more information on the safe use and operation of standby power units.

Alarm Systems

Use alarms to warn of high or low temperatures, power outages, fire, smoke, and other potentially dangerous situations. Alarm systems signal the need for attention to a situation and may prevent horse losses. Systems are commercially available.

Most alarms respond to power failure, but the thermostat-controlled alarm does not sound until conditions in the building are critical. Check dry-cell batteries periodically and replace if needed. Keep wet-cell batteries charged with a trickle-charger; and check the water level frequently. Systems and components should be designed to withstand the environment inside the stable and comply with NEC Article 547.

Common alarm system options include:
- Relay switch controlled, battery powered.
- Solenoid valve controlled, compressed gas horn.
- Thermostat controlled, battery powered.
- Automatic phone dialers.
- Pagers.
- 24-hr commercial monitoring service.

Water

Horses need water to function properly. Horses lose water primarily in urine, feces, sweat, and respiration. Horses replace lost water mainly from drinking but also from feeds and from oxidation of food during metabolism. Water intake of horses depends on many factors, including environmental temperature, water temperature, the activity level

of the horse, production stage of the horse, and type and amount of feed.

This section will discuss:
- Water quality
- Quantity and short-term water storage
- Water distribution

Water Quality

Water quality characteristics can greatly affect consumption, and a contaminated water supply may pose health problems for both people and animals. Characteristics that influence water quality include pH, salinity, nitrates, nitrites, toxic inorganic chemicals, organic toxins and microbial contamination, Table 11-4. Safety characteristics of water sources are listed in Table 11-5. Table 11-6 contains the recommendations for total dissolved solids (TDS) in water for horses, while Table 11-7 provides a more detailed breakdown on TDS based on activity level.

Some states require at least an annual analysis to verify water quality. Even if testing is not required, it is a good practice to test the water supply on an annual basis to check its quality because most incidents of poor water quality present no visible signs.

Table 11-4	Recommended limits of potentially toxic substances in livestock drinking water.
Substance	Safe upper concentration limit, mg/l Council of Agricultural Science and Technology (CAST)[a]
Arsenic	0.50
Boron	10.0
Cadmium	0.50
Chromium	5.00
Cobalt	1.00
Copper	0.50
Fluoride	3.00
Iron	NE
Lead	0.10
Mercury	0.01
Nickel	NE
Nitrate	1,320
Nitrite	33.0
Selenium	0.10
Vanadium	1.00
Zinc	25.0

[a] Report No. 26, Quality of Water for Livestock, 1974.

Table 11-5 Safety characteristics of water sources.

Water treatment may be needed to remove undesirable minerals.

Source	Primary uses	Safety	Treatment usually recommended to be safe for DOMESTIC use
Drilled well (properly located)	Domestic and livestock	Usually best of all sources	None, unless subject to contamination
Dug, jetted, driven, or bored well	Domestic and livestock	Subject to contamination	Automatic chlorination
Spring	Domestic and livestock	Subject to contamination	Automatic chlorination
Cistern (untreated water)	Domestic, livestock, and fire protection	Subject to contamination	Automatic chlorination and filtration
Farm pond	Livestock and fire protection	Subject to contamination	Automatic chlorination and filtration
Stream or lake	Livestock and fire protection	Subject to contamination	Stream not recommended for domestic use without extensive treatment
Controlled catchment	Domestic and livestock	Subject to contamination	Automatic chlorination and filtration
Hauled water	Domestic	Good if hauled from safe source in safe containers	None if safely stored, but chlorination is desirable
Community water system	Domestic, livestock, and fire protection	Good if properly maintained	None by user, but if stored underground, chlorinate

Table 11-6 Guideline for use of saline waters for horses.

Adapted from National Academy of Sciences, 1974, and *Livestock and Water*, AS954, Lardy, G. and Stoltenow, C. NDSU Extension Service, North Dakota State University of Agriculture and Applied Science, July 1999.

Total dissolved solids, (ppm)	Recommendations
less than 1,000	These waters should be satisfactory for horses.
1,000 to 3,000	Very satisfactory for horses. May cause temporary mild diarrhea in horses not accustomed to it. Low palatability.
3,000 to 5,000	Generally satisfactory. Temporary diarrhea and water refusal initially when horses not accustomed to them. May cause increased water consumption.
5,000 to 7,000	May be used with reasonable safety for horses, but should be avoided for pregnant or lactating mares, especially as the levels approach 7,000 ppm.
7,000 to 10,000	Considerable risks may exist with pregnant or lactating mares, or with horses subjected to heat stress, water loss, or disease conditions.
greater than 10,000	Unsuitable for horses.

Table 11-7 Recommended levels of dissolved solids for horses.

Adapted from *Livestock and Water*, AS954, Lardy, G. and Stoltenow, C. NDSU Extension Service, North Dakota State University of Agriculture and Applied Science, July 1999.

Activity level	Dissolved solids (ppm)				
	Excellent	Good	Fair	Poor	Limit
Working	0 to 1,000	1,000 to 2,000	2,000 to 3,000	3,000 to 5,000	6,000
Others	0 to 1,000	1,000 to 2,000	2,000 to 4,000	4,000 to 6,000	10,000

Coliform counts in water are an indication of the level of sanitation of the water. Coliforms, reported in coliforms per 100 milliliters (ml), indicate the presence of organic contamination in the water supply and may indicate the presence of pathogens.

The U.S. EPA in 1973 proposed that acceptable limitations for water used by livestock should not exceed 5,000 coliforms per 100 ml. A veterinarian or water quality expert should be consulted if bacteria are found in the water supply.

Treatment to improve water quality includes four methods: filters, reverse osmosis units, softeners, and chlorination. Generally, reverse osmosis units and water softeners are not cost effective for horse facilities.

Filters can remove dirt, sediment, and odors. They do not purify or soften water but only remove some dissolved organic compounds and suspended particles.

Chlorination is used to disinfect water. Proper disinfecting may be influenced by the presence of organic matter, water temperature, and time of contact between the microorganisms and the chlorine. Shock chlorination of wells may be done to disinfect the well overnight and flush the system. For continued chlorination, systems are available that add chlorine pellets to the well on a periodic basis. Contact a water treatment company for details.

Refer to *Private Water Systems Handbook*, MWPS-14, for additional information on water sources and quality.

Quantity and Storage

Having an ample and reliable water supply is very important, especially for larger horse facilities. A water well system's pressure tank provides a small amount of storage. The storage volume is usually 10 to 30% of the tank size, which provides small amounts of water without starting the pump. If a facility does not have access to a reliable supply of water other than the small amount stored in the pressure tank, some type of intermediate water storage should be considered to ensure that enough water is available for peak use times.

If an intermediate water storage is needed for fire protection, size a tank to provide 1,200 to 6,000 gallons of water to maintain 10 to 50 gpm of water flow for two hours; otherwise, the tank should be sized for its peak use capacity. Peak use capacity usually takes place when many activities occur simultaneously, such as water consumption, washing horses, washing stalls and vehicles, and even having enough water available for fire protection. Knowing facility water usage is essential to adequately size an intermediate water storage.

The first, and most important concern, is to supply water to the horses for consumption. The type and amount of feed, or more specifically dry matter intake, affects water consumption. The water content of feeds varies from fresh young grass with 70 to 80% water to hay and stored grains at 10%. Horses require about 1 to 2 quarts of water per pound of dry matter consumed—the greater the fiber content, the greater the excretion of water. Increased ash or mineral intake increases the amount of water needed. A 1,100-pound horse typically drinks 8 to 12 gallons of water per day. Smaller animals such as horses up to two years old and ponies typically drink 6 to 8 gallons of water per day. A horse can increase its water consumption by 15 to 20% when its environmental temperature increases from 55°F to 70°F. Table 11-8 shows some typical water consumption values for horses.

The activity level of a horse also dictates its water consumption. A moderate working horse can increase its water consumption by 60 to 80%, and a hard working horse by 120%, above the needs of a resting horse. The production stage of the horse also factors into its need for water. A mare in the last third of its gestation cycle drinks 8 to 10% more water than a non-pregnant mare. Because mare's milk is about 90% water, a lactating mare needs to drink more water, which can amount to an additional 50 to 70% more water depending on milk production. When no good information is available and a horse's activity level does not fit into one of the categories of Table 11-8, a rough rule-of-thumb for estimating

An intermediate water storage should be considered under these conditions:
- Water source and pressure tank cannot deliver the required peak flow rate.
- Water sources do not sufficiently meet peak two-hour capacity (the largest volume of water needed in any two hours).
- Standby power is not available. In this instance, elevate the water storage tank for gravity feed to waterers.

Table 11-8 **Estimated water intake per 1,100-pound horse.**

Environmental temperature 60 to 70°F.

Activity	Water Consumption (gallons per day)
Non-working	4-8
Gestation	7-9
Peak lactation	9-11
Medium work	9-15
Heavy work	12-15

Table 11-9 **Estimated water usage and flowrate.**

Environmental temperature 60 to 70°F.

Use	Flowrate (gpm)	Water Consumption (gallons)
Adult or child	—	50-100 per day
Automatic washer— (large farms)	5	30-50 per load
Automatic waterers	0.5-2 gpm	—
Bathroom lavatory	2	1-2 per use
Cleaning and manure removal for horse barn	5-10	—
Cleaning hose — horse wash stall	3-5	—
Fire protection[a]	10	1,200 per 2-hr period
Outdoor hydrant for uses other than firefighting	3-5	—
Outside hose faucet	5	—
Shower or tub[c] (in stable)	5	25-50 per use
Sink[b] (in stable)	3	2-4 per use
Toilet flush[c] (in stable)	3	4-7 per use
Water fountain	½	—
Water softener regeneration[d]	5	50-100 per time

[a] Absolute minimum for limited fire fighting at least 10 gpm with a ¼-inch nozzle at 30 psi for two hours per day; preferred minimum is 20 gpm at 60 psi or a total of 2,400 gallons per two-hour period.
[b] Water flow restricting valves and showerheads can reduce flow and water usage by up to 50%.
[c] Older toilet. Newer low flow toilets will reduce usage by 40% to 50%.
[d] Water usage can vary greatly depending on many factors including water hardness and softener size.

water consumption is that a horse will consume about one gallon of water per day per 100-pounds of body weight.

Water usage for other areas of a farm can vary greatly making estimating difficult, Table 11-9. Flushing gutters and washing down a stable can require 20 gallons of water per day. A toilet can require 6 gallons per flush for an older toilet, while newer toilets use 3 gallons per flush or less. A shower can use 2.5 to 5.0 gallons per minute of use. Fire protection

requires large quantities of water that need to be available on short notice.

Intermediate water storages are usually concrete, fiberglass, plastic, or steel tanks. Protect the storage from contamination. When the water source can deliver the required flow rate the majority of the time, size the intermediate water storage for two hours of peak flow.

A two-pump system commonly is used for intermediate water storage when the water source and pressure tank cannot deliver the required peak flow rate, Figure 11-7. The first pump (usually the well pump) has a low level cut-off and a capacity slightly less than the water source's production level to prevent pumping the source dry. This pump fills an intermediate water storage with water for peak use periods. A second pump draws the water from the intermediate water storage and forces it into a pressure tank. Size the second pump to provide the peak use flow rate. If the water source tends to decrease or dry up for short periods, size the storage to meet the operation's minimum requirement for one day's total water usage.

Distribution

Plumbing for horse facilities can encounter special corrosion and freezing problems. Use PVC, CPVC, or polyethylene pipe with nylon fittings and stainless steel fasteners whenever possible to improve corrosion resistance. Check with the manufacturer for the proper temperature and pressure rating of each type of pipe before installing.

Overhead pipes in naturally ventilated buildings are generally not recommended and will require extra measures to prevent freezing. Insulation of pipes alone usually will not prevent freezing in naturally ventilated buildings. Both heat tape and insulation are required to prevent freezing. If heat tape is not used, the piping system delivering water to waterers will require a loop configuration to allow water to continuously circulate in the delivery system. Drain water systems in unused buildings. Use antifreeze to protect traps that cannot be drained.

Buried lines solve most freezing problems but are difficult to repair. Frost penetration

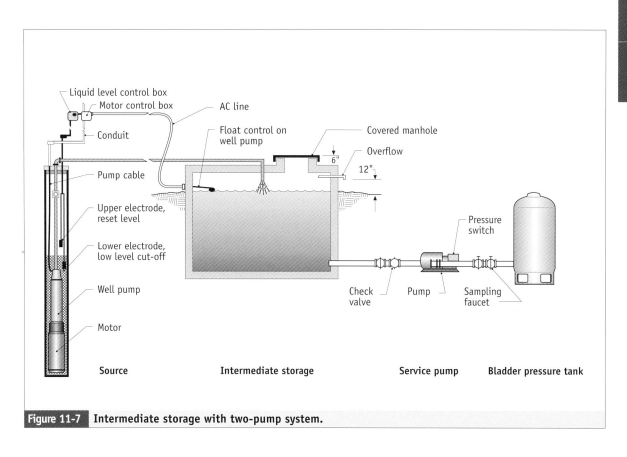

Figure 11-7 | **Intermediate storage with two-pump system.**

varies from 3 to 6 feet in the Midwest. The frost depth can increase by 2 feet in locations with compacted soil, such as under driveways and animal traffic areas, and in areas where snow cover is blown away or removed and the snow's insulating value is lost.

Where underground pipes are brought to the surface, run them through a larger diameter, rigid plastic pipe to protect them from abuse and to provide a warmed air film around the waterline. See Figure 11-8. Heavily insulated, non-heated frost-free waterers are commercially available with large diameter pipes to prevent freezing. They generally remain ice-free if water entering them is above 40°F and at least one tank full of water is consumed every four to six hours. Their success depends on the design, weather conditions, and number and size of the horses drinking.

See *Private Water Systems Handbook*, MWPS-14, for information on design of pipes, pumps, and water supplies.

Pipe and pump sizing

Size the water supply system to meet maximum instantaneous and daily needs. Size pipes and pumps to provide water required during the peak three-hour period. Estimate total water requirements from Table 11-9. When estimating water volumes for the peak three-hour period, include water:
- Consumed after feeding and exercise.
- Washing pens and equipment.
- Washing horses.

Select pipes from Table 11-10 based on the following guidelines:
- Maximum pressure loss from pressure tank to building: 5 psi.
- Maximum pressure loss from pressure tank to any isolated fixture: 10 psi.
- Maximum pressure loss per 100 feet of main supply line: 1 psi.
- Maximum water velocity: 4 feet per second (fps) to prevent water hammer.

Table 11-10	**Pressure loss in pipes due to friction.** (psi drop per 100 feet)

Table includes pressure losses in pipes less than or equal to 1.0 psi per 100 feet due to friction. See *Private Water Systems Handbook*, MWPS-14, for pressure losses in pipes greater than 1.0 psi per 100 feet due to friction. Losses are for straight lengths. Losses do not include bends or transition sections. PVC = Polyvinyl chloride material

Flow rate (gpm)	Nominal diameter (inches)	Steel (Schedule 40)	Copper (Type L)	PVC (Schedule 40)
½	0.90	—	0.5	—
¾	0.20	0.2	0.1	—
2	0.75	0.8	0.7	0.4
	1.00	0.3	0.2	0.1
5	1.00	—	1.0	0.8
	1.25	0.4	0.3	0.2
	1.50	—	0.2	0.1
10	1.25	—	—	0.7
	1.50	0.6	0.5	0.3
	2.00	0.2	0.1	0.1
15	1.50	—	—	0.7
	2.00	0.4	0.3	0.2
20	2.00	0.7	0.5	0.4
	2.50	0.3	—	0.2
30	2.50	0.6	—	0.3
40	2.50	1.0	—	0.5
	3.00	0.4	—	0.2
	4.00	0.2	—	0.0
50	2.50	—	—	0.8
	3.00	0.5	—	0.2
	4.00	0.2	—	0.0
60	3.00	0.7	—	0.3
	4.00	0.2	—	0.2
70	3.00	1.0	—	0.4
	4.00	0.3	—	0.2
80	3.00	—	—	0.5
	4.00	0.3	—	0.2
90	3.00	—	—	0.7
	4.00	0.4	—	0.2
100	3.00	—	—	0.8
	4.00	0.5	—	0.2

Design pumps to provide the flow required to overcome the total system head during the peak, three-hour period. Total head includes:

- Pressure loss due to friction.
- Pressure losses through elbows, tees, wyes, and transitions.
- Elevation differences between pump source and point of use.
- System operating pressure.

System operating pressures of 45 to 50 psi are common for farm water systems. Table 11-11 shows maximum recommended flowrates based on pipe size. Table 11-12 shows minimum recommended design pressures for various fixtures. If a single pump is to be used to supply the total farmstead, other on-farm water needs (e.g. house, other buildings), must be included in determining pipe size and pump capacity. Refer to *Private Water Systems Handbook*, MWPS-14, for more detail on sizing water pipes and pumps.

Waterers

Provide a constant supply of fresh, clean water. Each stall should have its own water supply. Outside pens or lots can have a unit waterer that will supply water for several horses. Ideally water should be between 40°F and 75°F. Extremely cold water may cause digestive problems, especially with sweating horses.

Access to water should be controlled. Horses that have finished exercising tend to drink an excessive amount of water. Unlimited

Table 11-11 Maximum recommended water flowrates through selected sizes of plastic pipe.

Nominal pipe diameter (inches)	Inside diameter (inches)	Maximum flowrate (gpm)
½	0.622	1.5
¾	0.824	3.1
1	1.049	5.7
1¼	1.380	12.0
1½	1.610	18.0
2	2.067	35.0
2½	2.469	55.0
3	3.216	100.0
4	4.134	140.0

Table 11-12 Outlet water pressures.

Recommended minimum pressures.

Fixture	Pressure
Lavatory, sink or bathtub	10 psi
Shower	12
Tank toilet	15
Flush-valve toilet	20
Hose faucet	20
Hose faucet for fire control	30
Livestock waterer	15

access to water can lead to colic, laminitis, or exertional rhabdomyolysis. Traditionally, horses that have just finished exercising were allowed only a few sips of water every three to five minutes until they cooled down. Some newer research studies suggest that allowing horses to drink longer may be permissible. Watch a horse after exercising and drinking water to make the best evaluation on proper care.

The two types of waterers are automatic waterers, Figure 11-8, and manually filled waterers. Manually filled waterers can be buckets, Figure 11-9, or troughs, Figure 11-10.

Automatic waterers are a good solution for watering many horses. As with all labor saving devices, compare the time saved to the cost of the appliance. There are many different kinds available. The advantage of automatic waterers is that clean water is always available as long as the waterer is checked and cleaned regularly. The disadvantage with automatic waterers is that they are much more expensive than buckets or troughs, can freeze if they are not kept in a warm location or do not have a heater, can overflow and create messes, and cannot be moved easily. Because most models need electricity, these waterers must be installed safely. A shut-off is required for times when a horse is not allowed water—such as after exercise. An option is to restrain the horse with cross ties.

When using waterers in stalls, locating one automatic waterer between two stalls can

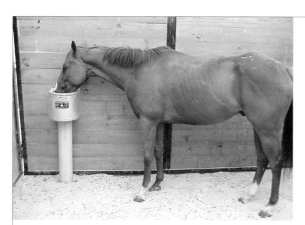

Indoor waterer.
Note the protective covering over the waterline.

Outdoor waterer.
Water placed on concrete pad so a horse must place its front hooves on to drink, but not back hooves. This arrangement helps to minimize the potential of the horse to defecate into the waterer.

Figure 11-8 Automatic waterers.

Figure 11-9 Bucket used to water horses.

Figure 11-10 Watering trough.

significantly reduce installation costs. Be certain that each horse allows the other to drink. This shared system can transmit harmful bacteria or allow fighting. Automatic waterers should be located away from doors. Protect pipes from horses. Some horses will play with water pipes and cause damage.

One advantage of using water buckets or troughs is that horses get more individual attention. Managers know how much water a horse has consumed. Large increases or decreases may signify sickness. Other advantages are that water can be taken away from one horse without turning off all the horses' water; horses are less apt to be injured on a rubber or heavy plastic bucket, and buckets and troughs are more easily cleaned on a regular basis. Stall waterers should be conveniently placed in

one corner of the stall, preferably the front, well away from the feeder, and about two-thirds the height of the horse at the withers off the floor.

All automatic waterers must have a way to prevent water from back siphoning. Use either an anti-back siphoning device in the water line or an air gap between the water inlet and the maximum water level. Include anti-back siphoning devices on all hose bibs. Heaters or heated water bowls may be required.

Automatic waterers installed in outdoor pens or lots should be placed on concrete slabs to reduce mud. Extend the slab away from the waterer at least 10 feet in each direction. Slope concrete ¼ to ½ inches per foot away from the waterer for good drainage. Having an elevated base around automatic waterers can help prevent horses from defecating in the waterer. Make the base wide enough so horses can easily put their front legs on it when they are drinking, but not their hind legs. Horses will not normally place only their hind legs on this base and therefore they typically will not defecate in the water. Placement and height of the base are the key to avoiding fecal contamination. Make the concrete surfaces rough so animals will not slip.

Equip all waterers with a drain to facilitate regular cleaning. Select waterers designed to allow easy cleaning. Install a fused disconnect switch for each waterer. Use a waterproof switch and a corrosion resistant box with appropriate fittings. Fuse only the hot wire with a fuse 25% larger than the total amperage rating of the waterer. Locate the switch on a pole or other suitable surface within sight of and within 50 feet of the waterer.

Enclose all wires mounted on a service pole in non-metallic conduit. Seal the top of the conduit, or extend it into a weatherhead to keep water out. Extend the conduit at least 24 inches into the ground. Install all switches and other electrical equipment where they cannot be damaged. Careful sizing of wiring for waterers is important for reliable and safe operations. All electrically heated waterers must have a grounding conductor as part of the electrical cable. A ground rod alone does not provide adequate protection. Install and connect equipment to an equipotential plane if possible. See the *Farm Buildings Wiring Handbook*, MWPS-28, for more information on equipotential planes.

Having a clean and reliable water supply can be negated if waterers, buckets, or troughs are not cleaned frequently. Dirty, contaminated, or stale water can result in reduced water consumption, which can lead to dehydration. Dirty and contaminated water is a host for disease organisms, which can allow disease to spread rapidly if other horses are drinking from the same trough. Sick animals should be isolated from the water trough and the trough cleaned and disinfected. Even when clean water is available, some horses may continue to consume dirty water if it is available; therefore, always makes sure to remove any dirty, contaminated, or stale water.

A dilute bleach solution is a good disinfectant to use in a waterer or trough after it has been thoroughly cleaned. After bleach application the trough must be thoroughly rinsed before filling with water for horses. Sprinkling baking soda into the trough periodically may reduce algae growth.

Other water supply locations

Provide hot water in the tack room or near the stable entrance for making hot feed mashes, cleaning equipment, and washing horses. Install hose bibs at least at each end and the middle of the alley—between each pair of stalls is ideal. Limit spacing to less than 50 feet when using 25-foot hoses. The cost of installing extra hose bibs typically is not very expensive. The main cost is installing water lines to the stable. Extra hose bibs cost little more to add on. Also consider hose bibs in the tack room, feed room, grooming/washing area, and stable yard. Most water needs are near the stalls. Additional water is needed for cleaning tack and buckets, filling outdoor water troughs, washing horses, etc.

In northern climates, install freeze-proof hydrants outside and inside cold barns, Figure 11-11. Provide a hydrant or other source of water near the stable yard or paddocks to allow for bathing of horses in warm weather,

Figure 11-11 Hydrant inside a stable.

for hosing lame legs, and for cleaning equipment, vehicles, and any other items needing washing or cleaning.

Heating Devices

In colder climates, providing heat to an arena, stable, or parts of the stable may be desired. Electrical space heating devices can be used safely to heat smaller areas such as a tack room or office. Heating larger areas may require the use of heaters using petroleum-based fuels. When operating a device that uses a petroleum-based fuel to produce heat, such as space and water heaters, the operator needs to have a working knowledge of the system and understand heater venting and safety requirements. The products of combustion must be ventilated to the outside. A few types of space heating devices do not used vents. For devices that do not use vents, it is essential to increase the ventilation rate for the structure. If a vent is used with a building negative pressure ventilation system, consider a powered vent fan to prevent combustion gases from being drawn into the building by the exhaust fan.

Heating Source

Propane (LP gas), natural gas, and fuel oil are commonly used to heat buildings and water. Careful planning is the key ingredient to designing a propane, natural gas, or fuel oil system that operates efficiently and safely.

Propane

Propane (LP gas) is less expensive than electricity but generally more expensive than natural gas. It has the advantage of being available anywhere a fuel storage tank may be located.

To maintain propane as a liquid, it is stored in special containers designed to withstand high pressure, but most gas appliances require gas delivered at low pressure. A UL listed first-stage regulator located at the supply tank and a second regulator located at the appliance are used to reduce the pressure to a level that accommodates gas appliances. In some instances, a third regulator or pressure-reducing valve is installed where the gas line enters a building. To be used safely, regulator vents must be pointed downward or be protected from the elements. They must not be painted or otherwise blocked.

Because propane is heavier than air, leaking propane can settle in low areas of buildings and can pose a risk of explosion and fire. To reduce the risk of propane seeping into a building and the risk of a deadly explosion in the event of a fire, propane tanks must be properly located. Table 11-13 and Figure 11-12 show spacing requirements for propane tanks. The pressure relief valve discharge must be at least 10 feet from any potential source of ignition, e.g., any ventilation air inlet.

Tanks should be positioned parallel to buildings since tank ends detach during an explosion. Use proper materials when installing propane systems. Use piping of wrought iron or steel (black or galvanized), brass, or copper. Seamless copper, brass, or steel tubing can be used. Make sure all piping or tubing complies with NFPA 58, *Storage and Handling Liquefied Petroleum Gases* and NFPA 54, *The National Fuel Gas Code*. All piping must be suitable for a working pressure of 125 psi. Flexible hose may be used on the low-pressure side of the second regulator. This is common practice where heaters are hanging from the ceiling and may have a tendency to swing when bumped. This hose must be AGA (American Gas Association) approved and should be preceded by a shut-off valve. Only appropriately trained persons should install and service propane systems and associated equipment.

Natural gas

Natural gas is an economical fuel in those areas where it is available. Gas is delivered to the point of use via a pressurized pipeline system. Installing a pressure reducing valve or regulator near the gas meter reduces pressure.

Natural gas is lighter than air and is odorless; however, an odorant is added to the gas to aid in leak detection. Care is necessary to protect a natural gas system to minimize the risk of damage to gas lines due to vehicle traffic or the digging of trenches or holes. Use proper materials when installing piping and associated equipment. Persons having appropriate training and experience should do installation and service. Systems must comply with the most current edition of NFPA 54, *The National Fuel Gas Code*.

Venting Heaters

Installation of an unvented heater must be accompanied by a continual source of combustion air. Examples of unvented heaters include kerosene heaters, hanging unit heaters, and gas-fired radiant or catalytic heaters.

Minimum requirements are:

- Mechanical ventilation system providing a CONTINUOUS airflow of at least 4 cfm per 1,000 BTU/hr of heater capacity. (**NOTE:** Timer controlled fans do not satisfy this requirement.)
- Two permanent outlets opening directly to the outside. One must be within 12 inches of the ceiling and one must be within 12 inches of the floor. Minimum size for each opening is 1 square inch per 2,000 BTU/hr of heater capacity. The minimum opening size is 3 x 3 inches. (**NOTE:** Periodic opening of building entrance/exit doors does not meet these requirements.)

Table 11-13 Spacing requirements for propane tanks.

National Fire Protection Association (NFPA) minimum spacing requirements. Separation distances listed also apply to tanks and large pieces of equipment using propane.

Rated tank capacity (gallons)	Minimum distance between tank and building (feet)		Separation distance between tanks (feet) Above ground
	Above ground	Underground	
Less than 125 gallons	0	10	0
126 to 250	10	10	0
251 to 500	10	10	3
501 to 2,000	25	10	3
Over 2,000 gallons	50	50	5

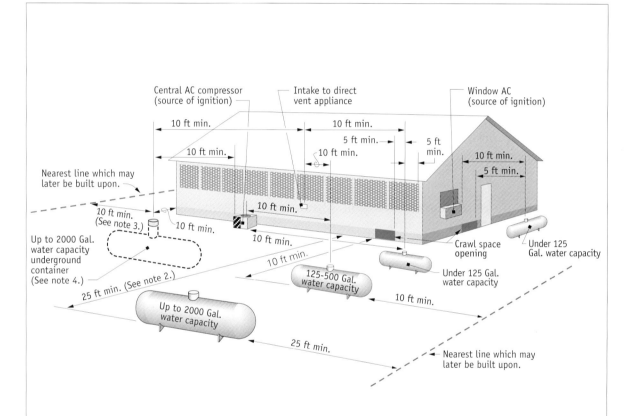

Notes:

1. Regardless of its size, any ASME tank filled on-site must be located so that the filling connection and fixed level gauge are at least 10 feet from external sources of ignition (i.e. open flame, window AC, compressor, etc.), intake to direct vented gas appliance or intake to a mechanical ventilation system.

2. May be reduced to a 10-foot minimum for a single container of 1,200 gallons water capacity or less if it is located at least 25 feet from any other LP Gas container of more than 125 gallons water capacity.

3. Minimum distances from underground containers shall be measured from the relief valve and filling or level gauge vent connection at the container, except that no part of the underground container shall be less than 10 feet from a building of line of adjoining property which may be built upon.

4. Where the container may be subject to abrasive action or physical damage due to vehicular traffic or other causes it must be either,

   (a) Placed not less than 2 feet below grade;
   (b) Otherwise protected against such physical damage.

Adapted from *NFPA 58, Appendix G, The National Fuel Gas Code.*

Figure 11-12 Location of propane storage containers.

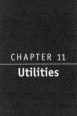

• Use fan-forced chimney venting in rooms using negative pressure ventilation to avoid drawing fumes from the heater or from down the chimney into the room.

Minimum ventilation openings are required to help ensure complete combustion and minimize the risk of carbon monoxide poisoning.

Heater Safety

Gas heaters for either air or water used in stables or horse facilities give off carbon monoxide fumes during combustion. Gas water heaters should be properly vented. Monitor the effectiveness of venting closely. Use forced venting in space where negative pressure is used for ventilation because the negative pressure of the ventilation system may bring flue gases back into the building.

All heaters should have control devices that stop fuel flow or shut down heater operation if necessary.

• If fuel does not ignite within approximately one minute of electrical igniter operation, the fuel and fan should shut off.

• If the gas supply is depleted, a manual reset flame sensor should shut down the heater.

• If no air is moving through the unit before ignition, a sensor that detects air movement should deactivate the ignition circuit.

• If airflow through the unit stops during operation, the main fuel valve is closed.

• If the temperature at the air discharge or at the burner becomes too high, the main fuel valve is closed.

• If the blower motor becomes overloaded, electrical overload protection should activate to prevent overheating and motor damage.

• If there is loss of electrical power, there should be a full shut down of the burner.

To ensure continued safe and efficient operation, install items properly and then maintain them well. Use a totally enclosed motor on the heater fan. Place flame arrestors on the gas lines that lead to heating units or generator engines. Mount regulators 18 inches or higher above ground with the vent facing down.

Establish a regular maintenance schedule. Clean the heating elements, fan blades, and output louvers to enhance complete fuel combustion and heating efficiency. Totally disconnect electric power before cleaning, and be sure no moisture remains in the electrical boxes before restoring power. Inspect electrical wiring and fuel line connections annually. Check LP gas regulators, which are usually mounted on the exterior of buildings. Make sure debris, or snow and ice are not covering the device or plugging the vent opening.

Wastewater Treatment

Wastewaters from sinks, toilets, and shower and baths need to be properly treated. Directly discharging untreated wastewater or septic tank effluent to the ground surface or into abandoned wells is unacceptable and in almost all states is illegal. Untreated discharges or failing systems potentially expose people to harmful bacteria or viruses through direct contact or transmission by vectors such as flies or family pets that come in contact with the untreated waste. The contamination of streams and lakes or of groundwater by nonexistent or failing onsite systems also brings the possibility of illness from drinking or swimming in the water. In addition, inadequately treated wastewater can create environmental problems by overloading natural waters with excess organic material and nutrients. Good design, construction, operation, and maintenance of an onsite treatment system will protect both health and the environment.

Often the wastewater system is the last component of a site to be planned and built when it actually needs to be planned and designed with the other facilities. Ideally the wastewater would be connected to a municipal sewer system. If access to a municipal sewer system is unavailable, an onsite (septic) wastewater treatment system is needed. The technology behind onsite wastewater treatment is a combination of well-established see the *Onsite Domestic Waste System Handbook*, MWPS-24, for more details on this technology.

The main types of treatment systems that are usually used for horse operations are:

- **Traditional Systems.** A septic system composed of a septic tank and absorption field is the most common onsite wastewater system for homes and can be applied to stable facility wastewaters, Figure 11-13. Treatment of the wastewater begins in the septic tank. Final treatment and absorption of the wastewater occur in the absorption field.

- **Lagoons (Wastewater Stabilization Ponds).** A lagoon is a constructed pond, 6 to 8 feet deep. Bacteria in the lagoon treat the wastewater. Air movement across the lagoon surface and algae growing in the lagoon aerate the upper part. For an impermeable, high-clay soil, a lagoon is an effective, inexpensive and practical option, if sufficient land is available. Lagoons require a minimum of two acres.

- **Alternative Systems (Pretreatment or Enhanced Treatment).** Alternative systems include mounds, aeration systems, sand filters, filters using other media, and rock-plant filters. Although *all* onsite systems require some maintenance, the mechanical and electrical parts or vegetation in alternative systems mean

that additional monitoring and maintenance is required for good performance and reliability. Having a contract for maintenance service with a technician, installer, or manufacturer is strongly recommended.

- **Discharging Systems/Disinfection.** In some states, the effluent from an onsite system may be applied to the surface of the ground. To do this, the system must have a discharge permit and the wastewater must be adequately pretreated by an alternative system and disinfected. Chlorine tablet systems are often used for disinfection. Other chlorination systems or ultraviolet radiation can be used. Taking samples of the final effluent and reporting the laboratory test results may be required.

The type and depth of soil determine which systems are candidates for a particular site. Deep, permeable, well-drained soil on a level site is ideal for a traditional system. If such conditions are not available on the site, options such as pressurized distribution, an alternative system, or a lagoon can be considered, as appropriate. The selection among the system types is based on constraints of the site, state and local codes, availability of the system, maintenance requirements, installation and operating costs, special requirements such as nutrient reduction, and preference.

Check with the local health (sanitarian), building, or zoning department to learn what regulations apply and what systems are allowable and successful in the area. *Onsite Domestic Sewage Disposal Handbook*, MWPS-24, explains the selection, design, installation, and maintenance needs for a household sewage disposal system. *Private Water Systems Handbook*, MWPS-14, contains details about water source selection, treatment, and distribution. Other sources of information are county or university extension staff and the EPA-sponsored National Small Flows Clearinghouse (1-800-623-8301).

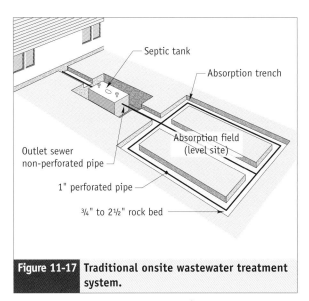

Figure 11-17 | **Traditional onsite wastewater treatment system.**

CHAPTER 12

Fire Protection

Many fires are not detected until they are beyond the point where the fire department can prevent major damage. Although many disasters are unavoidable (such as severe storms), good planning and preparation almost always can reduce losses.

A fire occurs when a fuel source comes in contact with an ignition source. An ignition source can be a spark or intense heat. Fuel sources can be almost any item but are usually items such as wood, plant material, plastic, paper, fabric, or combustible fuel.

Fires can start instantaneously once the ignition source contacts the fuel source, or as is more common with fires, the fire starts slowly after the ignition source contacts the fuel source and the fuel source starts to smolder. Oxygen availability, fuel type, and physical arrangement are factors that determine the length of the smoldering process. Smoldering can vary from minutes to hours. Fires caught during this stage have the greatest chances of being controlled with minimal damage, but are still extremely dangerous. Smoldering fires may also be difficult to detect and completely extinguish, especially with smoldering hay or wood shavings, when the fuel itself helps to insulate the fire and prevent water penetration. The time it takes a fire to grow and spread is again related to a number of factors, such as the fuel source, the fire temperature, and the time the fire has to burn.

Smoke and heat production increase as the fire smolders. By the end of this smoldering or incipient phase, enough heat has been generated to produce flames. Once flames are present, the fire is extremely dangerous and unpredictable. It grows rapidly, and the heat produced becomes intense. The capabilities of fire extinguishers as a line of defense will soon be surpassed. After flame eruption, it takes only a few minutes for ceiling temperatures to exceed 1,800°F. As ceiling temperatures continue to rise, the building acts as a boiler, and the flash point is soon reached. When fire has reached the flash point, often in as little as 3 to 5 minutes, the hot air temperature simultaneously ignites all combustibles within the space. At flash point, survival within the structure is unlikely, and the building contents are destroyed.

Smoke is produced in the earliest stages of fire development. The color and density of the smoke is dependent on fuel and burning conditions. Low-temperature fires produce more visible smoke particles, creating darker, thicker smoke, whereas hotter fires have smaller particles in the smoke, making it less visible. Smoke and heat are the fire's killing attributes. Smoke contains noxious gases and vapors specific to the fuel.

The most common products of combustion (fire) are carbon monoxide and carbon dioxide. As the fire consumes the available oxygen in the room, it releases carbon monoxide that combines with blood hemoglobin more readily than oxygen, resulting in suffocation, even if an adequate supply of oxygen is available. Elevated levels of carbon monoxide and carbon dioxide increase respiration in an attempt to obtain more oxygen, resulting in the inhalation of more deadly gases. The consequences are swift and thorough incapacitation and asphyxiation. Intense heat of the fire along with the smoke can increase the chance for lung damage. When this super-heated mass of gases is inhaled, the respiratory tract will be seared. Smoke damage can occur even before flames are visible.

Once all available fuel sources have been used, the fire will burn out. Unfortunately, this is not necessarily the end of the fire. Stables, barns, and other agricultural-type buildings often contain large quantities of fuel sources that can be impervious to water (e.g., hay, petroleum fuels, and fertilizers). It is common for some of these fuel sources to remain unburned during the initial fire, then to continue to smolder. These smoldering pockets often re-ignite or re-kindle another fire, requiring another visit from the fire department.

The remainder of this chapter will discuss causes of fire, especially the impact hay has on fire, and fire prevention and planning, detection, and suppression. More specific discussion of fire control methods for farms can be found in *Fire Control in Livestock Buildings* NRAES-39.

Fire Causes

Some of the ignition sources for fires are:
- Lightning.
- Faulty wiring.
- Sparks from motors.
- Portable heaters.
- Careless handling of matches.
- Careless smoking.
- Truck or machinery exhausts.
- Improperly cured baled hay.

The ignition source by itself cannot start a fire unless it comes into contact with a fuel source and adequate oxygen is available to feed the fire. Most people are familiar with many of the ignition sources in the list, but truck and machinery exhausts and baled hay are ones that many people do not think about being an ignition source. Trucks driven into the hay/bedding storage area have been known to ignite materials in contact with the hot exhaust and catalytic converters.

Baled hay can be its own ignition and fuel source. The majority of hay fires occur within 6 weeks of baling, usually caused by excessive moisture in the bale. Ideal moisture range for hay at baling is 15 to 18%. Even after grass and legume forages are harvested, plant respiration continues and generates a small amount of heat. In properly harvested forages, respiration decreases and will eventually cease during drying and curing. With acceptable moisture levels, the normal heat of respiration during curing is inconsequential. However, if moisture levels are too high, the respiratory heat will provide an environment suitable for the heat generating microorganisms that exist in the baled hay to grow and multiply. Once the bale interior reaches 170°F, most of these microorganisms die from the heat. Interior temperatures of 170°F can cause the bale to ignite if sufficient oxygen is present.

A burning bale of hay may be difficult to detect because the inside of the bale burns first. Hay fires are very difficult to extinguish completely. The tightly laced forages prevent water from penetrating to the core. Only a forceful blast of water can penetrate deep enough to extinguish the fire.

Hay temperature monitoring can be done to ensure that bale temperatures never reach critical levels. Check newly baled hay twice a day for heat buildup. If bale temperatures have reached 150°F, monitor the interior bale temperature frequently, as the temperature is most likely to climb. By the time the interior bale temperature reaches 175 to 190°F, a fire is about to occur, and at 200°F, a fire has already erupted.

Temperature probes are available at most farm supply companies and stores. Follow manufacturer's directions for using the probe. Most often the temperature probe is pushed or driven into the haystack, and a reading is taken after about 15 minutes. Use Table 12-1 to interpret readings, and take the needed actions based on probe readings.

An alternative to purchasing a temperature probe is to make one, using a metal rod 3/8 to ½ inches in diameter. Drive the rod into the hay and let it stand for at least 15 to 20 minutes before removing it. If

Table 12-1 Determining hay temperatures with a probe.

Follow manufacturer's directions for proper insertion of temperature probe. Take readings after about 15 minutes.
Table based on *Guarding Against Hay Fires,* ANR-964. C.B. Ogburn. Alabama Cooperative Extension Service, Agricultural Engineering, Auburn University.

Probe reading	Action
Below 130°F	• No problem
130 to 140°F	• No problem yet. • Temperature may go up or down. • Recheck in a few hours.
150°F	• Temperature will most likely continue to climb. • Move the hay to circulate and cool in the air. • Monitor temperature often.
175 to 190°F	• Fire is imminent or may be present a short distance from the probe. • Call the fire department. • Continue probing and monitoring the temperature.
200°F or above	• Fire is present at or near the probe. • Call the fire department. • Inject water to cool hot spots before moving hay. • Have a charged hose ready to control fire when moving hay.

the temperature within the bale is less than 130°F, you should be able to hold the metal comfortably in your bare hand. If the bale has reached a temperature of 160°F or greater, the rod will be too hot to hold comfortably in your bare hands. If the rod is too hot, let it cool for a few minutes and then reconfirm by taking another sample. When hot hay bales are found, summon the fire department. Be sure to tell the dispatcher that you have hot hay bales that may ignite instead of saying that you have a hay fire. This will help the fire company in planning on how to deal with your situation.

Most barn fires occur in the winter when forage and bedding are stored, electrical and heating fuel use are high, and equipment repairs and upgrades are traditionally made. Most of the components in a horse barn are highly flammable. Stall walls are frequently constructed with wood, and horses are usually standing in ample amounts of dried bedding, eating dried forages.

Fires can grow quickly and give no warning. In most cases, the sight of flames means that it is already too late.

Fire is extremely dangerous at any stage of growth, and controlling it is best left up to professionals.

Fire Prevention and Planning

There is no such thing as a fireproof building. Fire prevention starts with good design, management, and safety practices. Good design not only includes the buildings, but also the layout of the site. Many of the design features highlighted in this section have been discussed in more detail in other sections of this book. Using a professional who is knowledgeable about fire safety designs; such as an architect or engineer, can help ensure a fire-safe design.

It has been estimated that the root cause of 95% of preventable horse barn fires is from careless smoking, with faulty electrical systems second on the list.

Post and enforce a NO SMOKING policy. All smoking should be banned from the barn and immediate premises. If smokers do frequent the barn, provide them with a smoking area away from the barn, that is equipped with a receptacle for butts and matches.

Always contact the insurance company before finalizing building designs and starting construction. Designs that do not meet the insurance company's requirements may result in the building not being insurable. Generally, small, uninsulated metal clad buildings with openings on opposite walls (for ventilation) and used for storing non-powered equipment would be of low concern for fire spread. Some insurers have special rates for such low-hazard buildings. Also, the local building code may have building fire prevention requirements. Visit with the insurer about building or operation modifications that can increase safety and reduce premiums.

Post evacuation plans and practice fire drills with all persons and horses in the barn. Post by the phone all emergency numbers, written directions, a list of any chemicals stored on the premises, and any other important information that emergency operators will need. Providing a map of the facility to emergency services will greatly enhance reaction time once emergency medical services (EMS)/ fire is on site. This map should indicate where animals are housed, water sources that can be used to help extinguish a fire, and the location and quantity of commonly stored chemicals.

By practicing evacuation drills, both horse and handler can prepare for emergency situations. Teach the horses to walk out with their eyes covered, and accustom horses to firefighter turnout gear, loud noises that simulate sirens, and smoke. If horses are reluctant to walk blindfolded during the drills, chances are that they will be even more reluctant during an emergency situation. Some fire companies are willing to meet with you to train both you and the firefighters. Most firefighters are volunteers who may have little to no horse experience, making handling a frightened horse not only difficult and dangerous, but also potentially lethal.

Work with the local fire department and let them know where local water sources that can be used to fight fires are located. They can give good suggestions on making sure these sources are adequate when needed. Having local firefighters visit the site occasionally helps familiarize them with its location, layout, water storage and access situation.

Chapter 13. Emergency Response Planning has more information on enacting plans for fire emergencies.

Site Layout

Layout of the site should allow an unobstructed view of the buildings, as well as road vehicles, machinery, livestock and people traffic. The ground surfaces around farm buildings should be solid enough to support heavy fire equipment at all times of the year. In addition, access from the roadway must have adequate vertical and horizontal clearance for fire and emergency equipment to reach all buildings.

Building spacing for fire safety depends on building size, construction type, wall openings, and materials stored inside. Table 12-2 suggests building spacing based on buildings constructed to contain a fire for 45-minutes and the adjacent structure constructed with a reflective, non-combustible surface and having

no openings facing the burning building—to minimize the danger of fire spread between buildings. Provide a minimum of 75 feet clear space between buildings to allow for firefighting equipment access.

Field firebreak strips and areas can be used to protect farmsteads from fast-traveling, open-range type fires. Generally, such firebreak construction surrounds a farmstead and involves a tilled soil space greater than 100 feet wide and/or several tilled strips; the areas between tilled strips are often burned to reduce fuel for a spreading fire. Local range management or forestry agencies may have unique firebreak construction recommendations for hazards that may include grass, brush, and/or tree fires. Firebreak planning/ construction is a part of farmstead planning and should be done well before a fire approaches.

The farm needs to have access in all weather to a large supply of water, such as ponds, swimming pools, cisterns, and manure lagoons. Locating additional water sources around the barn will save valuable time for firefighters. The major reason for fire suppression problems in rural communities is a lack of water supply. Any potential water source must be no lower than 20 feet below the pump truck

Table 12-2	Building spacing to prevent radiation firespread.	
Building type	Dimension of building, overall height and length (feet)	Distance to adjacent structure (feet)
High hazard		
Fuel storage	10 x 14	40
Hay storage	10 x 50	70
Feed processing	20 x 30	80
Barn with furnace or heater	20 x 50	100
Moderate hazard		
Storage		
• Silage and grain	10 x 14	30
Machinery		
• Storage	10 x 100	80
• Maintenance	20 x 50	65
Barn—no heat	20 x 50	80

* Based on the burning building's ability to contain a fire for 45 minutes, and adjacent structure being constructed with reflective, non-combustible cladding and having no openings facing the burning building.

elevation, Figure 12-1. Some horse farms install a pond for recreational and aesthetic purposes. The water system should be able to supply at least 20-gpm flowrate. Have a backup power generator available if the fire should interrupt the utility power supply.

Buildings

Chapter 3. Stables and Chapter 5. Arenas and Training Facilities have addressed many fire safety features including materials, designs, and practices. This section will highlight these key fire safety design features and show additional features that can help enhance fire safety.

Construction practices and materials

All farm building electrical supply, wiring, and appliances should be installed according to the *National Electrical Code* for the environmental conditions found in that building. All LP gas fuel supplies and holding tanks should be designed according to *The National Fuel Gas Code*. These are some of the most important steps to fire prevention. *Chapter 11. Utilities* has more information on fire safe designs.

To reduce the potential for fire loss, use building materials and develop a building design for minimal fire-spread rating (ASTM-E119.88) and low potential for combustion. A supplier should know about ratings of specific building materials. Concrete, masonry, stucco, gypsum board, and fire-retardant treated plywood are considered fire and flame retardant materials. Steel and aluminum sheeting are only flame retardant (not fire retardant) as they readily conduct heat. Plywood, chipboard, and particleboard require a flame retardant treatment to reduce their fire hazard characteristics. Most plastics melt at about 200°F and then burn vigorously.

Fire-retardant treated plywood and studs have excellent fire-resistant properties and can withstand moisture in livestock buildings. A common requirement of insurance providers for farm construction is that lumber and plywood should be pressure-treated with fire-retardant chemicals to meet the Underwriters Laboratories Fire Rated System (FRS) rating denoting a surface-burning characteristic rating of 25 or less for flame spread and smoke developed in a test of thirty minutes duration.

While insulation is essential in heated buildings in colder climates, it can also add to the fire hazard if not used correctly. Most insulation is not fireproof and should be covered to protect it from physical and mois-

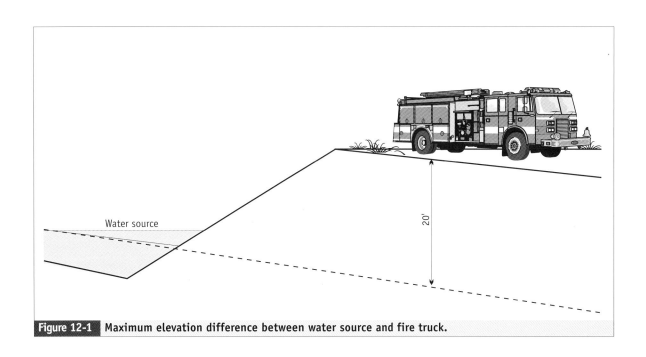

Figure 12-1 Maximum elevation difference between water source and fire truck.

Water source

20'

ture damage. Some is highly combustible. Check with a professional engineer or with the insurer to ensure that it is properly installed in the building.

Chapter 3. Stables has more information on fire safe materials and designs. *Fire Control in Livestock Buildings*, NRAES-39, explains the suitability and use of fire-resistant building construction.

Design layout

If practical, design stalls with two exits for the horse to use in an emergency. An adequate number of exits are needed so that the fire will not block horses and people from leaving the building. Provide easy entrances and exits from all stalls and rooms. Have exits open into an enclosed area so that horses escaping the stable will not have access to nearby roads and traffic. Be sure to keep all exits clear. A fire door is not an effective exit if it is blocked. Have halters and lead ropes available for each horse.

Swinging stall doors should open out of the stall. Frantic horses will catch a hip on half-open doors. Also, if there is only time for someone to run down the alley opening stall door latches, a horse pushing out on the door can escape on its own. Likewise, sliding doors can be unlatched and pushed open. All latches and fastenings on doors should work quickly to save time.

Having water hydrants (more than one) with adequate water volume and pressure located in and around the barn and feed storage areas helps in early suppression before the fire company arrives. Use a minimum of 1¼-inch waterlines. If enough hydrants are not available, an alternative is to have enough hose available to reach all areas in the barn. In all facilities, hydrants need to be frost free. Avoid using heat tapes on waterlines and pipes. Heat tapes can be a fire hazard if not properly installed. If heat tapes are used, be sure to read, understand, and follow all manufacturer warnings and directions.

Housekeeping

Keeping areas in and around buildings clean and organized can help minimize the potential for fires to start or spread. Mowing around buildings, eliminating any dried vegetation in the area, and removing debris piles can reduce fire spread between buildings. Keep any hay stored inside a stable confined to areas designed for its storage. Keep any potentially combustible materials well away from ignition sources such as heaters. Sweep up any spilled feed or hay. Store fuels only in buildings designated for their storage. Cobwebs, chaff, and even dust build up can be a fuel source for a fire. Sweep barns on a daily basis to minimize build up of cobwebs, chaff, and dust. Keeping the buildings clean inside and outside also increases the chances of escape during a fire.

Special Fire Safety Design Features

Larger and more expensive stables or stables housing many expensive horses may want to include additional design features that will minimize the spread of a fire. These features are not common to stables and will add some expense to the project, but may be warranted in some situations.

Firewalls and curtains

Large, inter-connected buildings are especially vulnerable to fire damage. These buildings can make good use of a firewall or curtain, especially at points where there is a change in building use. Preventing the exchange and redirection of super heated air and flame is the operating principle of a firewall or curtain. Firewalls or curtains should be located no more than 75 feet apart. Where multiple buildings are connected with enclosed walkways, a firewall should be constructed in the center of the passage length with fire doors that are kept closed.

A true firewall must be completely sealed in a fire and should provide at least one hour of fire protection, Figure 12-2. In a stable with a frame-constructed roof, firewalls should be constructed with moisture-resistant gypsum board or fire-retardant treated wood or masonry, and must extend through the attic and at least 18 inches above the roof; the higher the wall extends, the longer the fire protection. Firewalls should prevent airflow between building sections or compartments. Any doors in the wall need to be fire rated and self-closing, and any openings for wiring or pipes need to be sealed.

Fire curtains (Figure 12-3) or fire barriers are walls that divide up the open space in the roof trusses and prevent the spread of heat and smoke through the attic space. This

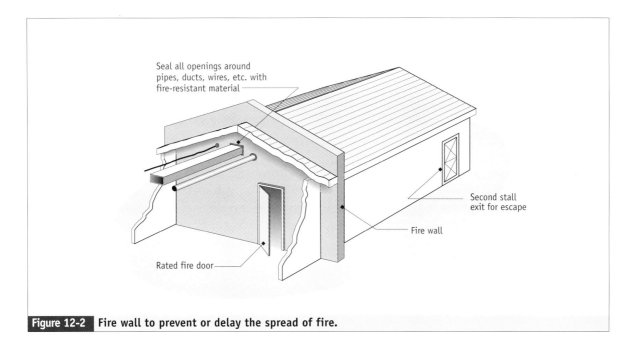

Figure 12-2 Fire wall to prevent or delay the spread of fire.

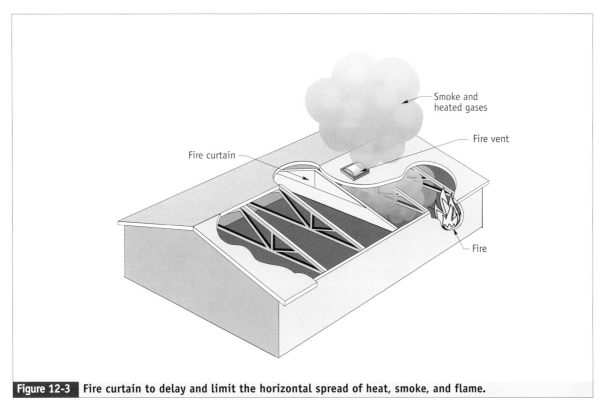

Figure 12-3 Fire curtain to delay and limit the horizontal spread of heat, smoke, and flame.

prevents the truss area from becoming a natural tunnel for heat and flame travel. Building design determines the size of the fire curtain; the taller the fire curtain, the greater the effectiveness.

If not properly installed, firewalls or curtains can disrupt the everyday airflow patterns needed for proper ventilation in the stable. An option more common at horse facilities is to compartmentalize by having entirely separate structures rather than dividing up one extra large building. This is one reason why many racetracks have several modest-sized stables rather than one huge stable.

Fire ventilation

Roof vents are an effective way to ventilate a barn during a fire. Proper ventilation will improve the removal of gases from occupied areas, direct the airflow currents and fire spread, and provide for the release of unburned gases before ignition. Recommended roof vent spacing and sizes are set by the National Fire Protection Association, based on building material types and area to be vented. The most important factor used to determine the space needed between vents is the rate at which burning material gives off heat. Horse barn fires burn with moderate-to-high heat production. Stables should have 1 square foot of ceiling vent space for every 100 square feet of floor area. Buildings with hay storage need 1 square foot for every 30 to 50 square feet of floor area.

Roof vent options include a continuous slot opening along the ridge; roof vent monitors with louvers or thin glass that are opened by the super-heated air; and unit vents that are designed to melt, collapse, or spring open at predetermined temperatures. Each of these vents increases gas removal during the fire. Vents on heat-triggered fuses (usually set to open at 212°F) may not open unless a hot, free-burning fire produces smoke temperatures high enough to activate fuses. This may mean that the fire has had time to progress, depending on its origin. Do not assume that just because vents are installed, the environment within a burning

barn is livable. A smoldering fire can produce enough toxic smoke to be an immediate threat to human and animal life.

Fire Detection

Early warning devices can be an effective tool in fire detection but few are suitable for barn use. In some situations, the main goal is to save the animals housed in the barn, but in other situations, minimizing property damage is the priority. Many early detection and fire suppression systems are available, but most were developed for residential use. This severely limits their practicality in horse or livestock facilities because these environments tend to be dustier, more humid, and colder than residential environments. When using early warning devices in stables and arenas, use industrial quality rather than residential quality detectors, and develop a routine inspection program to clean and service detectors every four to six months.

There are three basic types of fire detection devices: smoke, thermal, and flame detectors. Smoke detectors are the best line of defense for early warning of fires. They identify the fire while it is in the smoldering or early flame stages. Smoke detectors are not as reliable in the dusty and humid environment of horse barns. Airborne dust and dander or humidity may trigger false alarms. A smoke detector is better suited in more controlled low-dust, low-humidity environments, such as a lounge, an office, equipment storage areas, and tack rooms.

Thermal or heat detectors are more effective in dusty buildings than smoke detectors. However, their adequacy in a horse barn is debatable since they require the fire to be in the later stages of progression before the sensor recognizes and signals the alarm. The longer a fire has to develop, the greater damage it can cause and the more difficult it is to control, especially in a barn. This is why they are usually not permitted as the sole detection device in life safety applications, such as in residential use.

The most common thermal detectors are fixed temperature devices, set to operate when temperatures reach a predetermined level, usually 135° to 165°F. Rate-of-rise thermal detectors activate an alarm when the temperature climbs at an abnormally fast rate. Both fixed temperature and rate-of-rise detectors are spot detectors and activate sooner in a closer proximity to the source. A third type of thermal detector is the fixed temperature line detector. This detector does not require the sensor to be as close to the heat source for activation. The benefit of this detector is that it can cover more floor area at a lower cost.

Flame detectors are the most reliable and expensive early warning detection devices. These sensors are spot detectors; therefore, they must be looking directly at the fire source. Flame detectors sense a flame's wavelength, cycle, and consistency, so they can differentiate between hot objects and actual fires, minimizing false alarms. The greater the distance the flame is from the sensor, the larger it must be before the sensor will respond to it. These devices are highly reliable early detection devices especially for hot burning fires that are not likely to give off smoke, such as alcohol or methane fires.

One way to ensure that someone is alerted when a fire is detected by an early warning system alarm is to connect the alarm to a telephone dialer. A telephone dialer provides 24-hour alarm monitoring. The dialer can be connected to a professional monitoring service, family, neighbors, or directly to the fire department. These dialers can be connected to cell phones. It may be best to alert someone near the premises first, to prevent calling the fire department for any false alarms; however, best judgment should prevail, and if the nearest neighbor is too far away, contacting a 911 operator may be a better alternative. A phone dialer will need its own line, to ensure the availability of a phone connection after a fire has been detected.

When designing an early warning system, seek advice and recommendations from fire engineers or fire protection professionals familiar with the unique needs and situations found in horse facilities. The local fire department should be able to assist in locating fire protection professionals.

Fire Suppression

Fire can blaze out of control very quickly. In most all cases, leave the fire fighting to the professional firefighters, especially if it is a hay or building fire. Some fires can be put out by the use of fire suppression devices such as fire extinguishers or sprinkler systems. Choosing and designing the proper device can mean the difference in putting out a fire or spreading a fire.

Fire Extinguishers

Fire extinguishers should be located in all barns, feed storage areas, and rooms where people congregate. It is a good idea to have a fire extinguisher located in work vehicles such as the truck that pulls the trailer.

Most stable fires are ordinary combustibles burning such as hay. Electrical fires are the next major concern. NEVER store flammable liquids in a stable.

Three types of fire extinguishers as shown in Table 12-3 are available. These extinguishers are labeled A, B, and C. Extinguishers are not universal. Using a water-type extinguisher can spread fires fueled by flammable liquids, such as gasoline, or become a safety hazard in electrical fires.

Fortunately, many extinguishers available today can be used on different types of fires and will be labeled with more than one designator, e.g., A-B, B-C, or A-B-C. Dry chemical extinguishers are usually rated for multipurpose use. They contain an extinguishing agent and use a compressed, nonflammable gas as a propellant. The most versatile type of extinguisher is the ABC-type that extinguishes the broadest range of fires.

A fourth type of extinguishers, which is designed for use on flammable metals, also is available. These extinguishers are not for multipurpose use and would have no place in suppressing a fire in a stable.

Fire extinguishers need to be kept filled and regularly checked. Ten-pound ABC type extinguishers should be sufficient for most farms. Extinguishers should be placed near exits in all major buildings and in buildings that have extensive electrical equipment or

Table 12-3 Fire extinguisher types and codes.

Adapted from information obtained from the Hanford Fire Department and Staying Alive websites.

Class	Use	Types
 **A**	**Ordinary combustibles** These extinguishers will put out fires in ordinary combustibles, such as wood and paper. The numerical rating for this class of fire extinguisher refers to the amount of water the fire extinguisher holds and the amount of fire it will extinguish.	Water extinguishers contain water and compressed gas and should be used only on Class A (ordinary combustibles) fires.
 **B**	**Flammable liquids** These extinguishers should be used on fires involving flammable liquids, such as grease, gasoline, oil, etc. The numerical rating for this class of fire extinguisher states the approximate number of square feet of a flammable liquid fire that a non-expert person can expect to extinguish.	Carbon dioxide (CO_2) extinguishers are most effective on Class B and C (liquids and electrical) fires. Since the gas disperses quickly, these extinguishers are effective only from 3 to 8 feet. The carbon dioxide is stored as a compressed liquid in the extinguisher. As it expands, it cools the surrounding air.
 **C**	**Electrical Equipment** These extinguishers are suitable for use on electrically energized fires. This class of fire extinguishers does not have a numerical rating. The presence of the letter "C" indicates that the extinguishing agent is nonconductive.	Halon extinguishers contain a gas that interrupts the chemical reaction taking place when fuels burn. These extinguishers are often used to protect valuable electrical equipment since they leave no residue to clean up. Halon extinguishers have a limited range, usually 4 to 6 feet. Also, Halon is a carcinogenic and it can damage the ozone.

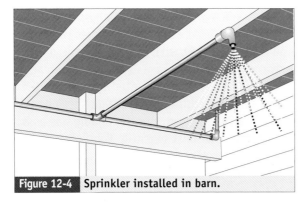

Figure 12-4 Sprinkler installed in barn.

that store flammable liquids. In a stable, fire extinguishers should be mounted in easily accessible locations at 50-foot intervals. The local fire department or insurance representative can also be helpful when deciding on the type of extinguisher to use and where to place extinguishers.

Sprinklers

Sprinkler systems are an effective tool for controlling fires but are not common in rural horse barns, Figure 12-4. Most sprinkler systems open to apply water to a fire when a sensing element in the individual sprinkler head comes in contact with intense heat. Only the sprinkler heads that come in contact with the fire's heat react, minimizing the water needed to extinguish the fire. A sprinkler system usually suppresses a fire with as few as two sprinkler heads and is very effective at controlling fires before they get out of hand.

For sprinkler systems to be effective, an adequate water supply needs to be available at all times to provide enough water flow and pressure to extinguish the fire. On average, one sprinkler head will deliver 25 gallons of water per minute to extinguish the blaze. As more sprinklers are activated, more water must be available to maintain pressure in the line

(47 gallons and 72 gallons per minute for activation of the second and third sprinklers, respectively). Water systems for many horse farms have difficulty providing enough water flow or pressure to meet these criteria. If water availability is a problem, a tank can be installed to provide temporary water storage. *Chapter 11. Utilities* shows how to size this tank. Temporary water storages can be an extremely expensive addition that will need regular service checks and maintenance.

If the facility's water supply is sufficient, three main types of sprinkler system options are available: wet-pipe system, dry-pipe system, and preaction system. A wet-pipe system sprinkler system holds water in the line at all times. These are the most inexpensive systems to install and require the least amount of maintenance. However, in buildings where the temperature goes below 32°F, they can freeze and burst.

A dry-pipe system is employed in environments where water freezing can occur. The supply lines are pressurized with air or nitrogen gas to hold a valve closed, preventing water from entering the system. In a fire, the sprinklers are activated, releasing the pressure and opening the valve. If the pressure is released through damage to the supply line, the valve is also released, which can pose a problem if the valve release is not found and temperatures are low enough for freezing to occur. Also, dry-pipe systems are more limited in design. The reliance on pressure to close a valve creates strict requirements on the overall size and location of the sprinkler heads and supply lines. The increased system complexity requires more components, has more opportunity for failure, and increases the costs of installation and maintenance.

A preaction system is designed to eliminate the danger of accidental valve release on a dry-pipe system. A preaction system uses an electronically operated valve to prevent water from prematurely entering the pipes. In order for the valves to be opened, an independent flame, heat, or smoke detection device must identify a fire or potential fire. Once a fire is detected, the valve is released, and the water is available to the sprinkler heads. The sprinklers open when triggered by heat, not by the valve detection device. As with an increasingly complex system, installation and maintenance costs increase along with the potential for malfunction.

Fire Protection Quick Summary

Fire protection requires consideration during design, layout, and construction and requires a regularly reviewed and updated plan to maintain that protection. Summarizing some of these design aspects:

- Site and separate buildings to minimize the potential for fire to spread.
- Design stalls with two exits that open into a secure, enclosed area.
- Be sure that no swinging door obstructs a pathway.
- Follow *National Electrical Code* and *National Fuel Gas Code* requirements.
- Use UL fire rated products.
- Seek advice and recommendations from fire engineers or fire protection professionals familiar with the unique needs and situations found in horse facilities.
- Check local zoning and building codebooks for fire regulations in your area.

In addition to good design, include some basic preparation for fire emergencies:

- Make local emergency-coping organizations aware of and familiar with the farm's identity and location.
- Be sure that the facility is accessible to emergency vehicles and that the ground around the buildings is firm enough to support them.
- Install communication/warning systems.
- Have an operational standby electric power system.
- Post and practice evacuation routes.

> If you do have a fire, don't put yourself or someone else in danger. Think out your actions first.

- Post written emergency information at each phone.
- Install fire extinguishers and other fire control devices.
- Have halters and lead ropes easily accessible on stall doors.
- Post and enforce a NO SMOKING policy.
- Keep the barn neat and clean. This will enhance aesthetic appeal, minimize the risk of fire, and increases the chances of escape during a fire.
- Have regular self-inspections to minimize malfunctions.

For fire alarms and suppression devices:
- Have multiple water hydrants around the barn.
- Know the location of additional water sources (e.g., ponds).
- Locate water hydrants on 1¼-inch water lines adjacent to barns and feed-storage areas.
- Install the water system on a separate power circuit that runs directly from the transformer pole.
- Have fire extinguishers adjacent to or in fuel storage areas, barns, hay and bedding storage areas, and vehicles.
- Have at least one charged and mounted ABC-type fire extinguisher of recommended size every 50 feet in stables.
- Install industrial quality early detection and fire suppression systems.

- Install fire alarm systems in buildings and arenas.
- Use sprinkler systems that have adequate water pressure and that do not freeze if they are located in a cold environment.

To minimize fire fuel and ignition sources:
- Store hay and organic bedding materials in a separate section of the barn or, preferably, in a separate building.
- Store fuel and other petroleum products in a separate building. Store all combustibles properly and be sure to provide appropriate receptacles to dispose of rags soiled with combustibles.
- Use fire retardant/resistant construction materials, such as masonry, heavy timber, and fire-retardant treated wood.
- Keep the grass and the weeds mowed in yards and around buildings to eliminate accumulations of dried plant materials.
- Keep the barn clean and free of cobwebs, chaff, and dust.
- Use space heaters only according to the manufacturer's guidelines, and do not leave them unattended.
- Have certified professionals install lightning protection systems on all buildings.
- Avoid having trucks or mechanized machinery driving into the hay/bedding storage area, especially if the materials are extremely dry.

CHAPTER 13

Emergency Response Planning

Even a well planned, constructed, operated and maintained operation will have problems. Equipment or power fails, people make mistakes, manure runs off, fires occur, a trailer overturns, or severe weather forecast warrants relocating horses. While the time of these occurrences cannot be predicted, a well conceived response to emergency situations could keep a small problem from turning into a major disaster.

Planning for emergencies can be relatively easy with a little thought and preparation. Developing a written plan to address each potential emergency situation and thoroughly reviewing these plans with each person who is associated with the horses can help minimize financial losses, litigation, and loss of life to people and horses. The larger the horse operation or the more expensive the horses and facilities, the more important is the need for written emergency action plans (EAP).

Emergency response planning:

- **Promotes safety**. A plan not only prevents accidents, but also can mean the difference between losing and not losing a limb or even between life and death. Every employee or family member needs to be familiar with the operation's day-to-day procedures and understand what to do in the event of an emergency.
- **Promotes environmental stewardship**. Everybody is responsible for maintaining a clean environment.
- **Promotes public relations**. The public will develop a better impression of a stable facility as a whole knowing that it is standard procedure to have emergency response plans.
- **Addresses government regulations**. Many state and local governments now require emergency response planning before allowing new facilities to be constructed.
- **Minimizes the potential for litigation**. The legal system views emergency response planning favorably. Litigation can be minimized or completely avoided with proper planning.

Steps for emergency response planning are:
- Prevention.
- Preparation.
- Action.
- Review.

Preventing Emergencies

Preventing emergencies around a site can be thought of as:

Prevention =
(Inspection and Maintenance) + (Education)

Regular and thorough inspection of facilities, equipment, and storage followed with immediate maintenance or replacement of damaged items is one of the most important approaches to preventing emergencies. Manage and design operations and procedures to minimize the chances of failure and to *fail safely* if a failure occurs within the operation. For example, if a gas heater malfunctions will it shut down the gas and have an alarm that contacts key personnel of its failure, or will it release gas into the stable where it could result in a catastrophic death loss. Proper management and operation will help lessen the odds of an emergency.

For all types of systems, perform the following tasks:
- Identify key areas and components of the operation.
- Develop a checklist, and inspect the operation on a predetermined regular schedule.
- Correct or repair necessary components of the operation.
- Keep a copy of each regular inspection report in an organized area such as a filing cabinet or bookbinder.

Another component to prevention is education. Family members or employees must be properly educated in the day-to-day procedures and tasks that they will perform for the operation or about any equipment they will use. If a person lacks the proper knowledge or ability to perform procedures or tasks or to operate equipment, the person should not be placed in a position that could result in an emergency situation. When educating people, have written goals for the person to learn, have written instructions for the function or operation of the equipment, and maintain written records showing that the person has the proper knowledge level. Young people can be especially prone to accidents. Contact the local extension service or farm safety advocacy group about selecting tasks to match a young person's ability.

Preparing for Emergencies

Proper preparation can help to minimize the negative effects of an emergency situation. Having a written plan and educating all people associated with the farm about emergency procedures can help minimize the impact of emergencies. Emergency kits can also help minimize the negative effects of an emergency.

Emergency Action Plans

A written plan (commonly called an Emergency Action Plan or EAP) is a common sense plan that will help people make sound decisions during an emergency. Having a written EAP is important because a written plan:
- Communicates clearly to people specific actions to be taken in case of an emergency.
- Shows responsible preparation.
- Lessens the impact of an emergency.
- May be required by local, state, or federal regulations.

The written EAP should be posted prominently in each building, in the employee area, and next to all phones. The EAP also should be written in the native language of farm employees that do not speak English. Having EAPs written in multiple languages can help increase responsiveness and minimize the negative impacts of an emergency situation. Because many people now carry cell phones, posting key contact information on main entrance doors can help someone unfamiliar with the farm contact key people even when buildings are locked.

Plans can be developed for:
- Catastrophic death loss.
- Fire.
- Horse injury.
- Human injury.
- Manure runoff.
- Over-turned trailer.
- Power or utility failure.
- Run away horses or loose horses.
- Severe weather, such as hurricane, tornado, or flood.

One key action that could be needed in the event of a fire or severe weather is to relocate horses. Make sure several locations are identified. Possible relocations areas are other private stables or pastures, racetracks, fair grounds, or humane societies or shelters.

All EAPs should have the following:
- Name of the site.
- Owner, operator, or key personnel associated with the site. List no more than three (3) people.
- Site address, or if available, the 911 address.
- Driving directions to the site from the nearest town or from several towns close by.
- Specific actions to take during an emergency situation
- Specific names and phone numbers for key contact people who can help correct an emergency situation.

Worksheet 13-1 shows an example EAP. Table 13-1 shows possible action items to include in an EAP and recommended preparations to help enact the EAP when needed. Local extension services and emergency rescue groups also can be helpful when developing an EAP.

After developing an EAP, make sure that all people associated with the farm are knowledgeable about its content and know how to enact the procedures. All personnel should practice implementing the plan. Practicing can help identify and correct missing elements or awkward procedures that are specified in the EAP. Practicing also allows personnel to provide input to improve the EAP. Practice running through the EAP at least annually or more frequently if there is a higher risk of loss. Periodically review and update the plan to reflect any changes in the operation.

Emergency Kits

A first aid kit is often the only emergency kit people are familiar with using, and is important to have in stables and arenas. Typical first aid kits have:
- First-aid manual
- Sterile gauze
- Adhesive tape
- Adhesive bandages in several sizes
- Elastic bandage

- Antiseptic wipes
- Soap
- Antibiotic cream (triple-antibiotic ointment)
- Antiseptic solution (like hydrogen peroxide)
- Hydrocortisone cream (1%)
- Acetaminophen and aspirin (aspirin is not recommended for children under age 12)
- Tweezers
- Sharp scissors
- Safety pins
- Disposable instant cold packs
- Calamine lotion
- Alcohol wipes or ethyl alcohol
- Fever thermometer
- Plastic gloves (at least 2 pairs)
- Flashlight and extra batteries
- Mouthpiece for administering cardiopulmonary resuscitation (CPR) (can be obtained from the local Red Cross)
- List of emergency phone numbers
- Blanket (stored nearby)

Another type of emergency kit that is important to have on hand is an emergency evacuation kit. This kit is used in the event that horses need to be moved quickly. The Maryland Department of Agriculture lists the following items to include in an emergency evacuation kit on their *Disaster Action Guidelines For Horse Owners* website:
- Plastic trash barrel with lid
- Water bucket
- Leg wraps
- Fire resistant non-nylon leads and halters
- First aid items
- Portable radio and extra batteries
- Flashlight
- Sharp knife
- Wire cutters
- Tarpaulins
- Lime, bleach

Also remember to have enough fresh water and hay available for the horses for their stay away from the farm. A 48- to 72-hour supply is usually enough for a hurricane event. Flood events vary based on the duration of the flood.

Worksheet 13-1 Example Emergency Action Plan (EAP).

Date: ______________

EMERGENCY Situation: ______________

____

Farm Name & Location (911 address): ______________

Driving directions from nearest town(s): ______________

____

____

____

EMERGENCY Actions:

1. Assess the extent of the emergency and determine how much help is needed.

____

____

____

2. Implement the following steps:

____

____

____

3. Available equipment/supplies for responding to emergency:

Equipment/supplies	Contact Person	Phone Number

4. Farm contacts:

Contact Person	Phone Number

5. Additional corrective measures or property restoration measures.

____

____

____

____

Table 13-1 Possible actions to address emergency situations.

Emergency situation	Possible actions	Plan preparation
Catastrophic death loss	• Call owner, operator, or key personnel • Contact needed state agencies such as the Department of Natural Resources or Water Quality Control • Contact insurance carrier	• Have state agencies phone numbers and name of contact person (if possible) • Have insurance carrier phone numbers and name of contact person (if possible)
Fire	• Call fire department • Call owner/operator • Remove horses (if possible, without putting people in danger) • Move horses to a safe location either on site or to an off site location • Show fire department water sources for the site • Contact insurance carrier	• Contact fire department and let them know the layout of site, types of buildings, and water sources for the site • Contact other horse farm(s) in case relocation is necessary and have the necessary phone numbers for these farms • Identify water sources for fire department • Have insurance carrier phone numbers and name of contact person (if possible)
Horse injury	• Call veterinarian • Stabilize horse (if possible, without putting either person or horse in danger)	• Have veterinarian phone number
Human injury	• Call doctor, rescue unit, fire department, or poison control • Stabilize person (if possible)	• Have phone numbers for: *Doctor* *Rescue unit* *Fire department* *Poison control*
Manure runoff	• Stop source of runoff • Stop runoff from advancing further (if needed call person who has earth moving equipment) • Call owner, operator, or key personnel • Contact needed state agencies ASAP	• Identify equipment needed to stop runoff • Have phone numbers for people who have equipment needed to stop runoff • Have state agencies phone numbers and name of contact person (if possible)
Over turned trailer	• Call owner/operator • Call fire department • Remove horses (if possible, without putting people in danger) • Return trailer to upright position	• Identify equipment and people needed to return an overturned trailer to its upright position • Have phone numbers for key people • Identify area to place horses
Power or utility failure	• Call owner, operator, or key personnel • Call utility company • Remove and relocate horses (if necessary) • Contact insurance carrier (if necessary)	• Have the utility company phone numbers • Have insurance carrier phone numbers and name of contact person (if possible)
Run away horses, or horses out of pasture/lot	• Call owner/operator • Prevent other horses from leaving confined area • Keep track of loose horses and move back into confined area if it can be done safely • Keep horses off of road • Flag drivers of possible horse hazard (only if it can be done safely)	• Have phone numbers for key people • Identify area to confine or place horses
Severe weather (Hurricane, flood)	• Remove and relocate horses to safer locations (if necessary) • Take emergency evacuation kit	• Contact other horse farms in case relocation is necessary and have the necessary phone numbers for these farms • Have emergency evacuation kit prepared and stored in an easy-to-find location

Taking Action During an Emergency

Even with prevention and planning, much confusion and anxiety can still occur during an emergency. The objective during an emergency is to remain calm and carefully follow the procedures outlined in the EAP. With proper education and practice, confusion and anxiety should be at a minimum. If the emergency is a chemical or manure spill, contain the spill first then contact the appropriate state environmental agency. Remember to be present until the emergency has been completely controlled, or responsibility can be transferred to the appropriate authorities (e.g. fire department, police, regulatory agency).

Reviewing Actions and Procedures after Emergencies

Within a few days after an emergency occurs, review the EAP. Identify areas of the plan that worked successfully, and identify areas that need improvement. For the areas that need improvement determine specifically:

Step 1. What was the problem?
Step 2. What caused the problem?
Step 3. How could the problem be avoided? (Identify at least three solutions.)
Step 4. What is the best solution to each problem?
Step 5. What is the best solution overall?

Many times problems have more than one cause. Identifying three or more solutions (Step 3) helps managers or operators expand their reviews. After the review, revise the EAP and other procedures.

Common Fly Species Found in Stables

Species/I.D.	Life Cycle	Comments	Management
House fly			
Has dabbing mouthparts; abdomen roundish with "waist".	Lays eggs in manure; larvae and pupae develop in manure; adults feed on decaying organic matter. Cycle complete in 7-10 days.	This non-biting fly causes economic losses due to annoyance of workers and horses and has been implicated in the spread of diseases. Good manure management is the key to control. Spot treatment of manure with larvacides should be avoided and done only when sampling of the manure pile for maggots shows populations warranting their use.	— Remove manure every 5-7 days. — Properly store or spread manure after removal. — Keep feeding and watering receptacles and areas clean and free of organic material. — Install screening. — Use insecticides: residual space or aerosol sprays; spot treatment of manure with larvacides. — Use sticky traps. — Use baited traps. — Install "Zappers".
Stable fly			
Has piercing mouthparts; abdomen roundish with "waist".	Lays eggs in decaying organic matter; larvae and pupae develop in decaying organic matter; adults (both sexes) feed on blood. Cycle complete in about 3 weeks.	The life cycle of the stable fly is similar to the house fly's, but it prefers to breed in decaying straw rather than manure. The stable fly causes losses due to annoyance of workers and horses and horse blood loss. Horses stamping their hooves is a good indication of stable flies. The fly feeds mainly on legs and the abdominal area.	— Remove wet straw, manure, spilled feeds and other wet or decaying organic matter. — Use insecticides: residual spray application to fly resting areas and horses; space or mist sprays. — Install screening. — Use sticky traps. — Use baited traps. — Install "Zappers".
Horsefly			
Large, helmet-shaped head; large, stout body; one inch long.	Lays eggs on objects near water; larvae aquatic, pupate and emerge as adults in spring; female adult fly bites and takes blood. Cycle complete in 70 days to 2 years.	Very large flies; the female delivers a painful bite. Alight on head, neck, shoulders and back of horses, cut through skin with knifelike mouthparts and feed on blood for several minutes. These wounds continue to bleed after the fly has left. Can fly long distances from breeding sites, making cultural control difficult.	— Use chemical: Residual spray application to fly resting areas and horses; mist sprays; ear tags; ear/face/tail tapes; self-application devices. — Use sticky traps.

Common Fly Species Found in Stables

Species/I.D.	Life Cycle	Comments	Management
Face fly			
Very similar to housefly; clusters around face.	Lays eggs in fresh manure on pasture; larvae and pupae develop in manure; adult feeds on decaying organic matter, hibernates in buildings. Cycle complete in 2-3 weeks.	Non-biting. Adults cause extreme annoyance to pastured horses by clustering around eyes, mouth, and muzzle. Adults feed on horse secretions, nectar, and dung liquids. Breed only in fresh, undisturbed droppings. Generally do not enter darkened buildings. Adults enter buildings (in fall) to hibernate.	— Drag or harrow pastures to break up fresh dropping. — Provide shelter for shade in pastures. —Use chemical: ear tags; ear/face/tail tapes; self-applicating devices.
Horse bot fly			
Body hairy; abdomen elongated with "waist".	Adult lays eggs on legs, shoulders, jaw, throat, or lips of horse; horse licks area and ingests eggs. Eggs hatch in mouth; larvae migrate to stomach and attach to lining; larvae passed with feces, burrow into soil to pupate. Cycle complete in several months.	Bot infestation causes decreased feed efficiency, resulting in reduced work and breeding performance, retarded growth of foals, of possibly, in severe cases, death. Rubbing due to itching results in hair loss. Horses pestered by adult bot flies toss their heads, stamp their front feet, or rub their noses; infected horses may show digestive problems, lowered vigor, and emaciation.	— Frequently groom, wash, and clip preferred egg-laying areas. — Deworming (consult your veterinarian for specific treatment information). — Clip hair and/or wash with 120°F water at around preferred egg-laying areas 30 days prior to worming. — Treat body areas where bot flies glue their eggs with insecticide wipes or sprays.

General Construction Plans

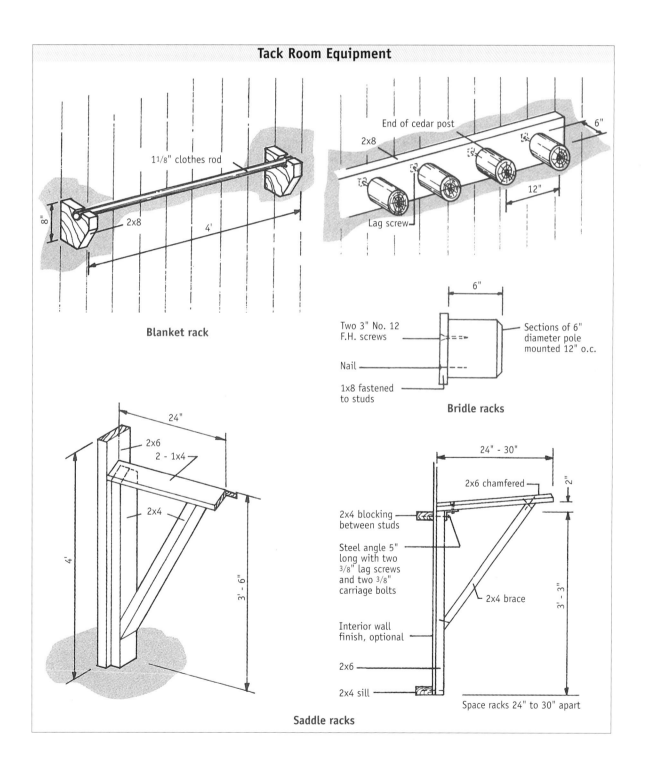

Tack Room Equipment

1¹/8" clothes rod

2x8

8"

4'

Blanket rack

End of cedar post

2x8

6"

12"

Lag screw

6"

Two 3" No. 12 F.H. screws

Sections of 6" diameter pole mounted 12" o.c.

Nail

1x8 fastened to studs

Bridle racks

24"

2x6

2 - 1x4

2x4

4'

3' - 6"

Saddle racks

24" - 30"

2x6 chamfered

2"

2x4 blocking between studs

Steel angle 5" long with two 3/8" lag screws and two 3/8" carriage bolts

Interior wall finish, optional

2x6

2x4 sill

2x4 brace

3' - 3"

Space racks 24" to 30" apart

Tack Room Equipment

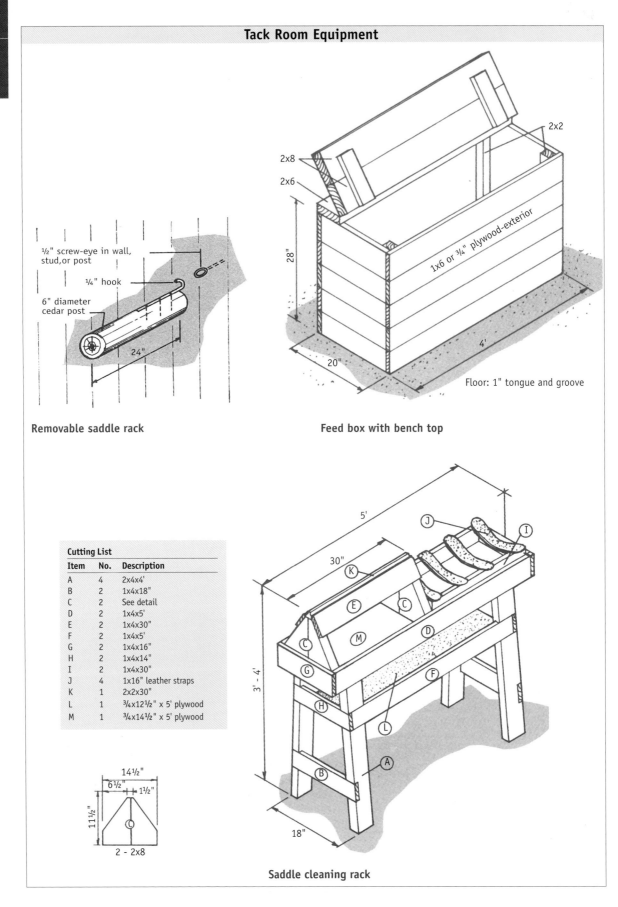

½" screw-eye in wall,
stud, or post

¼" hook

6" diameter
cedar post

24"

Removable saddle rack

2x2

2x8

2x6

28"

1x6 or ¾" plywood-exterior

20"

4'

Floor: 1" tongue and groove

Feed box with bench top

Cutting List

Item	No.	Description
A	4	2x4x4'
B	2	1x4x18"
C	2	See detail
D	2	1x4x5'
E	2	1x4x30"
F	2	1x4x5'
G	2	1x4x16"
H	2	1x4x14"
I	2	1x4x30"
J	4	1x16" leather straps
K	1	2x2x30"
L	1	¾x12½" x 5' plywood
M	1	¾x14½" x 5' plywood

5'

30"

3' - 4'

18"

14½"

6½"

1½"

11½"

2 - 2x8

Saddle cleaning rack

Show Box

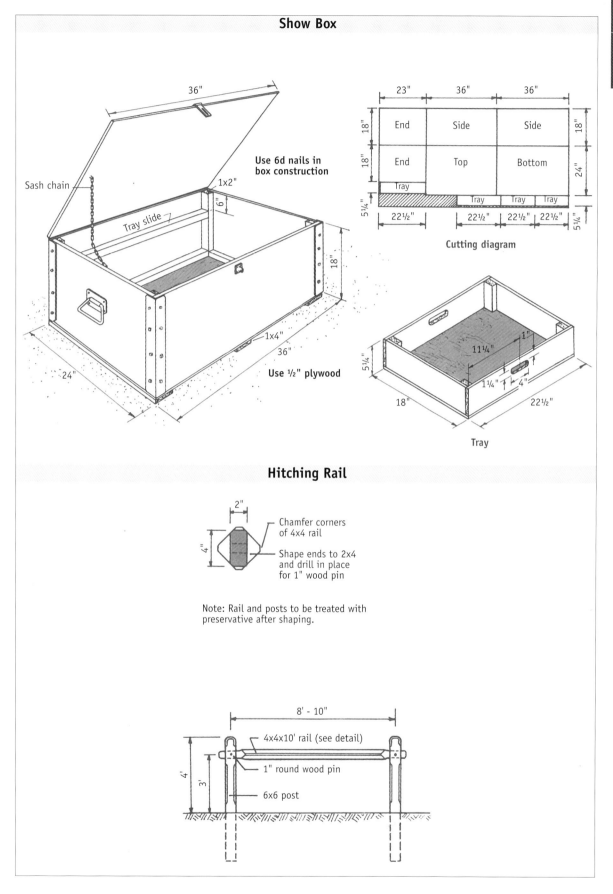

36"

Use 6d nails in box construction

Sash chain

1x2"

Tray slide

6"

18"

1x4"

36"

24"

Use ½" plywood

Cutting diagram

23"	36"	36"
End	Side	Side
End	Top	Bottom
Tray		

18"

18"

5¼"

22½"

22½"

22½"

22½"

18"

24"

5¼"

Tray

5¼"

1"

11¼"

1¼"

4"

18"

22½"

Hitching Rail

2"

4"

Chamfer corners of 4x4 rail

Shape ends to 2x4 and drill in place for 1" wood pin

Note: Rail and posts to be treated with preservative after shaping.

8' - 10"

4x4x10' rail (see detail)

1" round wood pin

6x6 post

4'

3'

Jumps

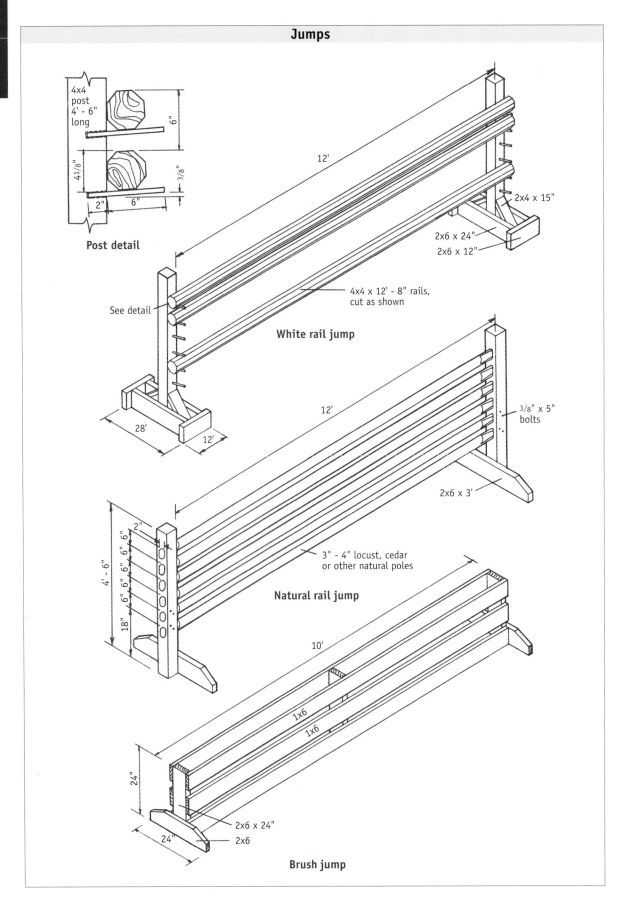

4x4
post
4' - 6"
long

6"

4 1/8"

3/8"

2"

6"

Post detail

12'

2x4 x 15"

2x6 x 24"

2x6 x 12"

4x4 x 12' - 8" rails,
cut as shown

See detail

White rail jump

12'

3/8" x 5"
bolts

2x6 x 3'

28'

12'

2"
6" 6"
6" 6"
6" 6"
6" 6"

4' - 6"

18"

3" - 4" locust, cedar
or other natural poles

Natural rail jump

10'

1x6

1x6

24"

24"

2x6 x 24"

2x6

Brush jump

216

Jumps

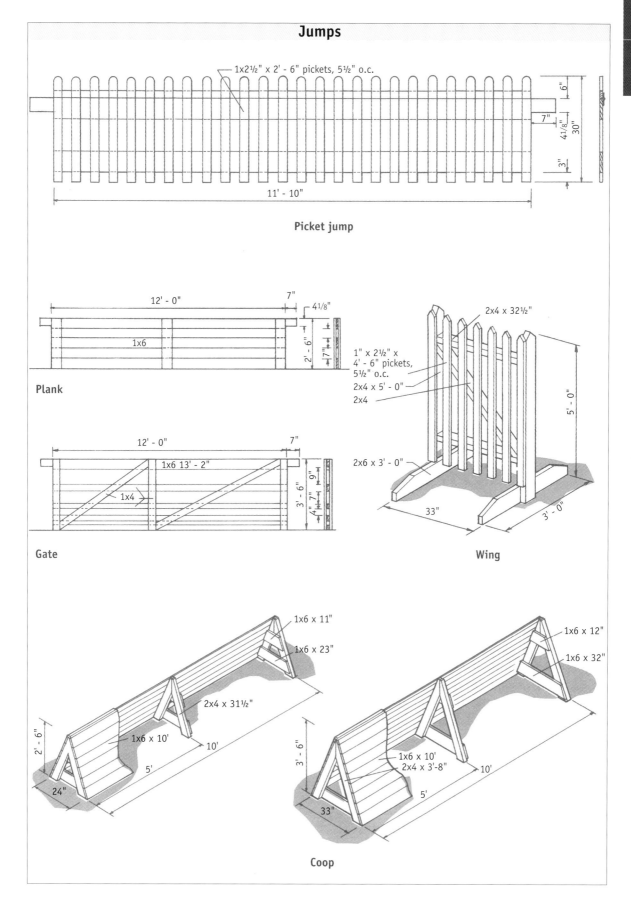

1x2½" x 2' - 6" pickets, 5½" o.c.

11' - 10"

6"

7"

4⅛"

30"

3"

Picket jump

12' - 0"

7"

4⅛"

1x6

2' - 6"

7"

Plank

2x4 x 32½"

1" x 2½" x 4' - 6" pickets, 5½" o.c.

2x4 x 5' - 0"

2x4

2x6 x 3' - 0"

5' - 0"

33"

3' - 0"

Wing

12' - 0"

7"

1x6 13' - 2"

1x4

3' - 6"

9"

7"

4"

Gate

1x6 x 11"

1x6 x 23"

2x4 x 31½"

1x6 x 10'

10'

2' - 6"

5'

24"

1x6 x 12"

1x6 x 32"

1x6 x 10'
2x4 x 3'-8"

10'

3' - 6"

5'

33"

Coop

Dutch Doors

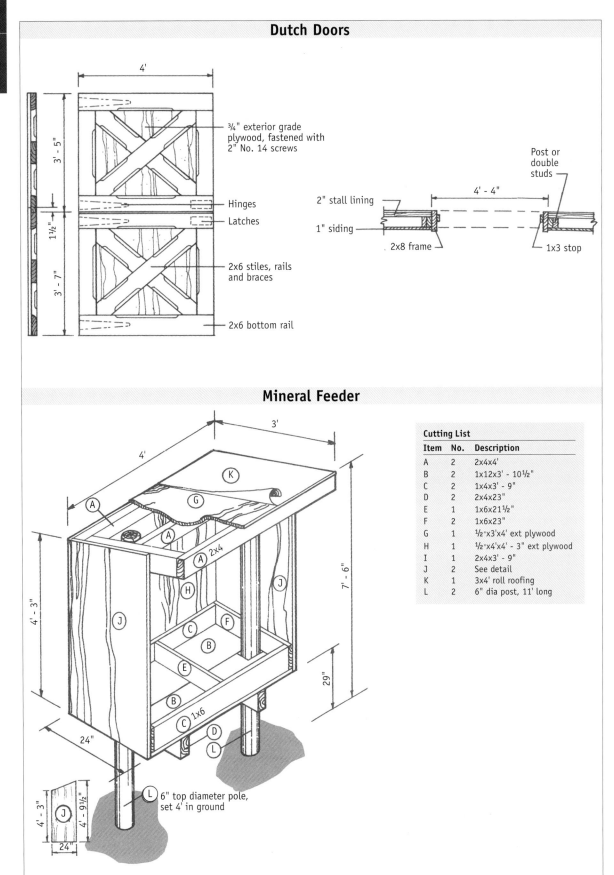

¾" exterior grade plywood, fastened with 2" No. 14 screws

Hinges

Latches

2x6 stiles, rails and braces

2x6 bottom rail

Post or double studs

2" stall lining

1" siding

2x8 frame

1x3 stop

4' - 4"

4'

3' - 5"

1½"

3' - 7"

Mineral Feeder

3'

4'

7' - 6"

4' - 3"

29"

24"

4' - 3"

4' - 9½"

24"

6" top diameter pole, set 4' in ground

6" dia post, 11' long

Cutting List

Item	No.	Description
A	2	2x4x4'
B	2	1x12x3' - 10½"
C	2	1x4x3' - 9"
D	2	2x4x23"
E	1	1x6x21½"
F	2	1x6x23"
G	1	½"x3'x4' ext plywood
H	1	½"x4'x4' - 3" ext plywood
I	1	2x4x3' - 9"
J	2	See detail
K	1	3x4' roll roofing
L	2	6" dia post, 11' long

Cupolas

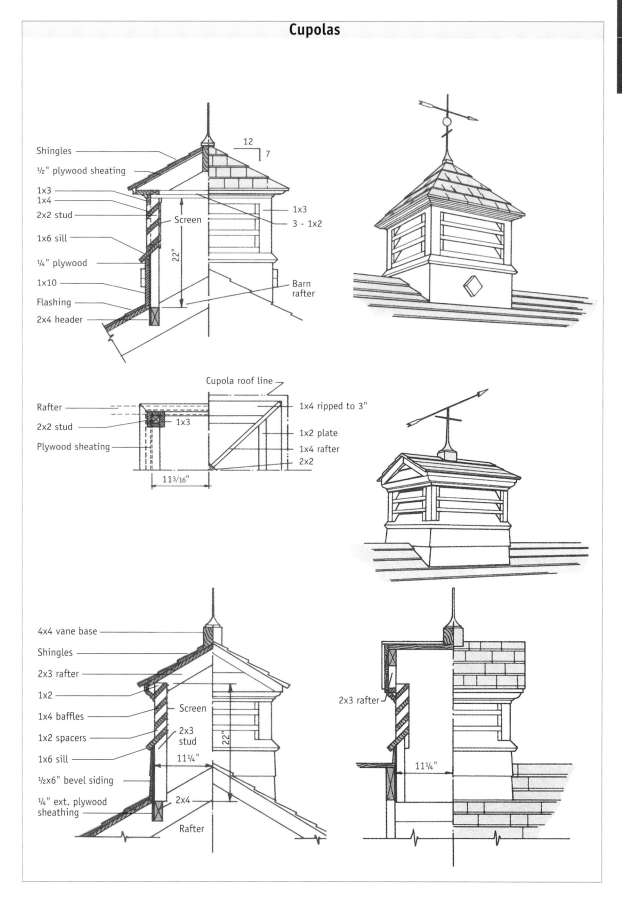

Top diagram (left):
- Shingles
- ½" plywood sheating
- 1x3
- 1x4
- 2x2 stud
- Screen
- 1x6 sill
- ¼" plywood
- 1x10
- Flashing
- 2x4 header
- 22"
- 12 / 7
- 1x3
- 3 - 1x2
- Barn rafter

Middle diagram (left):
- Rafter
- 2x2 stud
- Plywood sheating
- 1x3
- Cupola roof line
- 1x4 ripped to 3"
- 1x2 plate
- 1x4 rafter
- 2x2
- 11³/16"

Bottom diagram (left):
- 4x4 vane base
- Shingles
- 2x3 rafter
- 1x2
- 1x4 baffles
- 1x2 spacers
- 1x6 sill
- ½x6" bevel siding
- ¼" ext. plywood sheathing
- Screen
- 2x3 stud
- 11¼"
- 22"
- 2x4
- Rafter

Bottom diagram (right):
- 2x3 rafter
- 11¼"

Loading Chutes

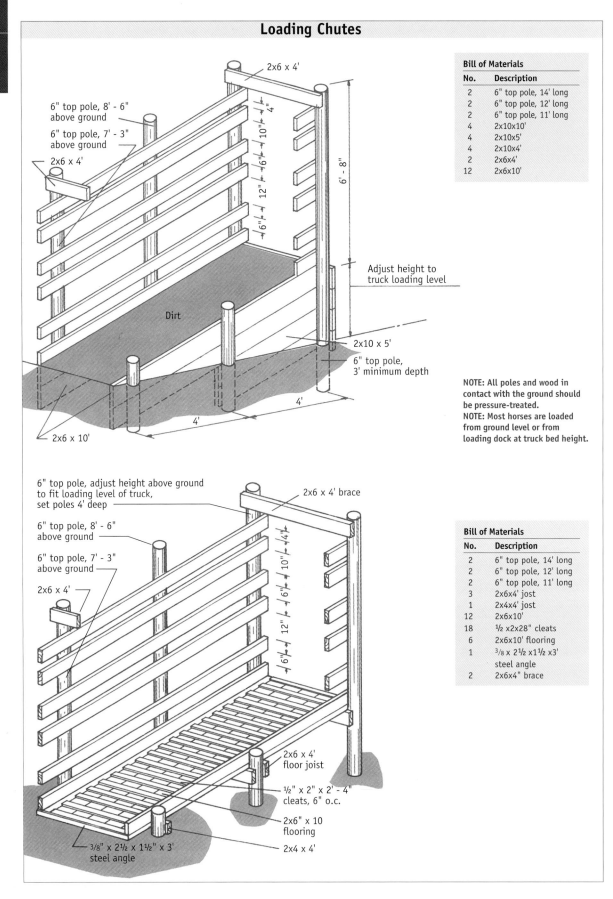

2x6 x 4'

6" top pole, 8' - 6"
above ground

6" top pole, 7' - 3"
above ground

2x6 x 4'

4"

10"

6"

12"

6"

6' - 8"

Adjust height to
truck loading level

Dirt

2x10 x 5'

6" top pole,
3' minimum depth

4'

4'

2x6 x 10'

Bill of Materials

No.	Description
2	6" top pole, 14' long
2	6" top pole, 12' long
2	6" top pole, 11' long
4	2x10x10'
4	2x10x5'
4	2x10x4'
2	2x6x4'
12	2x6x10'

NOTE: All poles and wood in
contact with the ground should
be pressure-treated.
NOTE: Most horses are loaded
from ground level or from
loading dock at truck bed height.

6" top pole, adjust height above ground
to fit loading level of truck,
set poles 4' deep

2x6 x 4' brace

6" top pole, 8' - 6"
above ground

6" top pole, 7' - 3"
above ground

2x6 x 4'

4"

10"

6"

12"

6"

2x6 x 4'
floor joist

½" x 2" x 2' - 4"
cleats, 6" o.c.

2x6" x 10
flooring

⅜" x 2½ x 1½" x 3'
steel angle

2x4 x 4'

Bill of Materials

No.	Description
2	6" top pole, 14' long
2	6" top pole, 12' long
2	6" top pole, 11' long
3	2x6x4' jost
1	2x4x4' jost
12	2x6x10'
18	½ x2x28" cleats
6	2x6x10' flooring
1	⅜ x 2½ x1½ x3' steel angle
2	2x6x4" brace

Wood Preservatives

Preservative wood treatments are used on lumber to extend its useful life against natural elements. The principal organisms that can degrade wood in horse buildings are:

- **Molds and stains.** Ordinarily they have little affect on the strength of wood; however, they occur in the conditions that are also favorable to decay fungi. Stains can impair the use of wood where appearance is important.

- **Decay-producing fungi.** Fungi can attack either heartwood or sapwood. Most tree-attacking fungi die after the tree is cut, but some decay fungi destroy logs or manufactured products, such as sawed lumber. Decay is relatively slow at temperatures below 50 F or above 90 F. Serious decay occurs only when the wood's moisture content is above 23%.

- **Insect damage.** Bark and ambrosia beetles can damage freshly cut timber or rustic structures where the bark is left in place. Powder-post beetles may attack the sapwood of either freshly cut or seasoned timber. Subterranean termites and carpenter ants can damage posts, structural timbers, or buildings. They use wood for shelter rather than food. Precautions that prevent termite attack and decay are usually effective against carpenter ants.

Pressure treated wood should be used in areas that are subject to decay and in ground contact such as fences. It is often recommended that all wood in contact with concrete, especially if on or near grade, be treated to the soil-contact level. Consider treated wood for below-grade millwork. Where termite attack is likely, treat all wood near the soil, because termites build tunnels from the soil and up concrete or other material to reach wood.

Pressure Treated Wood Preservatives

Two methods can be used to protect wood. One is the use of preservative oils and the other is a method of pressure treating wood. Wood using preservative oils is usually treated by brushing or dipping the wood, which results in very low penetration and retention. Pressure treatment forces preservatives throughout the sapwood and can achieve high retention. Use only pressure treated material or decay resistant wood species in contact with the ground or manure.

The three major types of preservatives for pressure treating wood are:

- Waterborne preservatives (inorganic arsenicals, and copper-amine and borate products)
- Oil-borne preservative (pentachlorophenol).
- Creosote and creosote solutions.

Waterborne Preservatives

Waterborne wood preservatives include chromated copper arsenate, CCA Type C; ammonical copper zinc arsenate, ACZA; amine copper quat (ACQ-B, ACQ-C, ACQ-D); copper azole (CBA-A, CA-B); and borates (SBX). These preservatives are often used when cleanliness and paintability are required. These treatments do not significantly affect ignition or flame spread on wood, although formulations with copper and chromium stimulate and prolong glowing combustion of wood. Fire retardant treatments are available for applications where reduction in flame spread is required.

For many years the inorganic arsenical chromated copper arsenate (CCA), also known as green salt, was used widely in residential and agricultural settings. CCA is a mixture of copper, chromium, and arsenic compounds. CCA is one of the most common preservatives in the wood treating industry and has been widely used for treatment of softwood lumber, plywood, poles, and fence posts. Ammonical zinc copper arsenate (ACZA) was a popular preservative that has been used for treatment of Douglas fir on the west coast. The arsenate in CCA and ACZA can be toxic at high enough levels. Because humans and animals can absorb arsenate through hand to mouth ingestion, through the lungs by inhaling sawdust, or by licking or chewing, the Environmental Protection Agency (EPA) has restricted the use of them. CCA and ACZA treatments are acceptable to use on building foundations, building posts, utility poles, and pilings.

With the restrictions placed on CCA and ACZA, copper-amines are now the accepted method of wood preservative treatment. Two types of copper amine wood preservatives are being used. These are copper azole (CBA-A, CA-B) and alkaline copper quat (ACQ-B, ACQ-C, ACQ-D). Like CCA, they are clean treatments and are paintable once dry. The preservatives react in the wood, become leach resistant in a similar manner to CCA and ACZA, and may be used in either interior or exterior applications. These products have lower toxicity levels than inorganic arsenical preservatives.

Borates are used only for interior applications that are protected from liquid water. Borates are most commonly used for sill plates and interior framing.

Oil-borne Preservatives

Pentachlorophenol solutions for wood preservation generally contain 5% penta; the remainder is volatile solvents or heavy oils. The heavy oil solvents remain in the wood for a long time and usually do not produce a paintable surface. The volatile solvents are used with penta when the natural wood finish must be maintained or a paint finish is required. More commonly called *penta*, the primary use of this product is in utility poles and posts and lumber for farm use.

Pentachlorophenol is toxic. Penta components are fat-soluble and can be absorbed through the skin. Because pentachlorophenol can accumulate in animal meat or milk, residues could be a problem. Toxic effects have occurred in cattle that have led to decreased growth rate and feed efficiency, and progressive anemia. Penta irritates skin, eyes, nose, and throat.

Creosote and Creosote Solutions

Creosote is the oldest common wood preservative. Coal tar creosote is a black or brownish oil made by distilling coal tar. It is highly toxic to wood destroying organisms, has low water solubility, low volatility, high permanence, easy application, easily determined penetration, low cost, and a long record of satisfactory use. Creosote is used in lumber, building poles, posts, utility poles, marine applications, and railroad ties.

Creosote has an objectionable odor and typically is unpaintable. Creosote vapors are harmful to growing plants, and some foodstuffs may take on the creosote smell. Freshly creosoted wood can be ignited easily, readily burns, and produces dense smoke. After seasoning, the more volatile oils disappear and creosoted wood burns like untreated wood. Creosote dumped in lakes or streams can be toxic to fish and other marine life.

Selecting a Preservative Treatment

Table D-1 shows uses and locations for the various wood treatments. Selecting wood with the proper amount of preservative treatment penetration and retention is important in obtaining a wood product that will satisfactorily meet the needs of the horse facility based on the location and use of the lumber. *Penetration* measures the depth to which the preservative is injected into the wood. It is expressed as inches of penetration into the wood or percent of sapwood penetrated. In sawn posts or poles, the minimum penetration may be 2.5 inches into the wood or 85% of the sapwood, depending on the species. In sawn lumber, penetration might be completely through the lumber thickness. In hard-to-treat species, such as Douglas fir or hem-fir, wood is generally incised to get the required penetration. Incising is a process in which slits are impressed into the surface of the wood to improve penetration. Ideally, the preservative treatment would penetrate the entire wood member.

The amount of preservative in the wood after treatment is called *preservative retention*. It is usually expressed in pounds of chemical per cubic foot of wood (pcf). Three treatment levels are common in agricultural and home construction: above ground, ground contact and fresh water exposure, and structural foundation. In CA-B treated wood, 0.31 pcf retention is used for structural members such as building

posts. Much of the lumber for decks, such as the 4x4 posts, is treated to 0.21-pcf retention. This is the recommended retention for wood in ground contact and fresh water exposure. The retention level is 0.10 pcf for treated wood used above ground, such as the deck boards. Retentions levels of various types of preservatives will vary. Always be certain that the treated wood you buy is marked for the appropriate end use. Table D-2 shows recommended levels of preservation retention.

To verify that a product is effectively treated, wood should be labeled with the type of preservative, standard to which it was treated, retention level, intended end use and the inspection agency. The American Lumber Standard Committee (ALSC) logo stamped on wood products means the wood has met the minimum ALSC requirements, Figure D-1. Treated lumber that carries this type of mark will be in compliance with building codes.

Table D-1 Selected uses for preservative-treated wood.

| | Waterborne | | | Oil-borne | |
Production agriculture	Copper-Amine	Inorganic arsenicals	Borate	Penta	Creosote
Components in ground contact (subject to decay or insect damage)	y	n [b]	n	y [a]	y [a]
Exterior fencing posts, gates, dividers (animals unlikely to crib, bite, or lick the wood)	y	y [b]	n	y	y
Feedbunk					
• Contact with feed (CCA, yes)		n	n	n	n
• Support structure	y	n [b]	n	y	y
Grain storage		n	n	n	n
Interior pen or stall dividers and liners (animals likely to crib, bite, or lick the wood)	y	n	n	n	n
Manure storage	y	n	n	y	y
Poles and timbers (structural framing)	y	y	n	y [a]	y [a]
Silage/feed storage and containers					
• Contact with feed (CCA, yes)		n	n	n	n
• Support structure	y	n [b]	n	y	y
Truck boxes for feed or foodstuffs		n	n	n	n
Trailer floors for livestock	y	n	n	y	n
Water tanks (CCA, yes)		n	n	n	n

[a] Penta- and creosote-treated wood require two coats of sealer in these applications. Urethane, epoxy, and shellac are accepted sealers for creosote-treated wood. Urethane, shellac, latex, epoxy, enamel, and varnish are acceptable for penta-treated wood. Select a sealer that can withstand the intended exposure or select a different treatment.

[b] CCA (inorganic arsenicals may be permitted in some locations when used for round piles or posts or for timbers larger than 5 inches where standards require treatment at 0.60 pcf or higher.

Table D-2   Recommended minimum preservative retentions, pcf.

Based on AWPA Standards C1, C2, C9, C15, C16 and C31
(1) Creosote and creosote solutions; (2) Pentachlorophenol; (3) Ammoniacal copper zinc arsenate (ACZA), amine copper quat (ACQ-B, ACQ-C, ACQ-D); (4) Chromated copper arsenate (CCA-C); (5) Copper azole; (6) Copper azole; and (7) Inorganic borate. Except for round structural members, levels are for all softwood species.

Material, use, or location	Creosote (1)	Penta (2)	ACQ[a], ACZA (3)	CCA-C (4)	CBA-A[a] (5)	CA-B[a] (6)	SBX (7)
Poles and posts, as round structural members:							
• Southern, Ponderosa pine	7.5	0.38	0.60	0.60	0.61	0.31	NR
• Red Pine	10.5	0.53	0.60	0.60	0.61	0.31	NR
• Coastal Douglas fir	9.0	0.45	0.60	0.60	0.61	0.31	NR
• Jack Pine, Lodgepole Pine	12.0	0.60	0.60	0.60	—	—	NR
• Western Red Cedar	16.0	0.80	0.60	0.60	0.61	0.31	NR
• Western Larch, intermountain Douglas fir	16.0	0.80	0.60	0.60	—	—	NR
Poles and Posts, sawn four sides as structural members:	12.0	0.60	0.60	0.60	0.61	0.31	NR
Fence posts							
• Round, half-round or quarter- round	8.0	0.40	0.40	0.40	0.41	0.21	NR
• Sawn 4 sides	10.0	0.50	0.50	N/A	0.41	0.21	NR
Lumber							
• In contact with soil	10.0	0.50	0.40	N/A	0.41	0.21	NR
• Not in contact with soil	8.0	0.40	0.25	N/A	0.20	0.10	NR
• Millwork	NR[b]	0.30	0.25	N/A	0.20	0.10	NR
Commercial-residential use, (AWPA Standard C15)							
Decking tongue-and-groove							NR
• Above ground	8.0	0.40	0.25	N/A	0.20	0.10	NR
• Soil and fresh water use	10.0	0.50	0.40	N/A	0.41	0.21	NR
Permanent Wood Foundation[c]	NR	NR	0.60	0.60	0.61	0.31	NR
Sawn posts and columns							NR
Sawn building poles and posts as structural members	12.0	0.60	0.60	0.60	0.61	0.31	NR
Square fence post, light	10.0	0.50	0.40	N/A	0.41	0.21	NR
Fencing slats, pickets, etc.	8.0	0.50	0.40	N/A	0.41	0.21	NR
Landscape ties	10.0	0.50	0.40	N/A	0.41	0.21	NR
Lumber and plywood roof decking, flooring, and subflooring	NR	NR	0.25	0.25	0.20	0.10	NR
Lumber floor plates, studs, joists, furring strips, beveled siding, sills, millwork, cant strips	NR	NR	0.25	N/A	0.20	0.10	0.17[d]

[a] Accepted replacement for chromated copper arsenate (CCA)

[b] NR-Not Recommended

[c] Permanent Wood Foundation: see AWPA Standard C22

[d] Borates for uses protected from liquid water; see AWPA Standard C31. 0.28 pcf when Forsoman termites are present.

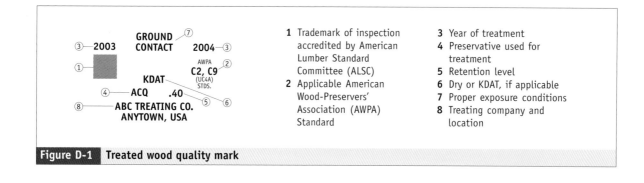

1. Trademark of inspection accredited by American Lumber Standard Committee (ALSC)
2. Applicable American Wood-Preservers' Association (AWPA) Standard
3. Year of treatment
4. Preservative used for treatment
5. Retention level
6. Dry or KDAT, if applicable
7. Proper exposure conditions
8. Treating company and location

Figure D-1   Treated wood quality mark

Handling Pressure Treated Wood Products

Wood preservatives must be toxic to protect the wood. The proper and safe use of preservative chemicals and pressure treated wood products protects both users and the environment. Take precautions when handling and disposing of treated wood. Exposure to green or unseasoned treated wood can be hazardous. Make sure that the wood is dry and has no surface residue.

Wear long sleeves, long pants, and gloves that are impervious to the chemicals (for example, vinyl-coated gloves) when handling creosote- or pentachlorophenol-treated wood. The chemicals can be absorbed through the skin with frequent or prolonged contact. To saw or machine treated wood, wear a dust mask, and if possible, work outdoors to reduce contact with airborne sawdust. Avoid frequent or prolonged inhalation of treated wood sawdust. Wear goggles to protect eyes from flying particles. After working with treated wood wash exposed areas such as hands and face thoroughly, especially before eating, drinking, or using tobacco products. If oily preservatives or sawdust accumulates on clothes, launder work clothes separately before reusing.

Dispose of treated wood by ordinary trash collection or burial. Do not burn treated wood in open fires, stoves, or fireplaces because toxic chemicals may be in the smoke and ashes. Treated wood from commercial or industrial use (e.g., construction sites) may be incinerated if in accordance with state and federal regulations.

REFERENCES AND RESOURCES

Chapter 1. Data Summary
- Brad Kruse, DraftResource.com (http://www.draftresource.com/).
- National Horse Show Association
- United States Dressage Federation

Chapter 2. Site Planning
- U.S. Geological Survey (USGS)
- *Coal Combustion By-products*. Ohio State University AEX-330-99 Fact Sheet (590 Woody Hayes Dr., Columbus OH 43210).
- *Farm & Home Concrete Handbook,* MWPS-35
- Using All-Weather Geotextile Lanes and Pads, AED-45, MWPS, 1999.
- American Association of State Highways and Transportation Officials (AASHTO), *A Policy on Geometric Design of Highways and Streets* (The Green Book), 2001.

Chapter 3. Stables
- *Housing for Horses, Flooring for Stalls*, by Kathy Anderson, Cooperative Extension, Institute of Agriculture and Natural Resources, University of Nebraska-Lincoln.
- *Horse Stable Flooring Materials and Drainage*, G-96. E. Wheeler and J. Smith, The Pennsylvania State University Extension Service. April 2000.

Chapter 4. Pasture, Paddocks, and Pens
- *Housing for Horses, Flooring for Stalls*, by Kathy Anderson, Cooperative Extension, Institute of Agriculture and Natural Resources, University of Nebraska-Lincoln.

Chapter 5. Arenas and Training Facilities
- *Horse Stable Flooring Materials and Drainage*, G-96. E. Wheeler and J. Smith, The Pennsylvania State University. April 2000.
- *Horse Facilities 6: Riding Arena Footing Materials*, College of Agricultural Sciences Agricultural Research and Cooperative Extension, Pennsylvania State University, State College, Pennsylvania.
- National Horse Show Association
- United States Dressage Federation

Chapter 6. Breeding, Maternity, and Foaling Facilities

Chapter 7. Environmental Control
- *Heating, Cooling and Tempering Air for Livestock Housing*, MWPS-34, 1990.
- *Horse Stable Ventilation*, UB039. E. Wheeler. The Pennsylvania State University. 2003.
- *Mechanical Ventilating Systems for Livestock Housing*, MWPS-32, 1989.
- *Natural Ventilating Systems for Livestock Housing*, MWPS-33, 1990.
- Anderson, K. 1996. *Winter Care for Horses*. NebGuide G96-1292-A. University of Nebraska-Lincoln Extension. (www.Ianr.unl.edu/pubs/horse/g1292.htm). December 29, 2003.
- Stotts, Donald. Symptoms Give Warning of Heat Stress in Horses. Oklahoma State University. (www.equiresource.com/usefulinfo/OSU_heat_stress.htm). December 30, 2003.
- Harper, Frederick. Ammonia and Foals Don't Mix. Animal Science Horse Information Series. University of Tennessee. (www.utextension.utk.edu/ansci). December 30, 2003.

Chapter 8. Manure Management
- Mills, D. S., S. Eckley, and J.J. Cooper. 2000. Thoroughbred bedding performance associated behavior differences and their implications for equine welfare. Animal Science. 70:95-106. British Society of Animal Science.
- *ASAE Standards*, 51st ed. 2004. D384.2: Manure Production and Characteristics. St. Joseph, Mich.: ASAE.
- *Manure Characteristics*, MWPS-18, Section 1
- Livestock and Poultry Environmental Stewardship (LPES) *Lesson 36: Land Application Equipment*.
- *On-Farm Composting Handbook*, NRAES-54, Tables 3.1 and A.1
- *Composting System for Small Horse Farms*, F-1729, Oklahoma Cooperative Extension Service.

Chapter 9. Bulk Feed and Bedding Storage
- *Aeration System Design for Cone-Bottom Round Bins*, Oklahoma State University Extension Facts F-1103.
- *Light Horses*, Ensminger, M. E. USDA Farmer's Bulletin 2127, 1965.

Chapter 10. Fencing
- *Fences for Horses*, Bulletin 1192, J.W. Worley and G. Heusner, The University of Georgia College of Agricultural and Environmental Sciences, Cooperative Extension Service, 2000.
- Red Brand guide, Figure 1

Chapter 11. Utilities
- *NFPA National Electrical Code®* (NEC, National Fire Protection Association)
- *Farm Buildings Wiring Handbook*, MWPS-28
- *Private Water Systems Handbook*, MWPS-14
- National Academy of Sciences, 1974 Guideline for use of saline waters
- NFPA 54, *The National Fuel Gas Code*
- NFPA 58, *Storage and Handling Liquefied Petroleum Gases* and NFPA 54, *The National Fuel Gas Cod*e
- *Onsite Domestic Sewage Disposal Handbook*, MWPS-24

Chapter 12. Fire Protection
- *Fire Control in Livestock Buildings,* NRAES-39. Natural Resource, Agriculture, and Engineering Service (NRAES) Cooperative Extension, Ithaca, New York. 1989.
- *Guarding Against Hay Fires*, ANR-964. C.B. Ogburn. Alabama Cooperative Extension Service, Agricultural Engineering, Auburn University.
- *Fire Safety in Horse Stables*. J. Zajaczkowski and E. Wheeler, The Pennsylvania State University. April 2002.

- Hanford Fire Department website (http://www.hanford.gov/fire/).
- Staying Alive website (http://www.stayingalive.ca/index.html).

Chapter 13. Emergency Response Planning
- Maryland Department of Agriculture website, Disaster Action Guidelines For Horse Owners

Appendix A. Common Fly Species Found in Stables

Appendix B. General Construction Plans

Appendix C. Wood Preservatives
American Wood-Preservers' Association, 801 Alabama Avenue, Second Floor, Selma, AL 36701:
- All Timber Products—Preservative Treatment by Pressure Processes, C1
- Lumber, Timber, Bridge Ties and Mine Ties—Preservative Treatment by Pressure Processes, C2
- Plywood—Preservative Treatment by Pressure Processes, C9
- Wood For Commercial-Residential Construction Preservative Treatment by Pressure Processes, C15
- Wood Used on Farms—Preservative Treatment by Pressure Processes, AWPA C16
- Lumber Used Out Of Contact With The Ground and Continuously Protected From Liquid Water—Treatment by Pressure Processes, C31

INDEX